"Mathematics is so much more than memorizing rules. It is learning to reason, to make connections, and to make sense of the world. We believe in Learning by Doing(TM)—you need to actively engage with the content if you are to benefi t from it. The lessons were designed to take you from your intuitive understanding of the world and build on your prior experiences to then learn new concepts. My hope is that these instructional materials help you build a deep understanding of math."

Sandy Bartle Finocchi, Senior Academic Officer

"You have been learning math for a very long time—both in school and in your interactions in the world. You know a lot of math! In this course, there's nothing brand new. It all builds on what you already know. So, as you approach each activity, use all of your knowledge to solve problems, to ask questions, to fix mistakes, and to think creatively."

Amy Jones Lewis, Director of Instructional Design

"At Carnegie Learning we have created an organization whose mission and culture is defined by your success. Our passion is creating products that make sense of the world of mathematics and ignite a passion in you. Our hope is that you will enjoy our resources as much as we enjoyed creating them."

Barry Malkin, CEO, Carnegie Learning

TABLE OF CONTENTS

High School Math Solution
Algebra I

Student Edition
Volume 2

Sandy Bartle Finocchi and Amy Jones Lewis

with Josh Fisher, Janet Sinopoli, and Victoria Fisher

501 Grant St., Suite 1075
Pittsburgh, PA 15219
Phone 888.851.7094
Customer Service Phone 412.690.2444
Fax 412.690.2444

www.carnegielearning.com

Cover Design by Anne Milliron

ISBN: 978-1-68459-281-4
Student Edition, Volume 2

Printed in the United States of America
 3 4 5 6 7 8 9 BB 21 20

LONG + LIVE + MATH

ACKNOWLEDGMENTS

High School Math Solution Authors
- Sandy Bartle Finocchi, Senior Academic Officer
- Amy Jones Lewis, Director of Instructional Design
- Josh Fisher, Instructional Designer
- Victoria Fisher, Instructional Designer
- Janet Sinopoli, Instructional Designer

Foundational Authors
- William S. Hadley, Co-Founder
- David Dengler
- Mary Lou Metz

Vendors
- Lumina Datamatics, Ltd.
- Mathematical Expressions, LLC

Images
www.pixabay.com

Special Thanks

- Alison Huettner for project management and editorial review.
- Jacyln Snyder for her contributions to the Teacher's Implementation Guide facilitation notes.
- Harry Lynch for his contributions and review of the Statistics and Probability strand.
- The members of Carnegie Learning Cognitive Scientist Team—Brendon Towle, John Connelly, Bob Hausmann, Chas Murray, and Martina Pavelko—for their insight in learning science and collaboration on MATHia® Software.
- John Jorgenson, Chief Marketing Officer, for all his insight and messaging.
- Carnegie Learning Education Services Team for content review and providing customer feedback.
- The entire Carnegie Learning staff for their hard work and dedication to transforming math education.
- The families of the authoring team for their continued support.

Module 2: Exploring Constant Change

Topic 1: Linear Functions

Topic 2: Solving Linear Equations and Inequalities

Topic 3: Systems of Equations and Inequalities

Module 3: Investigating Growth and Decay

Topic 1: Introduction to Exponential Functions

Topic 2: Using Exponential Equations

Module 4: Describing Distributions

Module 5: Maximizing and Minimizing

Topic 2: Solving Quadratic Equations

Topic 3: Applications of Quadratics

INVESTIGATING
Growth
&decay

The lessons in this module build on your experience with geometric sequences to learn about exponential functions. You will analyze and write equations to represent exponential functions and explore their graphs. You will extend your understanding of the rules of integer exponents to learn about rational exponents and solve simple exponential equations.

Introduction to Exponential Functions

You can recognize the graph of an exponential equation because it increasingly increases (or decreasingly decreases).

Module 3: Investigating Growth and Decay

TOPIC 1: INTRODUCTION TO EXPONENTIAL FUNCTIONS

In this topic, students build upon their previous understanding of sequences and common ratio to recognize that some geometric sequences are exponential functions and others are not. Next, students examine the structure of exponential functions, connecting the common ratio of a geometric sequence with the base of the power in an exponential function. Students explore the constant ratio between intervals of $\frac{1}{2}$, $\frac{1}{3}$, and $\frac{1}{4}$ for the function $f(x) = 2^x$. Through this exploration, they conclude that $2^{\frac{1}{2}} = \sqrt{2}$ and $2^{\frac{1}{3}} = \sqrt[3]{2}$. By graphing these values, the misconception that $f\left(\frac{1}{2}\right)$ is halfway between $f(1)$ and $f(2)$ is addressed. Finally, students transform exponential functions and generalize the effect of these transformations on (x, y).

Where have we been?

In middle school, students learned the rules of exponents and used those rules to rewrite expressions in equivalent forms. They transformed geometric objects in the coordinate plane and noted the effect of each transformation on the ordered pairs of the image. This topic begins where students left with geometric sequences in a previous topic. Students can already write a recursive and an explicit formula for a given geometric sequence.

Where are we going?

Throughout this topic, students apply what they know about the key characteristics of functions (e.g., intercepts, intervals of increase or decrease, domain and range, the rules of transformations) to include exponential functions. This prepares them for the work they will do with quadratic functions, both in this course and with more complex functions in subsequent courses.

Inside and Outside the Function

Different transformations of a function—such as a vertical stretching or compressing or horizontal stretching or compressing, vertical or horizontal translations, and reflections—can be specified when writing a function in transformation form.

Values inside the function affect the horizontal transformations of the graph, and values outside the function affect the vertical transformations of the graph.

outside the function

$$g(x) = A \cdot f(B(x - C)) + D$$

inside the function

The Matthew Effect

It might seem unfair, but some banks will charge you money for not having money. And they'll pay you money if you have a lot of it.

In 2015, the big three banks in the United States made about $6 billion in overdraft fees. By contrast, personal interest income in 2017 was over $1.4 trillion!

When you deposit money in a bank account that accrues interest, your money doesn't just sit there, waiting for you to withdraw it. The bank lends this money to people who want to buy cars, houses, and pay for college. Banks collect interest on these loans and reward you for your contribution. The more money you have in an interest-earning account, the more you are rewarded!

Talking Points

Exponential functions is an important topic to know about for college admissions tests.

Here is a sample question:

> **A biology class predicted that a population of animals will double in size every year. The population at the start of 2018 was about 500 animals. If P represents the population n years after 2018, what equation represents the model of the population over time?**

To solve this, students should know that this represents an exponential function, because the population doubles each year. This can be written as:

$$\text{initial value} \cdot (\text{growth rate})^{time}$$

The initial value is 500 animals, and the growth rate is 2, for doubling. So, the function $P(n) = 500 \cdot 2^n$ models the population over time in years, n.

Key Terms

exponential function
An exponential function is a function of the form $f(x) = a \cdot b^x$, where a and b are real numbers, and b is greater than 0 but is not equal to 1.

horizontal asymptote
A horizontal asymptote is a horizontal line that a function gets closer and closer to, but never intersects.

A Constant Ratio

Geometric Sequences and Exponential Functions

Warm Up

Use the explicit formula to generate the first 4 terms of each geometric sequence.

1. $g_n = 2 \cdot 3^{x-1}$

2. $g_n = 8240 \cdot 1.05^{x-1}$

3. $g_n = 100 \cdot \left(\frac{1}{2}\right)^{x-1}$

4. $g_n = (-2) \cdot 4^{x-1}$

Learning Goals

- Write a geometric sequence as an exponential function in the form $f(x) = a \cdot b^x$.
- Identify the constant ratio and y-intercept in different representations of exponential functions.
- Recognize when a relationship is exponential.
- Use algebra to show that, for an exponential function in the form $f(x) = a \cdot b^x$, the ratio $\frac{f(x + 1)}{f(x)}$ is constant and equal to b, and the y-intercept is represented by the ordered pair $(0, a)$.

You have learned about geometric sequences and have briefly explored exponential functions. How can you use geometric sequences to define exponential functions?

Compare and Contrast

Recall that a geometric sequence is a sequence of values in which consecutive terms are separated by a common ratio, or constant ratio. For example, the sequence shown is a geometric sequence with a constant ratio of 2.

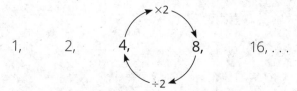

The graphs of six different geometric sequences are shown.

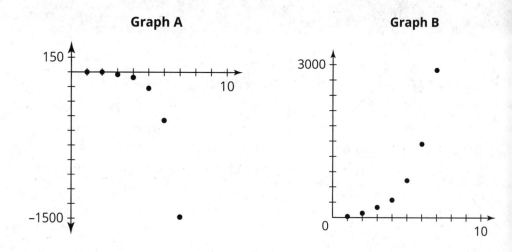

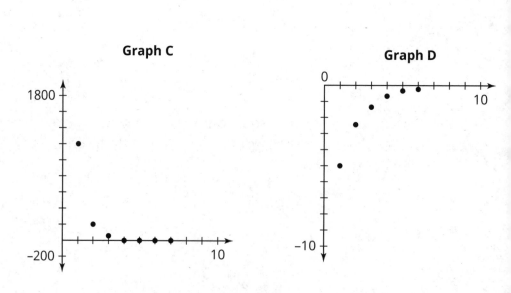

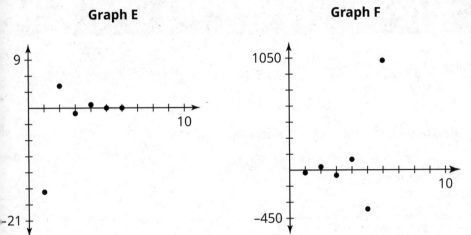

Graph E

Graph F

1. Identify similarities and differences among the graphs. What do you notice?

The explicit formula for a geometric sequence is $g_n = g_1 \cdot r^{n-1}$.

A table of values, a graph, and the explicit formula are given for six geometric sequences.

1. Identify the constant ratio in each representation.

a. Sequence A

x	y
1	−2
2	−6
3	−18

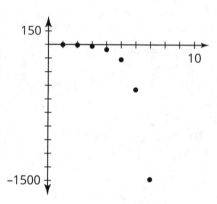

$y = -2 \cdot 3^{x-1}$

b. Sequence B

x	y
1	45
2	90
3	180

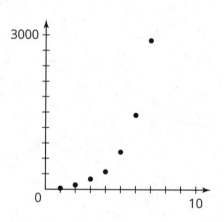

$y = 45 \cdot 2^{x-1}$

c. Sequence C

x	y
1	1234
2	123.4
3	12.34

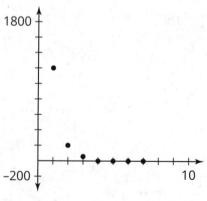

$y = 1234 \cdot 0.1^{x-1}$

d. Sequence D

x	y
1	−5
2	−2.5
3	−1.25

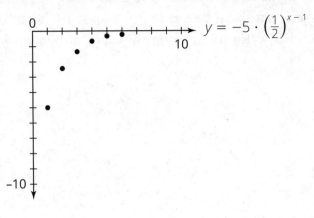

$$y = -5 \cdot \left(\tfrac{1}{2}\right)^{x-1}$$

e. Sequence E

x	y
1	−16
2	4
3	−1

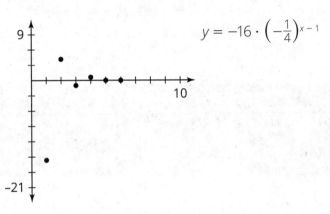

$$y = -16 \cdot \left(-\tfrac{1}{4}\right)^{x-1}$$

f. Sequence F

x	y
1	−4
2	12
3	−36

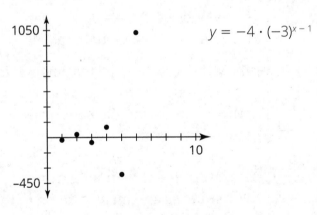

$$y = -4 \cdot (-3)^{x-1}$$

2. **What strategies did you use to identify the constant ratio for each sequence?**

All arithmetic sequences can be represented as linear functions. Is there a function family that can represent geometric sequences?

3. **Analyze the graphs of the geometric sequences. Do any of the graphs appear to belong to a specific function family? If so, identify the function family. Explain your reasoning.**

ACTIVITY 1.2 Exponential Growth

A famous legend tells the story of the inventor of the game of chess. When the inventor showed the new game to the emperor of India, the emperor was so astonished, he said to the inventor, "Name your reward!"

The wise inventor asked the emperor for 1 grain of rice for the first square of the chessboard, 2 grains for the second square, 4 grains for the third square, 8 grains for the fourth square, and so on.

Square Number	Number of Rice Grains	Power
1	1	
2	2	
3	4	
4	8	
5		
6		
7		
8		

1. **Determine the number of rice grains on the next 4 squares and include them in the table. Complete the third column by writing each number of rice grains as a power with the same base.**

2. **What pattern do you notice in the table?**

3. Graph the points from your table. The first few points have been plotted. Describe the meaning of the plotted points and then identify the function family represented.

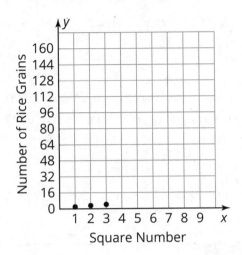

4. Identify the constant ratio in the graph, in the table, and in the situation.

5. Pat and George each used different methods to write an exponential function to represent the number of rice grains for any square number on the chessboard.

Pat
I compared the exponents of the power to the square number in the table. Each exponent is 1 less than the square number.
$$f(s) = 2^{s-1}$$

George
I know the constant ratio is 2. If I extend the pattern back, I get the y-intercept of $(0, \frac{1}{2})$, so I can rewrite the function as
$$f(s) = \frac{1}{2}(2)^s$$

Use properties of exponents to verify that 2^{s-1} and $\frac{1}{2}(2)^s$ are equivalent.

The function that George wrote is in exponential form. Recall that an exponential function is a function of the form $f(x) = a \cdot b^x$, where a and b are real numbers, and b is greater than 0 but is not equal to 1.

6. **What do the a-value and b-value represent in terms of the equation and graph?**

7. **Use the exponential function and a calculator to determine the number of rice grains that would be on the very last square of the chessboard. A chessboard has 64 squares.**

You can write the explicit formula for geometric sequences in function notation.

Think about:

The Product Rule of Exponents allows you to rewrite the product of two powers with the same base:

$2^n \cdot 2^{(-1)} = 2^{n-1}$
$6^x \cdot 6^y = 6^{x+y}$

Worked Example

Represent $g_n = 45 \cdot 2^{n-1}$ as a function in the form $f(x) = a \cdot b^x$.

$$g_n = 45 \cdot 2^{n-1}$$
$$f(n) = 45 \cdot 2^{n-1}$$

Next, rewrite the expression $45 \cdot 2^{n-1}$.

$f(n) = 45 \cdot 2^n \cdot 2^{-1}$	Product Rule of Powers
$f(n) = 45 \cdot 2^{-1} \cdot 2^n$	Commutative Property
$f(n) = 45 \cdot \frac{1}{2} \cdot 2^n$	Definition of negative exponent
$f(n) = \frac{45}{2} \cdot 2^n$	Multiply.

So, $g_n = 45 \cdot 2^{n-1}$ written in function notation is $f(n) = \left(\frac{45}{2}\right) \cdot 2^n$, or $f(n) = (22.5) \cdot 2^n$.

In the previous activity you identified some of the geometric sequences as exponential functions and some that were not exponential functions.

8. **Rewrite each explicit formula of the geometric sequences that are exponential functions in function form. Identify the constant ratio and the y-intercept.**

Sequence	Explicit Formula	Exponential Function $f(x) = a \cdot b^x$	Constant Ratio	y-Intercept
A	$-2 \cdot 3^{x-1}$			
B	$45 \cdot 2^{x-1}$			
C	$1234 \cdot 0.1^{x-1}$			
D	$-5 \cdot \left(\frac{1}{2}\right)^{(x-1)}$			

Based on the graphs of Sequences E and F, you can tell they do not represent exponential functions.

9. **Rewrite each explicit formula in function form and explain why these geometric sequences are not exponential functions.**

    a. **Sequence E:** $y = -4 \cdot (-3)^{x-1}$ b. **Sequence F:** $y = -16 \cdot \left(-\frac{1}{4}\right)^{x-1}$

10. **You know that all arithmetic sequences are linear functions. What can you say about the relationship between geometric sequences and exponential functions?**

11. **Complete the table by writing each part of the exponential function that corresponds to each part of the geometric sequence.**

Geometric Sequence $g_n = g_1 \cdot r^{n-1}$	Exponential Function $f(x) = a \cdot b^x$	Mathematical Meaning
g_n		
$\dfrac{g_1}{r}$		
r		
n		

Identifying Exponential Functions

As part of a project in health class, Aliyah, Kim, and Reese are raising awareness and challenging others to eat a healthy breakfast each morning. Today, they each sent selfies of themselves eating a healthy breakfast to 4 friends and challenged them to do the same the next day. This next day when others send selfies of themselves eating a healthy breakfast will be considered Day 1 of their results. The following day, only those contacted the previous day will send selfies to 4 friends, and the challenge will continue to spread. Assume everyone contacted completes the challenge and new participants are contacted each day.

> The constant ratio of an exponential function must be greater than 0 and not equal to 1.

1. **Write an exponential function, $f(x)$, to represent the number of new participants of the challenge as a function of the day number, x.**

The results after 4 days of the challenge are shown in the table.

Time (Day)	Number of New Participants
1	12
2	48
3	192
4	768

2. **The relationship between time and number of participants is exponential.**

   a. **Verify the relationship is exponential by identifying the constant ratio.**

b. What is the number of new participants for Day 0? Explain your answer.

c. If the number of new participants for Day 0 is represented by $f(x) = a \cdot b^x$, then the number of new participants for Day 1 can be represented by $f(x + 1) = a \cdot b^{(x+1)}$. Complete the table to show the number of new participants as a function of the day in terms of x and $f(x)$.

Time (Day)	Number of New Participants	Function Form
x	$f(x)$	$f(x) = a \cdot b^x$
0	$f(x)$	$f(x) = a \cdot b^x$
1	$f(x + 1)$	12	$f(x + 1) = a \cdot b^{(x+1)}$
2		48	
3		192	
4		768	

d. Use the expressions from the Function Form column of the table and algebra to prove that the table shows a constant ratio between consecutive output values of the function.

> Recall that the Quotient Rule of Powers states that when dividing powers with the same base you can subtract their exponents.
> $$\frac{b^{x+2}}{b^{x+1}} = b^{(x+2)-(x+1)}$$

The Amazing Aloysius is practicing one of his tricks. As part of the trick, he cuts a rope into many pieces and then magically puts the pieces of rope back together. He begins the trick with a 10-foot rope and then cuts it in half. He takes one of the halves and cuts that piece in half. He keeps cutting the pieces in half until he is left with a piece so small he can't cut it anymore.

1. **Complete the table to show the length of rope after each of Aloysius's cuts. Write each length as a whole number, mixed number, or fraction. Then graph the points from the table.**

Number of Cuts	Length of Rope (feet)
0	
1	
2	
3	
4	
5	

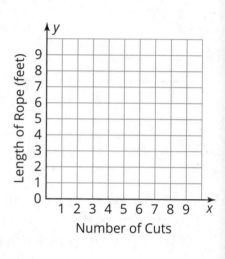

2. **Write the function, $L(c)$, to represent the length of the rope as a function of the cut number, c.**

3. **Use your function to determine the length of the rope after the 7th cut.**

. **Write an exponential function of the form $f(x) = a \cdot b^x$ for each table and graph.**

a.

x	y
0	4
1	2
2	1
3	$\frac{1}{2}$

b.

x	y
−2	$-\frac{1}{2}$
−1	−2
0	−8
1	−32

c.

x	y
0	1
1	4
2	16
3	64

d.

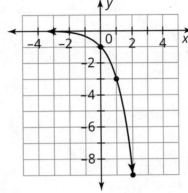

TALK the TALK

Did We Mention Constant Ratio?

1. For an exponential function of the form $f(x) = a \cdot b^x$, what is the relationship between the base of the power, the expression $\dfrac{f(x + 1)}{f(x)}$, and the common ratio of the corresponding geometric sequence?

2. How can you decide whether a geometric sequence of the form $g_n = g_1 \cdot b^{n-1}$ represents an exponential function?

Assignment

Write

Describe the differences between a linear function and an exponential function using your own words.

Remember

All sequences are functions, and some geometric sequences are exponential functions.

The form of an exponential function is $f(x) = a \cdot b^x$, where a and b are real numbers and $b > 0$, but $b \neq 1$. The a-value represents the y-intercept and the b-value represents the constant ratio, or constant multiplier.

Practice

1. Each table shows the population of a city over a three-year period. Write an exponential function to represent each population as a function of time.

a.

Blueville	
1	7098
2	7197
3	7298

b.

Youngstown	
1	12,144
2	12,290
3	12,437

c.

Greenville	
1	7860
2	7722
3	7587

2. Consider each situation. If possible, identify a constant ratio and write an exponential function to represent the relationship. Be sure to define your variables.

a. Manuel works in a lab. The number of bacteria over time in a petri dish he is studying is shown in the table.

Bacteria	
Time (hours)	Number of Bacteria
0	605
1	2420
2	9680
3	38,720

b. Jessica has been studying the honey bee population. The number of honey bees she documents over time is shown in the table.

Honey Bee Population	
Time (years)	Number of Honey Bees
1	52,910
2	43,069
3	35,058
4	28,537

c. Jackson started depositing money into a savings account. The amount of money over time in the account is shown in the table.

Savings Account	
Time (years)	Value ($)
5	875
10	1200
15	1525
20	1850

Stretch

Which of the functions does not fit with the others? Explain your answer.

A. The exponential function that goes through (0, −3) and (5, −96).

B. $f(x) = -1 \cdot 6^x$

C.

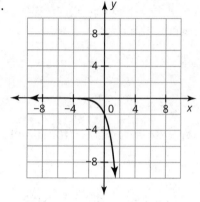

D.

x	y
1	$\frac{2}{3}$
2	$\frac{2}{9}$
3	$\frac{2}{27}$

Review

1. Solve each equation. Show your work.

   a. $|x - 4| = 7$

   b. $|3x + 5| = 11$

2. Determine the inverse of each function. Is the inverse also a function? Explain why or why not.

   a. $y = -4$

   b. $y = \left(\frac{1}{4}\right)x + \frac{3}{2}$

3. Solve each system of linear equations.

   a. $\begin{cases} y = -5x - 21 \\ -2x + 5y = -24 \end{cases}$

   b. $\begin{cases} 8x - 3y = 4 \\ 7x - 10y = -26 \end{cases}$

The Power Within

Rational Exponents and Graphs of Exponential Functions

Warm Up

Use the properties of exponents to rewrite each expression.

1. $\dfrac{b^3}{b^0}$

2. $\dfrac{a \cdot x^5}{a \cdot x^4}$

3. $a \cdot b^2 \cdot a^2 \cdot b^3$

4. $b^{-2} \cdot b^2 \cdot a^0$

Learning Goals

- Rewrite powers with rational exponents as radical expressions.
- Rewrite radical expressions as powers with rational exponents.
- Use the properties of exponents to interpret output values for non-integer input values in exponential functions.
- Construct exponential functions and identify a common ratio between output values in a graph, a table, and the equation.
- Solve simple exponential equations using common bases.

Key Terms

- horizontal asymptote
- extracting square roots

You have determined the constant ratio of exponential functions with integer inputs. How can you use a constant ratio to determine output values with non-integer inputs?

Squares and Cubes

Write an expression to represent the side length, s, of each square, given it area. Then approximate the value of s. Show your work.

1. Area = 5 ft²

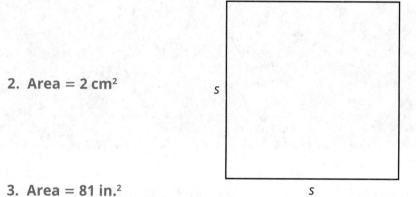

2. Area = 2 cm²

3. Area = 81 in.²

Write an expression to represent the side length, s, of each cube, given its volume. Then approximate the value of s. Show your work.

4. Volume = 51 ft³

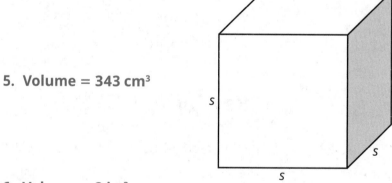

5. Volume = 343 cm³

6. Volume = 2 in.³

Characteristics of Exponential Growth

In a laboratory experiment, a certain bacteria doubles each hour.

1. **Suppose a bacteria population starts with just 1 bacterium.**

   a. **Complete the table to show the population of bacteria, $f(x)$, over time, x.**

x	1	2	3	4
$f(x)$				

   b. **Determine the constant ratio and y-intercept. Then write the exponential function that represents the growth of the bacteria population over time. Show your work.**

   c. **How is the constant multiplier evident in the problem situation?**

   > The constant ratio is a multiplier. To determine the next term of a geometric sequence, you multiply by this value.

2. **Graph the exponential function to show bacteria growth over time on the coordinate plane located at the end of the lesson.**

The Square Root Constant Ratio of an Exponential Function

An exponential function is continuous, meaning that there is a value $f(x)$ for every real number value x.

The table shown represents the function $f(x) = 2^x$, which models the laboratory experiment that a certain population of bacteria can double each hour.

x	0	1	2	3
$f(x)$	2^0	2^1	2^2	2^3
	1	2	4	8

In the table, the interval between the input values is 1, and the constant multiplier is 2 at the point when the interval changes. What effect, if any, is there on the constant multiplier if the input interval is different?

1. **Consider the ratio $\frac{f(2)}{f(0)}$.**

   a. **Describe the interval of input values. Then determine the multiplier.**

   b. **Write two additional ratios that have the same multiplier. Explain your reasoning.**

   c. **Write a new pair of ratios that have the same multiplier but span a different input interval than the intervals you have already analyzed. Justify your answer.**

Vicky, Nate, and Taylor are interested in the population of bacteria at each $\frac{1}{2}$-hour interval. They have values for the exponential function $f(x)$ when x is an integer. They need the values of the exponential function when x is a rational number between integers.

. The three students used the idea of the constant multiplier to estimate the value of $f\left(\frac{1}{2}\right)$ for the function $f(x) = 2^x$.

Vicky 👍

I know the constant multiplier for an interval of 1 is 2. I want to split each interval of 1 into two equal parts, which means I need two equal multipliers.

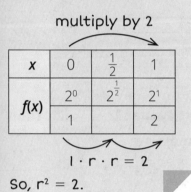

multiply by 2

x	0	$\frac{1}{2}$	1
$f(x)$	2^0	$2^{\frac{1}{2}}$	2^1
	1		2

$1 \cdot r \cdot r = 2$

So, $r^2 = 2$.

Nate 👍

If r is a constant multiplier for the function as it grows by consecutive integers, it can be split into two equal multipliers of $\sqrt{r}$, because r can be split into two equal factors of $\sqrt{r}$.

$$(\sqrt{r})^2 = r$$

Taylor 👎

If $f(0) = 2^0 = 1$ and $f(1) = 2^1 = 2$, then $f\left(\frac{1}{2}\right) = 2^{\frac{1}{2}}$ must be equal to 1.5.

a. Use Vicky's and Nate's thinking to determine $f\left(\frac{1}{2}\right)$. Write $f\left(\frac{1}{2}\right)$ as a power of 2 and in radical form. Then, enter the values in the table.

x	0	$\frac{1}{2}$	1	2	3
$f(x)$	2^0		2^1	2^2	2^3
	1		2	4	8

b. Use the graph you created in the previous activity to approximate $f\left(\frac{1}{2}\right)$ as a decimal.

c. Explain why Taylor's thinking is incorrect.

The expression $\sqrt{2} = 2^{\frac{1}{2}}$. The square root symbol ($\sqrt{}$) is interpreted as the rational exponent $\frac{1}{2}$. All the properties with integer exponents you previously learned continue to apply even when the exponent is a rational number.

The tables shown represent two different equivalent representations of the constant multiplier, $2^{\frac{1}{2}}$ or $\sqrt{2}$, for the function $f(x) = 2^x$.

The number 2 is a rational number because it can be represented as the ratio of two integers. The number $\sqrt{2}$ is an irrational number, because it cannot be represented as the ratio of two integers.

Rational Exponent Representation	
$f(0)$	2^0
$f\left(\frac{1}{2}\right)$	$2^{\frac{1}{2}}$
$f(1)$	2^1
$f\left(\frac{3}{2}\right)$	$2^{\frac{3}{2}}$

$2^0 \cdot 2^{\frac{1}{2}}$
$2^{\frac{1}{2}} \cdot 2^{\frac{1}{2}}$
$2^1 \cdot 2^{\frac{1}{2}}$

Radical Form Representation	
$f(0)$	1
$f\left(\frac{1}{2}\right)$	$\sqrt{2}$
$f(1)$	2
$f\left(\frac{3}{2}\right)$	$2\sqrt{2}$

$1 \cdot \sqrt{2}$
$\sqrt{2} \cdot \sqrt{2}$
$2 \cdot \sqrt{2}$

3. **Use the properties of exponents to justify that $2^1 \cdot 2^{\frac{1}{2}} = 2^{\frac{3}{2}}$. Then use the graph to estimate $2^{\frac{3}{2}}$ as a decimal.**

In the expression $\sqrt[n]{a}$, the n is called the index.

A rational exponent can be rewritten in radical form using the definition $a^{\frac{1}{n}} = \sqrt[n]{a}$. When the index is 2, it is usually implied rather than written.

Let's consider the properties of exponents to rewrite expressions in equivalent forms.

The process of removing perfect square numbers from under a radical symbol is called **extracting square roots**.

> ### Worked Example
>
> Consider the expression $2^{\frac{3}{2}}$.
> Using the Power to a Power Rule: $2^{\frac{3}{2}} = \left(2^{\frac{1}{2}}\right)^3$ or $(2^3)^{\frac{1}{2}}$.
> You can use the definition of rational exponents to rewrite each expression in radical form.
>
> $$\left(2^{\frac{1}{2}}\right)^3 = (\sqrt{2})^3 \qquad\qquad (2^3)^{\frac{1}{2}} = \sqrt{2^3}$$
> $$= \sqrt{2} \cdot \sqrt{2} \cdot \sqrt{2} \qquad\qquad\quad = \sqrt{2 \cdot 2 \cdot 2}$$
> $$= 2\sqrt{2} \qquad\qquad\qquad\qquad = \sqrt{2^2 \cdot 2}$$
> $$\qquad\qquad\qquad\qquad\qquad\quad = 2\sqrt{2}$$

The Product Property of Radicals states that $\sqrt{a} \cdot \sqrt{b} = \sqrt{a \cdot b}$ when a and b are greater than 0.

You can see that $\sqrt{2} \cdot \sqrt{2} \cdot \sqrt{2} = \sqrt{2 \cdot 2 \cdot 2}$.

4. **Use the worked example to explain the Product Property of Radicals**

Now let's consider how to use the Product Rule of Powers to rewrite the expression with rational exponents in radical form.

Worked Example

Consider the expression $2^{\frac{3}{2}}$.

Using the Product Rule of Powers:

$$2^{\frac{3}{2}} = 2^{\frac{1}{2} + \frac{1}{2} + \frac{1}{2}}$$
$$= \left(2^{\frac{1}{2}}\right)\left(2^{\frac{1}{2}}\right)\left(2^{\frac{1}{2}}\right)$$
$$= \sqrt{2} \cdot \sqrt{2} \cdot \sqrt{2}$$
$$= \sqrt{2 \cdot 2 \cdot 2}$$

You can use the definition of rational exponents to rewrite each expression in radical form.

---

5. **Analyze the worked examples.**

   a. **Explain why $\sqrt{2} \cdot \sqrt{2} = 2$.**

   b. **Explain why $\sqrt{2^2} = 2$.**

6. **Tony and Bobby each calculate the population of bacteria when $t = \frac{5}{2}$ hours.**

   Tony says that when $t = \frac{5}{2}$ hours, $f\left(\frac{5}{2}\right) = \left(\sqrt{2}\right)^5$ bacteria.

   Bobby says that $f\left(\frac{5}{2}\right) = 4\sqrt{2}$ bacteria.

   Who's correct?

   Use definitions and rules to justify your reasoning. Then use the graph to estimate the value of $f\left(\frac{5}{2}\right)$ as a decimal on the graph.

You will learn and practice more with rational exponents later in this lesson.

ACTIVITY 2.3 | The Cube Root Constant Ratio of an Exponential Function

Think

about:

What is the constant multiplier you can use to build this relationship over intervals of $\frac{1}{3}$?

In the previous activity, you looked at the exponential function $f(x) = 2^x$. When the input interval is 1, the constant ratio is 2^1, and when the input interval is $\frac{1}{2}$, the constant multiplier is $2^{\frac{1}{2}}$.

Now, let's think about the constant multiplier when the input interval is $\frac{1}{3}$.

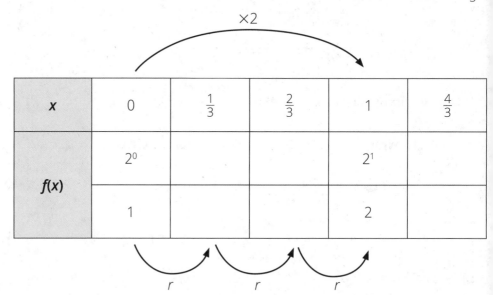

x	0	$\frac{1}{3}$	$\frac{2}{3}$	1	$\frac{4}{3}$
$f(x)$	2^0			2^1	
	1			2	

In the expression $\sqrt[n]{a}$, only $n = 2$ is implied rather than written. All other index values must be written.

1. **Complete the table of values for the exponential function $f(x) = 2^x$. Represent $f(x)$ as a rational exponent and in radical form. Show your work.**

2. **Write the points represented in the table as ordered pairs. Use the graph you created in the previous activity to estimate each output value as a decimal.**

Negative Exponents and Asymptotes

You have explored output values with integer and rational exponents for the exponential function $f(x) = 2^x$. What happens when x is a negative value?

1. **Use what you know about negative exponents to complete the table for the function $f(x) = 2^x$.**

x	-4	-3	-2	-1	0
$f(x)$					2^0
					1

Remember:

The Negative Power Rule states that
$a^{-1} = \frac{1}{a}$,
$a^{-2} = \frac{1}{a^2}$,
and so on.

2. **Consider the table of values you just completed. How does $f(x)$ change as x approaches negative infinity?**

An exponential function has a *horizontal asymptote*. A **horizontal asymptote** is a horizontal line that a function gets closer and closer to, but never intersects.

3. **Label the function $f(x) = 2^x$ on the coordinate plane shown. Identify the horizontal asymptote.**

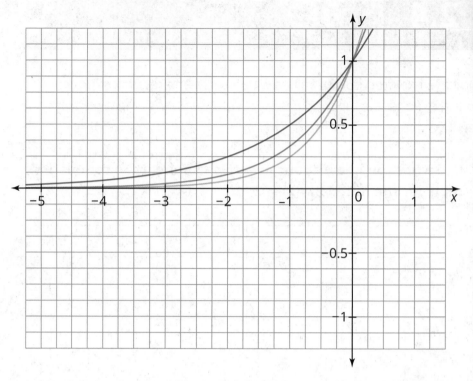

4. **The functions $g(x) = 3^x$ and $h(x) = 4^x$ are also shown on the coordinate plane.**

   a. **Identify each function, and explain how you know.**

   b. **Determine the horizontal asymptotes for the functions. Compare these with the horizontal asymptote of $f(x) = 2^x$.**

5. **Compare how each of the three functions approaches its horizontal asymptote. What is the same and what is different?**

In this lesson, you have been writing powers with rational exponents. You have shown that you can rewrite a rational exponent in radical form, $a^{\frac{1}{n}} = \sqrt[n]{a}$.

1. **Rewrite each expression as a power.**

   a. $\sqrt[3]{7}$ b. $\sqrt[5]{x}$ c. $\sqrt{y}$

2. **Rewrite each expression in radical form.**

   a. $8^{\frac{1}{4}}$ b. $z^{\frac{1}{5}}$ c. $m^{\frac{1}{3}}$

3. **Use the properties of exponents to rewrite $a^{\frac{m}{n}}$ in radical form.**

4. **Rewrite each expression in radical form.**

a. $4^{\frac{3}{2}}$ b. $5^{\frac{3}{4}}$ c. $x^{\frac{4}{5}}$ d. $y^{\frac{2}{3}}$

5. **Rewrite each expression as a power with a rational exponent.**

a. $\left(\sqrt[4]{2}\right)^3$ b. $\left(\sqrt{5}\right)^4$ c. $\left(\sqrt[5]{x}\right)^8$ d. $\left(\sqrt[5]{y}\right)^{10}$

Let's analyze the product of radicals.

Worked Example

You can rewrite the numeric expression $\left(\sqrt[3]{2}\right)^2\left(\sqrt{2}\right)$ in radical form using the rules of exponents.

$\left(2^{\frac{1}{3}}\right)^2 (2)^{\frac{1}{2}}$	Defintion of rational exponents
$\left(2^{\frac{2}{3}}\right)\left(2^{\frac{1}{2}}\right)$	Power to a Power Rule
$2^{\frac{2}{3}+\frac{1}{2}}$	Product Rule of Powers
$2^{\frac{7}{6}}$	Add fractions.
$\sqrt[6]{2^7}$	Definition of rational exponents

6. **Tonya rewrote the expression $\sqrt[6]{2^7}$ in a different way.**

$$2^{\frac{7}{6}} = 2^{\frac{6}{6}} \cdot 2^{\frac{1}{6}} = 2\sqrt[6]{2}$$

Is she correct? Justify your reasoning.

Let's revisit the Product Property of Radicals and the process of extracting roots.

Suppose you have the product $\sqrt{15} \cdot \sqrt{5}$. You can use properties of exponents to rewrite this radical expression.

Worked Example

$$\sqrt{15} \cdot \sqrt{5} = 15^{\frac{1}{2}} \cdot 5^{\frac{1}{2}} \qquad\qquad \sqrt{15} \cdot \sqrt{5} = \sqrt{15 \cdot 5}$$
$$\qquad\qquad = (15 \cdot 5)^{\frac{1}{2}} \qquad\qquad\qquad = \sqrt{3 \cdot 5 \cdot 5}$$
$$\qquad\qquad = (3 \cdot 5 \cdot 5)^{\frac{1}{2}} \qquad\qquad\qquad = \sqrt{3 \cdot 5^2}$$
$$\qquad\qquad = (3 \cdot 5^2)^{\frac{1}{2}} \qquad\qquad\qquad = 5\sqrt{3}$$
$$\qquad\qquad = 3^{\frac{1}{2}} \cdot 5$$
$$\qquad\qquad = 5\sqrt{3}$$

Rewrite each radical expression by extracting perfect squares.

a. $\sqrt{50}$

b. $\sqrt{24}$

c. $3\sqrt{20}$

d. $\sqrt{3} \cdot \sqrt{6}$

e. $\sqrt{3} \cdot \sqrt{12}$

f. $\sqrt{8} \cdot \sqrt{12}$

Explain how the properties of rational exponents extend from the properties of integer exponents.

9. Consider the calculations you made throughout this lesson and the definition of a rational number to answer each question.

a. Is the product of a nonzero rational number and an irrational number always, sometimes, or never a rational number? Explain your reasoning.

b. Is the product of an irrational number and an irrational number always, sometimes, or never a rational number? Explain your reasoning.

Worked Example

You can rewrite the numeric expression $\dfrac{\sqrt[3]{x}\,\sqrt{x}}{\sqrt[6]{x}}$ in radical form using rules of exponents.

$\dfrac{x^{\frac{1}{3}}x^{\frac{1}{2}}}{x^{\frac{1}{6}}}$	Rewrite using rational exponents.
$\dfrac{x^{\frac{1}{3}+\frac{1}{2}}}{x^{\frac{1}{6}}}$	Apply the Product Rule of Powers.
$\dfrac{x^{\frac{5}{6}}}{x^{\frac{1}{6}}}$	Add fractions.
$x^{\frac{4}{6}}$	Apply the Quotient Rule of Powers.
$x^{\frac{2}{3}}$	Rewrite fraction.
$\sqrt[3]{x^2}$	Rewrite in radical form.

0. **Rewrite each expression using the rules of exponents. Write responses in radical form.**

a. $\left(3^{\frac{3}{2}}\right)^3$

b. $\dfrac{\left(2^{-\frac{1}{2}}\right)^3}{\left(2^{\frac{1}{2}}\right)^{-1}}$

c. $\left(2x^{\frac{1}{2}}y^{\frac{1}{3}}\right)\left(3x^{\frac{1}{2}}y\right)$

d. $\left(\dfrac{24m^{\frac{3}{4}}n^{\frac{5}{2}}}{36m^{\frac{2}{7}}n^{\frac{2}{5}}}\right)^0$

Suppose a population of rabbits triples every year. The table shows their numbers.

Time (years)	Rabbit Population
0	2
1	6
2	18
3	54

1. **Write a function, f, to represent the rabbit population over time.**

2. **Use your equation to evaluate the population of rabbits for each number of years.**

   a. $f(10)$ b. $f(20)$ c. $f(30)$

How long did it take for the population of rabbits to reach a population of 4374? To answer this question, you must solve the equation $4374 = 2(3)^x$. This is equivalent to the equation $2187 = 3^x$.

Remember:

You know that a number is divisible by 3 when the sum of the digits is divisible by 3.

Worked Example

To solve the exponential equation $2187 = 3^x$, first determine the power of 3 that gives the result of 2187:

$$(3)(3)(3)(3)(3)(3)(3) = 2187$$

$$3^7 = 2187$$

Then rewrite the equation to show common bases:

$$3^7 = 3^x$$

Because the expressions on both sides of the equals sign have the same base, you can set up and solve an equation using the exponents:

$$7 = x$$

So, it will take 7 years for the rabbits to reach a population of 4374.

3. Use the method from the worked example to determine approximately how long it will take the rabbit population to reach 1 million. Explain your reasoning.

4. Solve each equation for x.

a. $3^x = 81$

b. $2^{4x} = 1$

c. $4^{8-x} = \frac{1}{64}$

d. $5^{9x} = 1$

e. $\frac{1}{3^{x+5}} = 243$

f. $2^{-x} = \frac{1}{2}$

TALK the TALK

May the Fourths Be With You

1. Consider the exponential function $f(x) = 2^x$.
   Complete the table. Then compare the table of fourths to the tables you completed for halves and thirds. What patterns do you notice in the multiplier?

x	0	$\frac{1}{4}$	$\frac{2}{4}$	$\frac{3}{4}$	1
$f(x)$	2^0				2^1
	1				2

2. Match each rational expression with the appropriate radical expression.

Rational Expression	Radical Expression
1. $2^{\frac{5}{10}}$	A. $\sqrt[5]{10^2}$
2. $10^{\frac{5}{2}}$	B. $\sqrt[5]{2^{10}}$
3. $10^{\frac{2}{5}}$	C. $\sqrt[10]{2^5}$
4. $5^{\frac{10}{2}}$	D. $\sqrt[2]{10^5}$
5. $2^{\frac{10}{5}}$	E. $\sqrt[2]{5^{10}}$
6. $5^{\frac{2}{10}}$	F. $\sqrt[10]{5^2}$

3. Solve for x and explain each step.
   $$4^x = \left(\frac{1}{2}\right)^{x-15}$$

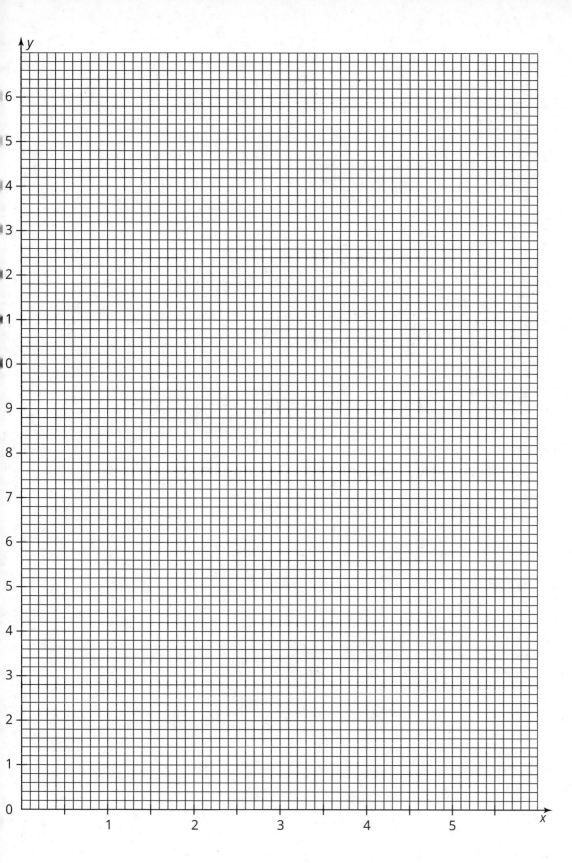

Assignment

Write

Describe how the components of radical form and rational exponent form of an equivalent expression are related.

Remember

If the difference in the input values is the same, an exponential function shows a constant multiplier between output values, no matter how large or how small the gap between input values.

If n is an integer greater than 1, then $\sqrt[n]{a} = a^{\frac{1}{n}}$.

Practice

Rewrite each radical using a rational exponent.

1. $\sqrt[4]{88}$
2. $\sqrt[10]{46}$
3. $\sqrt[6]{x}$
4. $\sqrt{z}$

Rewrite each power in radical form.

5. $9^{\frac{1}{3}}$
6. $5^{\frac{1}{2}}$
7. $20^{\frac{1}{5}}$
8. $41^{\frac{1}{8}}$

Rewrite each power in radical form. Simplify your answer, if possible.

9. $16^{\frac{3}{2}}$
10. $5^{\frac{7}{4}}$
11. $12^{\frac{2}{5}}$
12. $8^{\frac{4}{3}}$
13. $2^{\frac{5}{6}}$
14. $15^{\frac{6}{7}}$

Rewrite each expression using a rational exponent. Simplify your answer, if possible.

15. $(\sqrt[5]{10})^4$
16. $(\sqrt[4]{t})^4$
17. $(\sqrt{w})^6$
18. $(\sqrt[9]{h})^3$

Rewrite each radical expression by extracting perfect squares.

19. $\sqrt{12}$
20. $\sqrt{30}$
21. $\sqrt{27}$
22. $3\sqrt{75}$
23. $\sqrt{15} \cdot \sqrt{6}$
24. $\sqrt{14} \cdot \sqrt{2}$
25. $\sqrt{8} \cdot \sqrt{7}$
26. $\sqrt{10} \cdot \sqrt{15}$

Solve each exponential equation for x.

27. $4^x = 256$
28. $6^{3x} = 36$
29. $2^{5-x} = \frac{1}{16}$
30. $3^{-2x} = \frac{1}{81}$
31. $4^{x+3} = 4$
32. $\frac{1}{5^{x+4}} = 625$

Stretch

1. How do rational exponents help you to multiply or divide two radicals with different indices ($\sqrt[m]{a} \cdot \sqrt[n]{a}$ or $\frac{\sqrt[m]{a}}{\sqrt[n]{a}}$, when $m \neq n$)? Include two examples to support your answer.

Review

1. Complete the table.

Explicit Formula	Exponential Function	Constant Ratio	y-Intercept
$840 \cdot 3^{x-1}$			
$-3 \cdot \left(\frac{1}{5}\right)^{x-1}$			

2. Graph each function.

   a. $y = -3|x + 4| - 2$

   b. $y = 2|x - 1| + 2$

3. Solve each system of linear inequalities.

   a. $\begin{cases} y > -\frac{5}{4}x - 2 \\ x \geq -5 \end{cases}$

   b. $\begin{cases} 2x - 3y > -3 \\ x + 3y > -6 \end{cases}$

Now I Know My A, B, C, Ds

Transformations of Exponential Functions

Warm Up

1. Describe the effect of changing the *A*-value of the function $A \cdot f(x)$, given the basic function $f(x) = x$.

2. Describe the effect of changing the *D*-value of the function $f(x) + D$, given the basic function $f(x) = x$.

Learning Goals

- Graph exponential functions and transformations of exponential functions.
- Graph and analyze vertical translations and horizontal translations of exponential functions.
- Graph and analyze horizontal and vertical reflections of exponential functions.
- Graph and analyze horizontal dilations of exponential functions.
- Write equations of transformed functions from a graph.
- Write equations of transformed functions from a description.
- Rewrite exponential functions in different forms.

You know how to transform linear and absolute value functions. Do transformations of exponential functions behave in the same way?

H, I, J, . . .

Consider the function graphed.

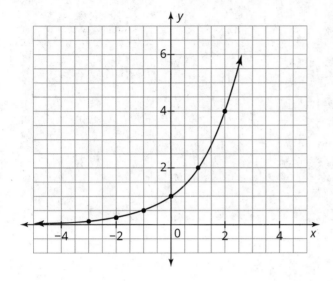

1. **Identify each part of the graphed function.**

   a. **the domain**

   b. **the range**

   c. **the horizontal asymptote**

Recall that the transformation form of a function $y = f(x)$, can be written as shown.

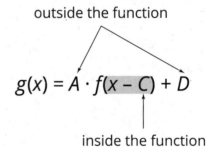

$$g(x) = A \cdot f(x - C) + D$$

2. **How do the A, C, and D values affect the graph of f(x)?**

Vertical Translations of Exponential Functions

Consider the three exponential functions: h, s, and t.

$$h(x) = 2^x \qquad s(x) = 2^x + 3 \qquad t(x) = 2^x - 3$$

In this case, $h(x) = 2^x$ is the basic function because it is the simplest exponential function with a base of 2. It is in the form $f(x) = a \cdot b^x$, where $a = 1$ and $b = 2$.

1. **Write the functions $s(x)$ and $t(x)$ in terms of the basic function $h(x)$. Then, describe the operation performed on the basic function $h(x)$ to result in each of the equations for $s(x)$ and $t(x)$.**

   $s(x) =$ _____

   $t(x) =$ _____

2. **Explain how you know that the graphs of $s(x)$ and $t(x)$ are vertical translations of the graph of $h(x)$.**

3. **Sketch and label the graphs of each function. Identify key points.**

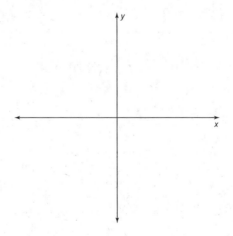

When graphing an exponential function, consider the points when $x = -1$, 0, and 1.

4. Compare the *y*-intercepts of the graphs of *s*(*x*) and *t*(*x*) to the *y*-intercept of the graph of the basic function *h*(*x*). What do you notice?

5. Compare the horizontal asymptotes of the graphs of *s*(*x*) and *t*(*x*) to the horizontal asymptote of the graph of the basic function *h*(*x*). What do you notice?

6. Write the *y*-value of each of the corresponding reference points on *s*(*x*) and *t*(*x*).

$h(x) = 2^x$	$s(x) = 2^x + 3$	$t(x) = 2^x - 3$
$\left(-2, \frac{1}{4}\right)$	(−2, ____)	(−2, ____)
$\left(-1, \frac{1}{2}\right)$	(−1, ____)	(−1, ____)
(0, 1)	(0, ____)	(0, ____)
(1, 2)	(1, ____)	(1, ____)
(2, 4)	(2, ____)	(2, ____)

7. Use the table to compare the ordered pairs of the graphs of *s*(*x*) and *t*(*x*) to the ordered pairs of the graph of the basic function *h*(*x*). What do you notice?

8. Complete each sentence with the coordinate notation to represent the vertical translation of each function.

a. $s(x) = h(x) + 3$

Each point (x, y) on the graph of $h(x)$ becomes the point _____ on $s(x)$.

b. $t(x) = h(x) - 3$

Each point (x, y) on the graph of $h(x)$ becomes the point _____ on $t(x)$.

Recall that for the basic function, the D-value of the transformed function $y = f(x) + D$ affects the output values of the function. For $D > 0$, the graph vertically shifts up. For $D < 0$, the graph vertically shifts down. The magnitude of the shift is given by $|D|$.

9. What generalization can you make about the effects of vertical translations on the domain, range, and asymptotes of exponential functions?

ACTIVITY

3.2

Horizontal Translations of Exponential Functions

Consider the three exponential functions shown, where $h(x) = 2^x$ is the basic function. The operations are performed on x, which is the argument of the function.

- $h(x) = 2^x$
- $v(x) = 2^{(x + 3)}$
- $w(x) = 2^{(x - 3)}$

You can write the given functions $v(x)$ and $w(x)$ in terms of the basic function $h(x)$.

Remember:

Recall that the argument of a function is the variable on which the function operates.

Worked Example

To write $v(x)$ in terms of $h(x)$, you just substitute $x + 3$ into the argument for $h(x)$, as shown.

$$h(x) = 2^x$$

$$v(x) = h(x + 3) = 2^{(x + 3)}$$

So, $x + 3$ replaces the variable x in the function $h(x) = 2^x$.

---

1. Write the function $w(x)$ in terms of the basic function $h(x)$.

2. Sketch and label the graph of each function. Identify key points.

Sketch the graphs one at a time to help you see which is which.

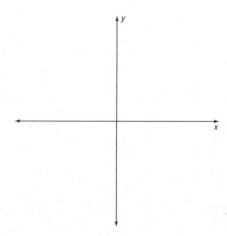

3. Compare the graphs of $v(x)$ and $w(x)$ to the graph of the basic function. What do you notice?

4. Write the x-value of each of the corresponding reference points on $v(x)$ and $w(x)$.

$h(x) = 2^x$	$v(x) = 2^{(x + 3)}$	$w(x) = 2^{(x - 3)}$
$\left(-2, \frac{1}{4}\right)$	$\left(\underline{\quad}, \frac{1}{4}\right)$	$\left(\underline{\quad}, \frac{1}{4}\right)$
$\left(-1, \frac{1}{2}\right)$	$\left(\underline{\quad}, \frac{1}{2}\right)$	$\left(\underline{\quad}, \frac{1}{2}\right)$
$(0, 1)$	$(\underline{\quad}, 1)$	$(\underline{\quad}, 1)$
$(1, 2)$	$(\underline{\quad}, 2)$	$(\underline{\quad}, 2)$
$(2, 4)$	$(\underline{\quad}, 4)$	$(\underline{\quad}, 4)$

5. Use the table to compare the ordered pairs of the graphs of $v(x)$ and $w(x)$ to the ordered pairs of the graph of the basic function $h(x)$. What do you notice?

Think about:

Notice there are no negative y-values in this table. Are negative values included in the range of h, v, or w?

If a constant is added or subtracted outside a function, like $g(x) + 3$ or $g(x) - 3$, then only the y-values change, resulting in a vertical translation.

And, if a constant is added or subtracted inside a function, like $g(x + 3)$ or $g(x - 3)$, then only the x-values change, resulting in a horizontal translation.

6. **Complete each sentence with the coordinate notation to represent the horizontal translation of each function.**

   a. $v(x) = h(x + 3)$
      Each point (x, y) on the graph of $h(x)$ becomes the point _____ on $v(x)$.

   b. $w(x) = h(x - 3)$
      Each point (x, y) on the graph of $h(x)$ becomes the point _____ on $w(x)$.

7. **Describe each graph in relation to the basic function $h(x) = b^x$.**

   a. **Compare $f(x) = h(x - C)$ to the basic function for $C > 0$.**

   b. **Compare $f(x) = h(x - C)$ to the basic function for $C < 0$.**

Recall that for the basic function, the C-value of the transformed function $y = f(x - C)$ affects the input values of the function. The value $|C|$ describes the number of units the graph of $f(x)$ is translated right or left. If $C > 0$, the graph is translated to the right. If $C < 0$, the graph is translated to the left.

8. **What generalization can you make about the effects of horizontal translations on the domain, range, and asymptotes of exponential functions?**

Consider the three exponential functions shown, where $h(x) = 2^x$ is the
basic function.

- $h(x) = 2^x$
- $m(x) = -(2^x)$
- $n(x) = 2^{(-x)}$

1. **Write the functions $m(x)$ and $n(x)$ in terms of the basic
   function $h(x)$.**

   $m(x) =$ _____

   $n(x) =$ _____

2. **Compare $m(x)$ to $h(x)$. Does an operation performed on $h(x)$ or
   on the argument of $h(x)$ result in the equation for $m(x)$? What is
   the operation?**

3. **Compare $n(x)$ to $h(x)$. Does an operation performed on $h(x)$ or
   on the argument of $h(x)$ result in the equation for $n(x)$? What is
   the operation?**

4. Use technology to sketch and label each function.

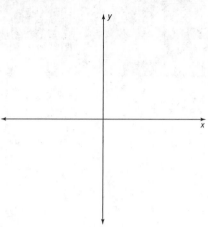

5. Compare the graphs of m(x) and n(x) to the graph of the basic function h(x). What do you notice?

6. Write the y-value of each of the corresponding reference points on m(x) and n(x).

$h(x) = 2^x$	$m(x) = -(2^x)$	$n(x) = 2^{(-x)}$
$(-2, \frac{1}{4})$	$(-2, \underline{\quad})$	$(\underline{\quad}, \frac{1}{4})$
$(-1, \frac{1}{2})$	$(-1, \underline{\quad})$	$(\underline{\quad}, \frac{1}{2})$
$(0, 1)$	$(0, \underline{\quad})$	$(\underline{\quad}, 1)$
$(1, 2)$	$(1, \underline{\quad})$	$(\underline{\quad}, 2)$
$(2, 4)$	$(2, \underline{\quad})$	$(\underline{\quad}, 4)$

7. Use the table to compare the ordered pairs of the graphs of m(x) and n(x) to the ordered pairs of the graph of the basic function h(x). What do you notice?

When the negative is on the outside of the function, like −g(x), all the y-values become the opposite of the y-values of g(x). The x-values remain unchanged.

Remember, a reflection of a graph is a mirror image of the graph about a line of reflection. A line of reflection is the line that the graph is reflected across. A horizontal line of reflection affects the y-coordinates, and a vertical line of reflection affects the x-coordinates.

. Consider the graphs of *m*(*x*) and *n*(*x*).

a. **Which function represents a reflection of *h*(*x*) across a horizontal line? Name the line of reflection.**

> When the negative is on the inside of the function, like *g*(−*x*), all the *x*-values become the opposite of the *x*-values of *g*(*x*). The *y*-values remain unchanged.

b. **Which function represents a reflection of *h*(*x*) across a vertical line? Name the line of reflection.**

. Complete each sentence with the coordinate notation to represent the reflection of each function.

a. ***m*(*x*) = −*h*(*x*)**

Each point (*x*, *y*) on the graph of *h*(*x*) becomes the point _____ on *m*(*x*).

b. ***n*(*x*) = *h*(−*x*)**

Each point (*x*, *y*) on the graph of *h*(*x*) becomes the point _____ on *n*(*x*).

Recall that for the basic function, the *A*-value of the transformed function $y = A \cdot f(x)$ affects the output values of the function. For $|A| > 1$, the graph vertically stretches. For $0 < |A| < 1$, the graph vertically compresses. For $A = -1$, the graph is reflected across the line $y = 0$, or the *x*-axis.

In this activity, you considered a different transformation that affects the input values of a function. For the basic function, the *B*-value of the transformed function $y = f(Bx)$ affects the input values of the function. For $B = -1$, the graph is reflected across the line $x = 0$, or the *y*-axis.

Let's consider different *B*-values and their effect on a basic function.

Consider the exponential functions, where $h(x) = 2^x$ is the basic function.

- $w(x) = 2^{\frac{1}{2}x}$
- $z(x) = 2^{2x}$

10. Write the function w(x) and z(x) in terms of h(x).

11. Use technology to sketch and label the graph of each function.

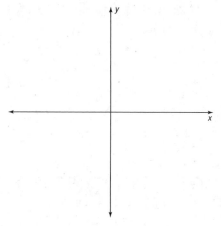

12. Compare the graphs of w(x) and z(x) to the graph of the basic function h(x). What do you notice?

13. Write the x-value of each of the corresponding reference points on w(x) and z(x).

$h(x) = 2^x$	$w(x) = 2^{\left(\frac{1}{2}x\right)}$	$z(x) = 2^{(2x)}$
$\left(-2, \frac{1}{4}\right)$	$\left(\underline{\quad}, \frac{1}{4}\right)$	$\left(\underline{\quad}, \frac{1}{4}\right)$
$\left(-1, \frac{1}{2}\right)$	$\left(\underline{\quad}, \frac{1}{2}\right)$	$\left(\underline{\quad}, \frac{1}{2}\right)$
$(0, 1)$	$(\underline{\quad}, 1)$	$(\underline{\quad}, 1)$
$(1, 2)$	$(\underline{\quad}, 2)$	$(\underline{\quad}, 2)$
$(2, 4)$	$(\underline{\quad}, 4)$	$(\underline{\quad}, 4)$

4. Use the table to compare the ordered pairs of the graphs of $w(x)$ and $z(x)$ to the ordered pairs of the graph of the basic function $h(x)$. What do you notice?

5. Given that the point (x, y) is on the graph of the function $y = f(x)$, what ordered pair describes a point on the graph of $g(x) = f(Bx)$?

Interpreting and Graphing Exponential Functions

There are different ways to interpret equations of exponential functions and transformations of exponential functions.

1. Jacob and Kate are comparing the two graphs shown.

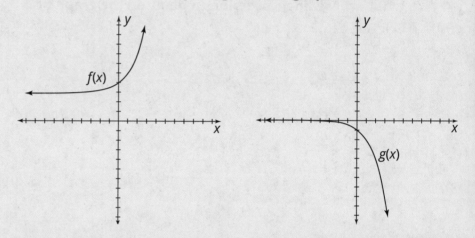

Jacob says that to get the graph of $g(x)$, first translate $f(x)$ down 3 units, and then reflect across the line $y = 0$. Kate says that to get the graph of $f(x)$, first reflect $g(x)$ across the line $y = 0$, and then translate up 3 units. Who is correct? Explain your reasoning.

2. Consider the function $f(x) = -2^{(x-3)} + 4$.

  a. Mike and Amy used the basic function in different ways to graph $f(x)$. Provide the step-by-step reasoning used by each student.

Mike 👍

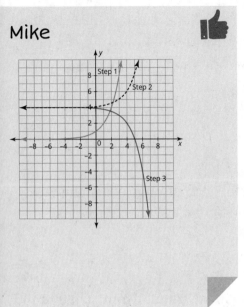

Amy 👍

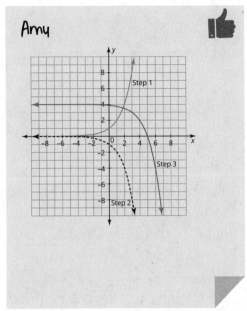

  b. Explain how changing the order of the transformations affects the line of reflection.

3. Use the given characteristics to write an equation and then graph $f'(x)$, given the basic function $f(x) = 2^x$. Label key points.

> One way to indicate the transformation of a function is by using the prime symbol. The function $f'(x)$ is a transformation of $f(x)$.

  a. $f'(x) = f(x) + 5$

    Equation: $f'(x) = $ _____

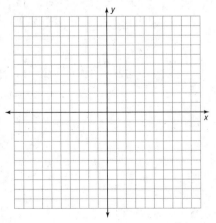

  b. $f'(x) = -f(x) + 5$

    Equation: $f'(x) = $ _____

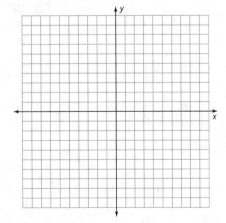

c. $f'(x) = f(-x) + 5$

Equation: $f'(x) =$ _____

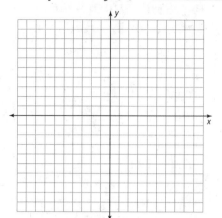

d. $f'(x) = -f(x) - 5$

Equation: $f'(x) =$ _____

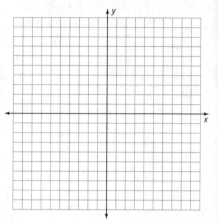

You have analyzed different ways to graph transformations of the basic function $h(x) = 2^x$. Now, let's consider different ways to interpret the equations of function transformations.

4. Andres and Tomas each described the effects of transforming the graph of $f(x) = 3^x$, such that $p(x) = 3f(x)$. Who's correct? Explain your reasoning.

Andres

$p(x) = 3f(x)$

The A-value is 3 so the graph is stretched vertically by a scale factor of 3.

Tomas

$p(x) = 3f(x)$
$p(x) = 3 \cdot 3^x$
$p(x) = 3^{(1+x)}$
$p(x) = f(x + 1)$

The C-value is -1 so the graph is horizontally translated 1 unit to the left.

5. Devonte says that you can rewrite the equation for $n(x) = 2^{(-x)}$ with a b-value equal to $\frac{1}{2}$. Is Devonte correct? Explain why or why not.

An exponential function can be rewritten to show an expression with no C- or B-value transformations.

Given the function $h(x) = 2^x$, consider the functions $v(x) = h(x + 3)$ and $t(x) = h(3x)$.

$v(x) = h(x + 3)$ $t(x) = h(3x)$

$v(x) = 2^{x+3}$ $t(x) = 2^{3x}$

You can rewrite $v(x)$ with no C-value and $t(x)$ with no B-value.

$v(x) = 2^{x+3}$ $t(x) = 2^{3x}$

$\quad = 2^x \cdot 2^3$ $\quad = (2^3)^x$

$\quad = 8 \cdot 2^x$ $\quad = 8^x$

6. Explain the steps to rewrite a function with no C-value and with no B-value. What effect does rewriting have on the b-value of the original function?

7. Given the function $f(x) = 2^x$.

   a. Rewrite $c(x) = f(x - 2)$ as an exponential function with no C-value transformation.

   b. Rewrite $b(x) = f(-2x)$ as an exponential function with no B-value transformation.

Writing Exponential Functions Given Graphs and Descriptions

1. **Consider the function, $f(x) = 2^x$. Write the function in transformation function form in terms of the transformations described, then write the equivalent equation.**

Transformation	Transformation Function Form	Equation
a. Reflection across the y-axis		
b. Reflection across the x-axis		
c. Horizontal translation of 2 units to the left and a vertical translation of 3 units up		
d. Vertical stretch of 2 units and a reflection across the line $y = 0$		
e. Reflection across the line $y = 3$		
f. Horizontal translation of 3 units to the right, a vertical translation down 2 units, and a vertical dilation of $\frac{1}{2}$		
g. Horizontal compression by a factor of 3		
h. Horizontal stretch by a factor of 3		
i. Vertical compression by a factor of 4		
j. Vertical stretch by a factor of 4		

2. Analyze the graphs of $f(x)$ and $g(x)$. Describe the transformations performed on $f(x)$ to create $g(x)$. Then, write an equation for $g(x)$ in terms of $f(x)$. For each set of points shown on $f(x)$, the corresponding points are shown on $g(x)$.

a. $g(x) =$ _____

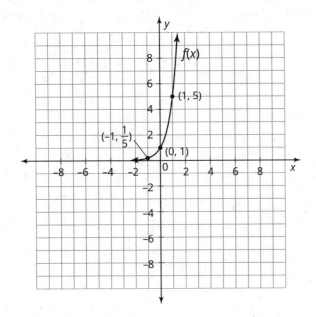

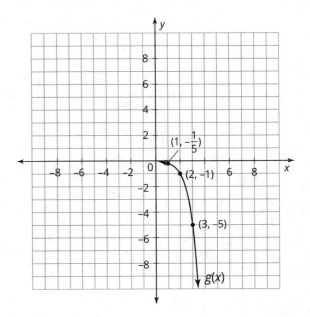

b. $g(x) =$ _____

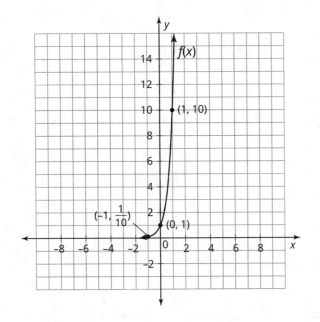

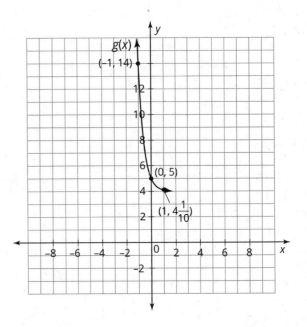

c. g(x) = _____

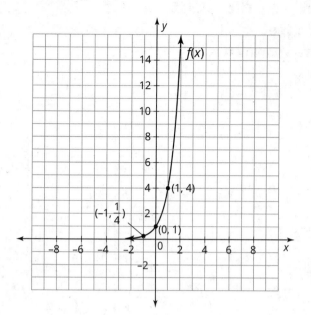

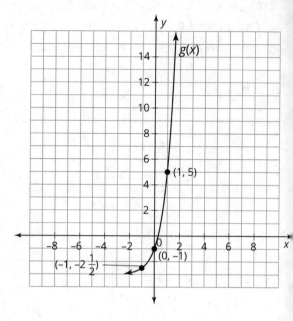

TALK the TALK

Next Time, Won't You Sing With Me?

1. Determine whether each statement is true or false. If the statement is false, rewrite the statement as true.

   a. In the transformation form of $f(x)$, $g(x) = Af(B(x - C)) + D$, the D-value translates the function $f(x)$ horizontally, the C-value translates $f(x)$ vertically, the A-value horizontally stretches or compresses $f(x)$, and the B-value vertically stretches or compresses $f(x)$.

   b. Key characteristics of basic exponential functions include a domain of non-negative numbers, a range of real numbers, and a vertical asymptote at $y = 0$.

   c. The domain of exponential functions is not affected by translations or dilations.

   d. Vertical translations do not affect the range and the horizontal asymptote of exponential functions.

   e. Horizontal translations do not affect the range and the horizontal asymptote of exponential functions.

   f. Vertical dilations do not affect the range and the horizontal asymptote of exponential functions.

   g. Horizontal dilations do not affect the range and the horizontal asymptote of exponential functions.

2. The basic exponential function can be written as $A \cdot 2^{B(x - C)} + D$. When $A = 1$, $B = 1$, $C = 0$, and $D = 0$, the function is equivalent to $f(x) = 2^x$. Complete the graphic organizer to summarize the transformations of an exponential function.

Graphic Organizer

A-Value

$$y = A \cdot 2^x$$

$|A| > 1$

$0 < |A| < 1$

$A = -1$

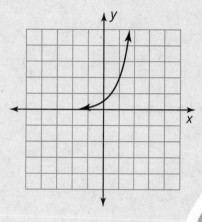

B-Value

$$y = 2^{Bx}$$

$|B| > 1$

$0 < |B| < 1$

$B = -1$

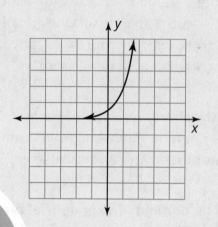

$$y = 2^x$$

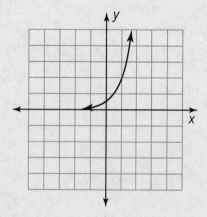

$C > 0$

$C < 0$

$$y = 2^{x - C}$$

C-Value

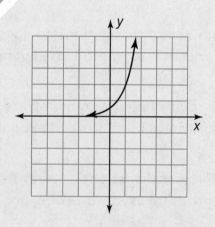

$D > 0$

$D < 0$

$$y = 2^x + D$$

D-Value

Assignment

Write

Given a basic function and the equation for a reflection of a basic function, explain how to determine whether the line of reflection will be the *x*-axis or the *y*-axis.

Remember

Transformations performed on any function $f(x)$ can be described by the transformation function $g(x) = Af(B(x - C)) + D$ where the *D*-value translates the function $f(x)$ vertically, the *C*-value translates $f(x)$ horizontally, the *A*-value vertically stretches or compresses $f(x)$, and the *B*-value horizontally stretches or compresses $f(x)$.

Practice

1. Complete the table to determine the corresponding points on $c(x)$, given reference points on $f(x)$. Then, graph $c(x)$ on the same coordinate plane as $f(x)$ and state the domain, range, and asymptotes of $c(x)$.

a. $f(x) = 2^x$

$c(x) = f(x - 1)$

Reference Points on $f(x)$	Corresponding Points on $c(x)$
$\left(-1, \frac{1}{2}\right)$	
$(0, 1)$	
$(1, 2)$	

b. $f(x) = 4^x$

$c(x) = -f(x) - 2$

Reference Points on $f(x)$	Corresponding Points on $c(x)$
$\left(-1, \frac{1}{4}\right)$	
$(0, 1)$	
$(1, 4)$	

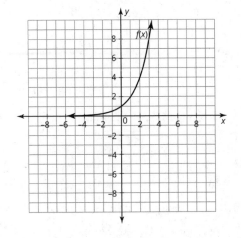

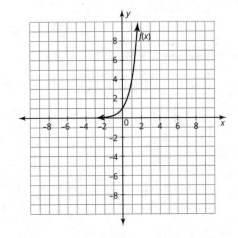

c. $f(x) = 2^x$

   $c(x) = 4f(x)$

Reference Points on $f(x)$	Corresponding Points on $c(x)$
$\left(-1, \frac{1}{2}\right)$	
$(0, 1)$	
$(1, 2)$	

d. $f(x) = 4^x$

   $c(x) = f(-x)$

Reference Points on $f(x)$	Corresponding Points on $c(x)$
$\left(-1, \frac{1}{4}\right)$	
$(0, 1)$	
$(1, 4)$	

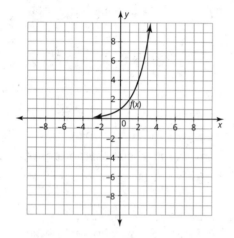

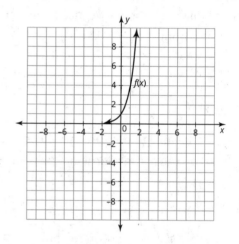

2. Describe the transformations performed on $m(x)$ that produced $t(x)$. Then, write an exponential equation for $t(x)$.

   a. $m(x) = 3^x$

      $t(x) = -m(x + 1)$

   b. $m(x) = 5^x$

      $t(x) = 3m(x) - 2$

   c. $m(x) = 5^x$

      $t(x) = m(-x)$

   d. $m(x) = 7^x$

      $t(x) = m(x - 2) + 3$

Stretch

Research real-world examples for which exponential functions provide good models. Write a short paragraph explaining why an exponential model works well for at least one of the examples.

Review

1. Rewrite each expression using properties of powers. Write the simplified expression in radical form.

   a. $(\sqrt{2})^3 \sqrt[3]{2}$

   b. $\dfrac{(\sqrt[3]{3})^2}{\sqrt[4]{3}}$

2. Solve each linear absolute value equation. Show your work.

   a. $6 - 7|x - 4| = -36$

   b. $-8|-10x| + 1 = -79$

3. Graph the piecewise function.

$$f(x) = \begin{cases} x + 2, & -5 < x \le -1 \\ y = 1, & -1 < x < 3 \\ -x + 4, & 3 \le x < 5 \end{cases}$$

4. Write a piecewise function to model the transformed absolute value function shown.

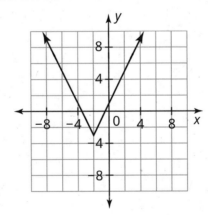

Introduction to Exponential Functions Summary

KEY TERMS

- horizontal asymptote
- extracting square roots

LESSON 1	A Constant Ratio

An exponential function is a function of the form $f(x) = ab^x$, where a and b are real numbers, and b is greater than 0 but is not equal to 1.

Geometric sequences with positive common ratios belong in the exponential function family. The common ratio of a geometric sequence is the base of an exponential function.

If a geometric sequence represents an exponential function, you can use the Product of Powers Rule and the definition of negative exponents to rewrite the explicit formula for the sequence as an exponential function.

For example, to represent $g_n = 45 \cdot 2^{n-1}$ using function notation, first rewrite it as $f(n) = 45 \cdot 2^{n-1}$. Next, rewrite the expression $45 \cdot 2^{n-1}$.

$f(n) = 45 \cdot 2^n \cdot 2^{-1}$ Product Rule of Powers
$f(n) = 45 \cdot 2^{-1} \cdot 2^n$ Commutative Property
$f(n) = 45 \cdot \frac{1}{2} \cdot 2^n$ Definition of negative exponent
$f(n) = \frac{45}{2} \cdot 2^n$ Multiply

So, $g_n = 45 \cdot 2^{n-1}$ written in function notation is $f(n) = \frac{45}{2} \cdot 2^n$.

The variable a in $f(x) = a \cdot b^x + c$ is the y-intercept, and b is the constant ratio.

The Power Within

An exponential function is continuous, meaning that there is a value $f(x)$ for every real number value x. If the difference in the input values is the same, an exponential function shows a constant ratio between output values, no matter how large or how small the gap between input values. A constant ratio can be used to determine output values for integer and for non-integer inputs.

An exponential function has a **horizontal asymptote**, which is a horizontal line that a function gets closer and closer to but never intersects.

Consider the table and graph represented by the function $f(x) = 4^x$.

x	f(x)
−2	$\frac{1}{16}$
−1	$\frac{1}{4}$
0	1
1	4
2	16

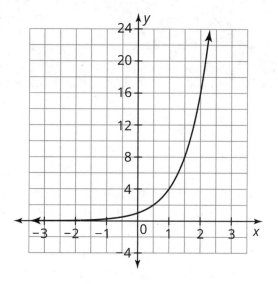

There are no x-intercepts. The y-intercept is at $(0, 1)$. The horizontal asymptote is $y = 0$. The domain is all real numbers and the graph increases over the entire domain. The range is $y > 0$.

A rational exponent is an exponent that is a rational number. You can write each nth root using a rational exponent. If n is an integer greater than 1, then $\sqrt[n]{a} = \frac{1}{a^n}$.

For example, $\sqrt[4]{b} = b^{\frac{1}{4}}$ and $6^{\frac{1}{5}} = \sqrt[5]{6}$.

Write expressions with rational exponents in radical form using the known properties of integer exponents. Write the power as a product using a unit fraction. Use the power of a power rule and the definition of a rational exponent to write the power as a radical.

For example, consider the expressions $8^{\frac{2}{3}}$ and $(\sqrt[7]{c})^3$.

$$8^{\frac{2}{3}} = 8^{\left(\frac{1}{3}\right)(2)} \qquad\qquad (\sqrt[7]{c})^3 = c^{\left(\frac{1}{7}\right)(3)}$$
$$= (\sqrt[3]{8})^2 \qquad\qquad\qquad\qquad = c^{\frac{3}{7}}$$

Rewrite radical expressions with an index of 2 by **extracting square roots**. This is the process of removing perfect squares from under the radical symbol.

For example, consider the irrational number represented by the radical expression $\sqrt{40}$.

$$\sqrt{40} = \sqrt{(4 \cdot 10)}$$
$$= \sqrt{4} \cdot \sqrt{10}$$
$$= 2\sqrt{10}$$

The product $2\sqrt{10}$ is an irrational number. The product of a nonzero rational number and an irrational number is always an irrational number, but the product of two irrational numbers can be irrational or rational.

Common bases and properties of exponents are used to solve simple exponential equations.

For example, to solve the exponential equation $2187 = 3^x$, first determine the power of 3 that gives the result of 2187: $(3)(3)(3)(3)(3)(3)(3) = 2187$, or $3^7 = 2187$.

Then rewrite the equation to show common bases: $3^7 = 3^x$.

Because the expressions on both sides of the equals sign have the same base, you can set up and solve an equation using the exponents: $7 = x$.

Now I Know My A, B, C, Ds

For the basic exponential function $f(x) = a \cdot b^x$, where $a = 1$, the transformed function can be written as $y = A \cdot b^{B(x-C)} + D$.

For the basic function, the *D*-value of the transformed function $y = f(x) + D$ affects the output values of the function. For $D > 0$, the graph vertically shifts up and for $D < 0$, the graph vertically shifts down. The amount of shift is given by $|D|$.

For example, consider $d(x)$.

$$d(x) = h(x) - 2$$

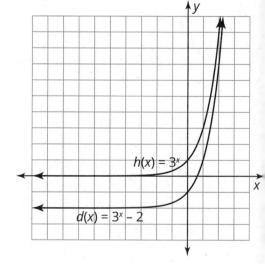

For the basic function, the *C*-value of the transformed function $y = f(x - C)$ affects the input values of the function. The value $|C|$ describes the number of units the graph of $f(x)$ is translated right or left. If $C > 0$, the graph is translated to the right, and if $C < 0$, the graph is translated to the left.

For example, consider $k(x)$.

$$k(x) = h(x - 2)$$

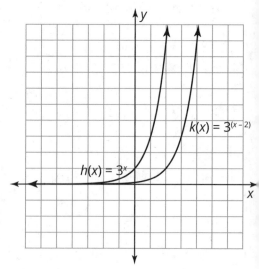

A basic function is multiplied by −1 to result in a reflection across the x-axis, or $y = 0$. The argument of a basic function is multiplied by −1 to result in a reflection across the y-axis, or $x = 0$.

For example, consider $s(x)$ and $v(x)$.

$$s(x) = -t(x)$$
$$v(x) = t(-x)$$

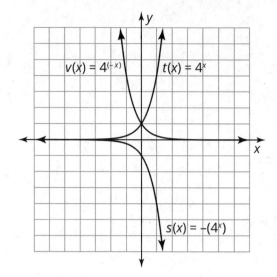

For the basic function, the A-value of the transformed function $y = A \cdot f(x)$ affects the output values of the function. For $|A| > 1$, the graph vertically stretches. For $0 < |A| < 1$, the graph vertically compresses. For $A = -1$, the graph is reflected across the x-axis.

For the basic function, the B-value of the transformed function $y = f \cdot (Bx)$ affects the input values of the function. For $|B| > 1$, the graph horizontally compresses. For $0 < |B| < 1$, the graph horizontally stretches. For $B = -1$, the graph is reflected across the y-axis.

Using Exponential Equations

Exponential functions become steeper and steeper or flatter and flatter. This slide comes down steeply and flattens out, rather like an exponential function.

Module 3: Investigating Growth and Decay

TOPIC 2: USING EXPONENTIAL EQUATIONS

In this topic, students explore strategies for distinguishing exponential functions that represent growth scenarios versus those that represent decay, and methods for solving exponential equations. Students begin by comparing the value of a simple interest account and a compound interest account. They graph and write equations for these two scenarios and then compare the average rate of change of each for a given interval. Students then examine the structure of the exponential equations to recognize scenarios in which exponential functions grow or decay by a certain percent. Throughout the rest of the topic, students solve real-world problems that can be modeled by exponential functions, including one that requires students to combine function types to best model the scenario.

Where have we been?

Students know the rules of exponents and are familiar with the structure of exponential functions from their work in the previous topic. Their previous work to transform an exponential function has prepared them to make sense of real-world scenarios that they are modeling in this topic. Students understand what it means to determine a solution for an equation.

Where are we going?

This topic represents students' first deep dive into solving equations that represent nonlinear functions. As students gain proficiency in solving increasingly complex equations, they are able to model more interesting and complex real-life phenomena.

Exponential Growth and Decay

An exponential growth function has a b-value greater than 1 and is of the form $y = a \cdot (1 + r)^x$, where r is the rate of growth. The b-value is $1 + r$. An exponential decay function has a b-value greater than 0 and less than 1 and is of the form $y = a \cdot (1 - r)^x$, where r is the rate of decay. The b-value is $1 - r$.

I Feel the Earth. Move.

How do scientists measure the intensity of earthquakes? You may know that scientists who study earthquakes—seismologists—refer to a scale known as a Richter scale when reporting the strength of an earthquake. The Richter scale is a kind of exponential scale.

The scale generally goes from 1 to 9 (though it doesn't really have an upper limit), but an earthquake which has an intensity of 6 on the Richter scale is 10 times more powerful than an earthquake which measures 5.

One of the strongest earthquakes in history occurred in Chile on May 22, 1960. This earthquake measured an amazing 9.5 on the Richter scale—over 30,000 times stronger than a magnitude 5 earthquake!

Talking Points

Exponential functions in real-world contexts is an important topic to know about for college admissions tests.

Here is a sample question:

A car valued at $21,000 depreciates at a rate of 17% per year. What is the value of the car after 5 years?

To solve this, students should know to use the model for exponential decay, $y = a \cdot (1 - r)^x$, where a represents the initial value, r represents the rate of decrease, and x represents time.

$$y = a(1 - r)^x$$
$$y = a(1 - 0.17)^x$$
$$y = 21,000(0.83)^5$$
$$y = 8271.99$$

In 5 years, the car will be worth $8271.99.

Key Terms

simple interest

In a simple interest account, a percent of the starting balance is added to the account at each interval. The formula for simple interest is $I = Prt$, where P represents the starting amount, or principal, r represents the interest rate, t represents time, and I represents the interest earned.

compound interest

In a compound interest account, the balance is multiplied by the same amount at each interval.

Uptown and Downtown

Exponential Equations for Growth and Decay

Warm Up

Determine the constant ratio for each geometric sequence.

1. 10, 10.5, 11.025, 11.57625, 12.1550625 . . .

2. 27, 9, 3, 1, $\frac{1}{3}$ . . .

3. 1, $\frac{3}{4}$, $\frac{9}{16}$, $\frac{27}{64}$ . . .

Learning Goals

- Classify exponential functions as increasing or decreasing.
- Compare formulas for simple interest and compound interest situations.
- Compare the average rate of change between common intervals of a linear and an exponential relationship.
- Write an exponential function that includes a percent increase or decrease with a b-value that is a decimal number.
- Solve exponential equations using graphs.

Key Terms

- simple interest
- compound interest
- exponential growth function
- exponential decay function

You have analyzed linear and exponential functions and their graphs. How can you compare linear and exponential functions as increasing and decreasing functions?

Up or Down?

Consider each function shown.

What does the structure of each function equation tell you?

$$f(x) = -2x + 5 \qquad g(x) = 2^x - 1 \qquad h(x) = 0.95^x$$

$$p(x) = 6 \cdot \left(\frac{5}{8}\right)^x + 2 \qquad q(x) = 3(x - 4) - 1 \qquad r(x) = 2 \cdot (1 - 0.5)^x$$

$$v(x) = 4 \cdot 1.10^{(x + 5)} \qquad w(x) = -5 \cdot 3^x + 1 \qquad z(x) = -x + 10$$

1. **Sort the functions into two groups. Justify your choices.**

    Increasing Functions   **Decreasing Functions**

Simple and Compound Interest

Suppose that your family deposited $10,000 in an interest bearing account for your college fund that earns simple interest each year. A friend's family deposited $10,000 in an interest bearing account for their child's college fund that earns compound interest each year.

Time (years)	Simple Interest Balance (dollars)	Compound Interest Balance (dollars)
0	10,000	10,000
1	10,400	10,400
2	10,800	10,816
3	11,200	11,248.64
10	14,000	14,802.44

In a **simple interest** account, a percent of the starting balance is added to the account at each interval. The formula for simple interest is $I = Prt$, where P represents the starting amount, or principal, r represents the interest rate, t represents time, and I represents the interest earned. In a **compound interest** account, the balance is multiplied by the same amount at each interval.

1. **Study the table of values.**

   a. **Sketch a graph of each account balance in dollars as a function of the time in years.**

   Simple Interest Balance

   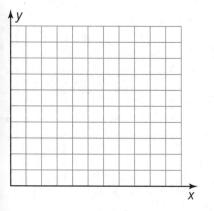

   Compound Interest Balance

   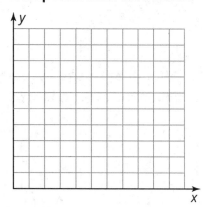

   b. **Write a function, $s(x)$, to represent the simple interest account and a function, $c(x)$, to represent the compound interest account.**

How accurate does your answer need to be?

2. Use the functions $s(x)$ and $c(x)$ to determine each value.

a. $s(5)$ b. $c(5)$

c. $c(4)$ d. $s(4)$

3. Determine the average rate of change between each pair of values given for each relationship.

Time Intervals (years)	Simple Interest Function (dollars)	Compound Interest Function (dollars)
Between $t = 0$ and $t = 1$		
Between $t = 1$ and $t = 2$		
Between $t = 2$ and $t = 5$		
Between $t = 5$ and $t = 10$		

4. Compare the average rates of change for the simple and compound interest accounts.

a. What do you notice?

b. What does this tell you about the graphs of linear and exponential functions?

Use technology to determine when each account will reach the given dollar amount.

a. When does the simple interest account reach $15,600?

b. Approximately when does the compound interest account reach one million dollars?

6. Chloe says that given any increasing linear function and any exponential growth function, the output of the exponential function will eventually be greater than the output of the linear function. Is Chloe correct? Use examples to justify your thinking.

Identifying Exponential Growth and Decay

At this moment, the population of Downtown is 20,000, and the population of Uptown is 6000. But over many years, people have been moving away from Downtown at a rate of 1.5% every year. At the same time, Uptown's population has been growing at a rate of 1.8% each year.

1. **What are the independent and dependent quantities in each situation?**

2. **Which city's population can be represented as an increasing function, and which can be represented as a decreasing function?**

Let's examine the properties of the graphs of the functions for Downtown and Uptown.

Downtown: $D(t) = 20,000(1 - 0.015)^t$ Uptown: $U(t) = 6000(1 + 0.018)^t$

3. **Sketch a graph of each function. Label key points.**

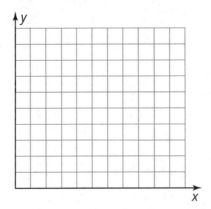

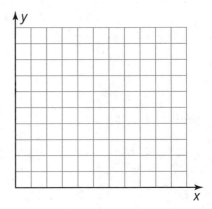

4. The functions $D(t)$ and $U(t)$ can each be written as an exponential function of the form $f(x) = a \cdot b^x$.

   a. What is the a-value for each function? What does each a-value mean in terms of this problem situation?

   b. What is the b-value for each function? What does each b-value mean in terms of this problem situation?

   c. Compare and explain the meanings of the expressions $(1 - 0.015)^t$ and $(1 + 0.018)^t$ in terms of this problem situation.

5. Analyze the y-intercepts of each function.

   a. Identify the y-intercepts.

   b. Interpret the meaning of each y-intercept in terms of the problem situation.

   c. Describe how you can determine the y-intercept of each function using only the formula for population increase or decrease.

Think about:

A decreasing exponential function is denoted by a decimal or fractional b-value between 0 and 1, not by a negative b-value.

An **exponential growth function** has a b-value greater than 1 and is of the form $y = a \cdot (1 + r)^x$, where r is the rate of growth. The b-value is $1 + r$. An **exponential decay function** has a b-value greater than 0 and less than 1 and is of the form $y = a \cdot (1 - r)^x$, where r is the rate of decay. The b-value is $1 - r$.

Comparing Exponential Functions

Consider the six different population scenarios.

1. **Match each situation with the appropriate function. Explain your reasoning.**

Functions

$f(x) = 7000 \cdot 0.969^x$

$f(x) = 7000 \cdot (1 + 0.028)^x$

$f(x) = 7000 \cdot 1.012^x$

$f(x) = 7000 \cdot (1 - 0.0175)^x$

$f(x) = 7000 \cdot 1.014^x$

$f(x) = 7000 \cdot 0.9875^x$

Blueville has a population of 7000. Its population is increasing at a rate of 1.4%.

Greenville has a population of 7000. Its population is decreasing at a rate of 1.75%.

Youngstown has a population of 7000. Its population is increasing at a rate of 1.2%.

North Park has a population of 7000. Its population is decreasing at a rate of 3.1%.

West Lake has a population of 7000. Its population is increasing at a rate of 2.8%.

Springfield has a population of 7000. Its population is decreasing at a rate of 1.25%.

And More, Much More Than This...

A scientist is researching certain bacteria that have been found recently in the large animal cages at a local zoo. He starts with 200 bacteria that he intends to grow and study. He determines that every hour the number of bacteria increases by 25%.

1. **Write a function and sketch a graph to represent this problem situation. Then estimate the number of hours the scientist should let the bacteria grow to have no more than 2000 bacteria.**

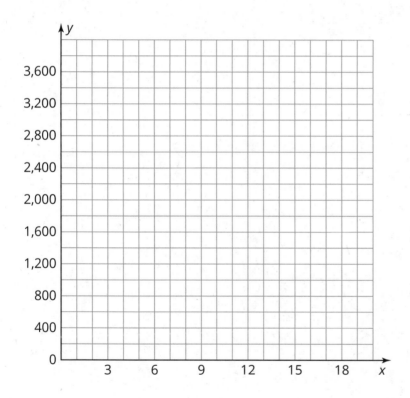

Write

Explain the difference between simple interest and compound interest.

Remember

An exponential growth function has a b-value greater than 1 and is of the form $y = a \cdot (1 + r)^x$, where r is the rate of growth. An exponential decay function has a b-value greater than 0 and less than 1 and is of the form $y = a \cdot (1 - r)^x$, where r is the rate of decay.

Practice

1. Chanise just received a $2500 bonus check from her employer. She is going to put it into an account that will earn interest. The Basic savings account at her bank earns 6% simple interest. The Gold savings account earns 4.5% compound interest.
   a. Write a function for each account that can be used to determine the balance in the account based on the year, t. Describe each function.
   b. Use your answers to part (a) to create a table of values for each function.
   c. Use technology to graph the functions for the Basic and Gold savings accounts. Then, sketch the graphs.
   d. Into which account would you recommend that Chanise deposit her money? Explain your reasoning.
   e. After reading the pamphlet about the different accounts a little more closely, Chanise realizes that there is a one-time fee of $300 for depositing her money in the Gold account. Does this change the recommendation you made in part (d)? Why or why not?
   f. Compare the rates of change for the Basic and Gold savings accounts. Explain what the rates of change tell you about the accounts.
   g. What do the rates of change for linear and exponential functions tell you about the graphs of the functions?

2. Ainsley works for the owners of a bookstore. Her starting salary was $24,500, and she gets a 3% raise each year.
   a. Write an equation in function notation to represent Ainsley's salary as a function of the number of years she has been working at the bookstore.
   b. What will Ainsley's salary be when she begins her fourth year working at the bookstore? Show your work.

Stretch

Consider a piece of paper that is 0.1 mm thick. How many times must it be folded so that it reaches the top of the Eiffel Tower? Assume the paper is as large as needed, and it is possible to fold it as many times as required.

Review

1. Roberto and Maeko open a pet store and start with 5 hamsters for sale. Hamster populations usually triple every cycle. One cycle is equal to 4 months. Write an equation in function notation to represent the change in the number of hamsters as a function of the cycle number, c. Explain how you determined your equation.

2. Write an exponential function to model this table of values.

x	$g(x)$
1	0.6
2	0.06
3	0.006
4	0.0006

3. Write a function, $g(x)$, and sketch a graph that is translated 3 units up from and 4 units to the right of $f(x) = \left(\frac{1}{2}\right)^x$.

4. Write a function, $h(x)$, and sketch a graph that is translated 2 units down from $f(x) = -3^x$, and is a reflection of $f(x) = -3^x$ across the line $x = 0$.

5. Given $f(x) = |x|$.

   a. Sketch the graph for $g(x) = f(x - 2)$.   b. Sketch the graph of $h(x) = -2f(x + 3) + 5$.

Powers and the Horizontal Line

Interpreting Parameters in Context

Warm Up

Rewrite each expression using the Order of Operations.

1. $3 - (4 \cdot 5) + 6^{-1}$

2. $8 + (9^{\frac{1}{2}} - 2) \div 2$

3. $1 - \frac{5^{\frac{1}{2}}}{2} + \sqrt{5}$

Learning Goals

- Analyze equations and graphs of exponential functions.
- Match equations and graphs of exponential functions using the horizontal asymptote.
- Write and interpret exponential growth and decay functions.
- Use the properties of exponents to rewrite exponential functions.

You have written exponential functions for problem situations. What strategies can you use to write and solve exponential equations?

Match Game

Consider the four graphs shown.

1. **Match each graph with the correct function.**

Equations
$f(x) = 3(5)^x + 2$
$f(x) = 5(2)^{-x}$
$f(x) = -3(2)^x + 5$
$f(x) = -2(5)^{-x} - 3$

Graph 1

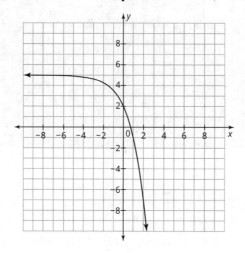

Graph 2

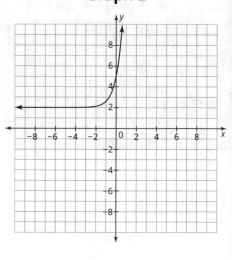

Graph 3

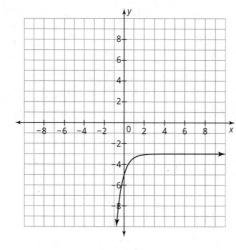

Graph 4

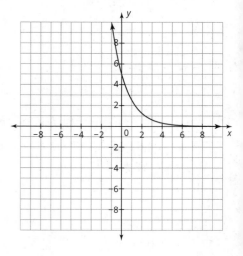

2. **Describe the strategies you used.**

3. **Lucy and Michael disagree about the equation for Graph 2.**

Lucy

The equation for Graph 2 is $f(x) = 5(2)^{-x}$.

The graph intersects the y-axis at 5.

In the form $f(x) = ab^x$, a is the y-intercept.

$f(x) = 5(2)^{-x}$ is the only equation with a=5.

Michael

The equation for Graph 2 is $f(x) = 3(5)^x + 2$.

I know this because the graph has an asymptote of $y = 2$, and 2 is the D-value in the equation.

a. **What is the error in Lucy's thinking. Does Lucy's method sometimes work? Explain your reasoning.**

b. **What characteristic does Michael use? Will his method always work?**

Solving Exponential Equations by Graphing

Depreciation is a decline in the value of something. Vehicles usually depreciate over time, meaning their value decreases over time. This decrease can often be represented by an exponential decay function.

A construction company bought a new bulldozer for $125,000. The bulldozer depreciates exponentially, and after 2 years, the value of the bulldozer is $80,000.

1. **Write a function to represent the value of the bulldozer as a function of the number of years it is owned. Then complete the table and graph.**

Number of Years Owned	Value of Bulldozer
0	
2.5	
5	
7	
8.5	
10	
12.5	

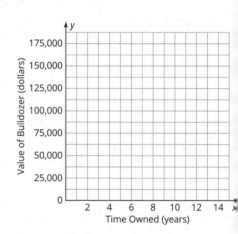

2. **The company wants to sell the bulldozer and get at least $25,000 from the sale. Use the graph to estimate the amount of time the company has to achieve this goal.**

Ask yourself:

What does each point on the graph represent?

3. **Estimate when the bulldozer will be worth:**

   a. **$50,000.**   b. **$10,000.**

4. **When will the bulldozer be worth $0?**

Interpreting the B-value

Simone has invested $500 in a mutual fund which has shown an annual increase of about 10%.

1. **Write a function, $f(t)$, that represents Simone's investment in terms of t, time in years.**

Suppose Simone is interested in determining the monthly rate of increase. What is the approximate equivalent monthly rate of increase for her mutual fund?

2. **Consider the responses from two of Simone's friends. Describe the differences in their reasoning and why Rahsaan is correct.**

Chitra
Because we are dividing up the annual rate of increase over twelve months, divide the constant ratio by 12.

$$\frac{1.10}{12}$$

Rahsaan
Because the annual rate of increase is represented as a multiplier, take the 12th root of the constant ratio.

$$1.10^{\frac{1}{12}}$$

Kirk wants to write a function that is equivalent to the annual rate of increase but reveals the monthly rate of increase.

3. **Explain why Kirk's reasoning is not correct.**

> ### Kirk
> Since Simone's monthly rate of increase is the twelfth root of the annual rate of increase, I can use the function
>
> $f(x) = 500 \cdot \left(1.10^{\frac{1}{12}}\right)^{t}$.

To rewrite the function representing Simone's annual increase as an equivalent function that reflects the monthly rate of increase, you must change the B-value. The B-value of an exponential function can be written as the coefficient of x.

$$f(x) = a \cdot (b)^{Bx}$$

Worked Example

You can use what you know about common bases to rewrite the expression in an equivalent form.

$\left(1.10^{\frac{1}{12}}\right)^{Bx} = (1.10)^x$

$(1.10)^{\frac{Bx}{12}} = (1.10)^x$ Apply the Power to a Power Rule.

$\frac{Bx}{12} = x$ The bases are the same, so the exponents must be equivalent expressions.

$Bx = 12x$ Multiply both sides by 12.

$B = 12$

So, the function $f(x) = 500 \cdot \left(1.10^{\frac{1}{12}}\right)^{12x}$ is equivalent to the function $f(x) = 500 \cdot (1.10)^x$.

4. Suppose Simone wants to determine how much her mutual fund increases each quarter. Rewrite the original function in an equivalent form that reveals the approximate equivalent quarterly rate of increase.

5. What is Simone's monthly increase, as a percent?

TALK the TALK

Is This Uptown or Downtown?

In 2005, the population of a city was 42,500. By 2010, the population had grown to approximately 51,708 people.

1. **Identify any equations that are appropriate exponential models for the population of the city. Explain why. Then explain why the equations you did not choose are not appropriate models for the situation.**

$$f(t) = 51{,}708(1.04)^t \qquad\qquad f(t) = 51{,}708(0.96)^t$$

$$f(t) = 42{,}500(1.04)^{5t} \qquad\qquad f(t) = 51{,}708(1.04)^{\frac{1}{5}t}$$

$$f(t) = 42{,}500(1.04)^t \qquad\qquad f(t) = 42{,}500(0.96)^t$$

2. **Create a presentation to explain the differences between the *b*-value and the *B*-value of an exponential function. Use at least one example in your presentation that is not in this lesson.**

Assignment

Write

Explain how an asymptote can be identified from an exponential equation and its graph.

Remember

You can estimate the solution to an exponential equation graphically. First, graph both the exponential function and the constant function for the given y-value. Next, determine the point of intersection of the graph of the exponential function and the horizontal line. Lastly, identify the x-value of the coordinate pair as the solution.

Practice

1. Ryan bought a brand new car for $18,000. Its value depreciated at a rate of 1.2%.
   a. Write a function to represent the value of the car as a function of time.
      Use technology to estimate the number of years it will take for the value to reach each given amount.
   b. $17,000
   c. $15,000
   d. half of the starting value
   e. one-third the starting value
   f. $0
   g. $10,000

2. In 2012, the population of a city was 63,000. By 2017, the population was reduced to approximately 54,100. Identify any equations that are appropriate models for the population of the city, and explain why the others are not.
   a. $f(x) = 63,000(1.03)^t$
   b. $f(x) = 52,477(1.03)^t$
   c. $f(x) = 63,000(0.97)^t$
   d. $f(x) = 52,477(0.97)^t$
   e. $f(x) = 63,000(0.97)^{\frac{1}{5t}}$
   f. $f(x) = 52,477(0.97)^{5t}$

3. Oscar wants to own a bee colony so that he can extract honey from the hive. He starts a colony with 5,000 bees. The number of bees grows exponentially with a growth factor of 12% each month.
   a. Write a function, $f(x)$, for the bee population that can be used to determine the number of bees in the colony, based on the month, x.
   b. Use technology to graph the function, $f(x)$.
   c. Oscar feels that in order to get a decent amount of honey, there should be at least 15,000 bees in the colony. Estimate how many months it will take Oscar until he has 15,000 bees.

Stretch

Julissa and Megan developed a new art app for smart phones. The table shows the number of customers who downloaded the app by month.

Month	Number of Downloads
0	4
1	8
2	16
3	32
4	64
5	128

1. Julissa thinks that the equation that represents the data in the table is $y = 4(2)^x$. Determine whether Julissa is correct. Explain your reasoning.

2. Determine a different exponential equation that represents the data in the table. Use the equation $y = a \cdot b^{f(x)}$, where $f(x)$ is a function of x and $a = 2$.

Review

1. Rewrite each expression in rational exponent form.

   a. $(\sqrt[3]{6})^4$

   b. $(\sqrt[8]{8})^{12}$

   c. $(\sqrt[7]{x})^3$

   d. $(\sqrt[10]{y})^5$

2. Eleanor receives $1500 for her birthday. She is going to spend $500 and wants to put the rest into an account that will earn interest. She is considering two different accounts. Account A earns 6.5% annual simple interest. Account B earns 4.5% annual compound interest.

   a. Write a function for each account that can be used to determine the balance in the account based on the year, t.

   b. Graph the functions for Accounts A and B using technology. Then, graph the functions. Be sure to label your graph.

   c. If Eleanor plans on leaving the money in the account for 12 years, which account should she use to deposit her money? Explain your reasoning.

   d. If Eleanor plans on leaving the money in the account for 25 years, which account should she use to deposit her money? Explain your reasoning.

3

Savings, Tea, and Carbon Dioxide

Modeling Using Exponential Functions

Warm Up

While driving to their vacation spot, the Mitchell family kept a record of their gas purchases. Their information is recorded in the table.

Amount of Gas (gallons)	Total Cost (dollars)
9	21.33
16.6	40.00
11.8	26.08
10	24.70
13.2	28.91

1. Use technology to write the linear regression equation.

2. What is the correlation coefficient, r? What does this value imply?

Learning Goals

- Write an exponential function to model a table of values and a graph.
- Add an exponential function and a constant function.
- Write an exponential function to model a data set.
- Use exponential models to solve problems.

You can interpret exponential scenarios, equations, tables and graphs. How can you use an exponential function to model real-world data?

The Elephants in the Room

Two elephant populations over time are shown, each within a different small area in Africa.

Population A

Time (years)	Elephant Population
3	3218
5	3628
7	3721
9	3871

Population B

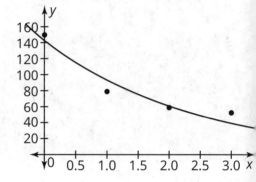

1. **Estimate an exponential function for each population change over time. Explain how you determined your functions.**

2. **Use your functions and the features of each situation to describe the change in the populations over time.**

Adding Functions

Autumn has two different methods of saving her money. Analyze her situation using functions.

1. Autumn received a graduation gift of $1000 from her wealthy aunt. She placed this money in a savings account with a 4% interest rate, compounded annually.

   a. Write a function $f(x)$ to model this situation. Define the variables.

   b. What will be the balance in Autumn's account after 5 years? 10 years? 15 years?

   c. Estimate when Autumn will have $1600 in her account.

2. Autumn also saved $500 that she keeps in a safe at home. She never touches it nor adds to it.

   a. Write a function $g(x)$ to model this situation. Define the variables.

   b. How much money will Autumn have in the safe after 5 years? 10 years? 15 years?

   c. When will Autumn have $1600 in the safe?

3. Autumn's total savings can be represented as $h(x) = f(x) + g(x)$. Write a function $h(x)$ to represent this sum and predict what the graph of $h(x)$ will look like.

4. Graph $f(x)$, $g(x)$, and $h(x)$ on the coordinate plane. Label each function.

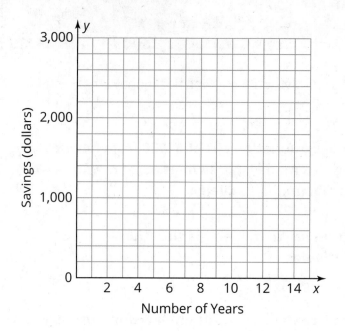

5. Did the graph of $h(x)$ appear as you predicted? How does it relate to what you learned about transformations?

6. How does the graph of $h(x)$ relate to the graphs of $f(x)$ and $g(x)$?

7. The exponential function $h(x)$ can be written in the form $h(x) = Ab^{B(x-C)} + D$. Identify three places where the value of D is evident in the graphs of the three functions.

Caroline loves drinking green tea. One morning, after making herself a cup of hot tea, she sat in her kitchen to enjoy it.

The table shows the temperature of a cup of Caroline's tea over time.

Time (minutes)	Temperature (degrees Fahrenheit)
0	180
5	169
11	149
15	142
18	135
25	124
30	116
34	113
42	106
45	102
50	101

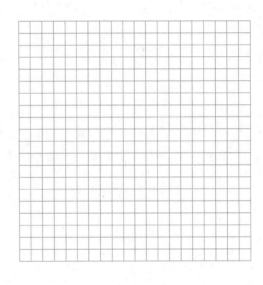

1. **Model this situation.**

   a. **Create a scatter plot. Label your axes.**

   b. **Use technology to write the exponential regression equation. Define the variables. Identify the correlation coefficient.**

   c. **Sketch the function on the same graph as your scatter plot.**

2. State the domain and range of the function you sketched. How do they compare to the domain and range of this problem situation?

3. Use the equation to predict the temperature of Caroline's tea after an hour.

4. Use the equation to predict the temperature of Caroline's tea after 4 hours.

5. Does your prediction make sense in terms of this problem situation? Explain your reasoning.

Determining the Best Fit to Model Data

One measure of climate change is the amount of carbon dioxide in Earth's atmosphere.

The table shows the carbon dioxide concentration in Earth's atmosphere in parts per million from 1860 to 2017.

Year	Carbon Dioxide Concentration (parts per million)
1860	286
1880	291
1900	296
1920	303
1940	311
1960	317
1980	339
2000	370
2010	389
2017	406

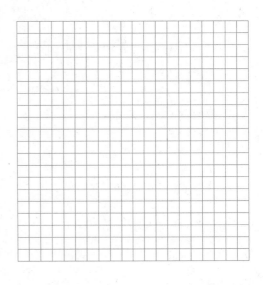

1. **Model this situation.**

   a. **Create a scatter plot using 1860 as Year 0. Label your axes.**

   b. **Use technology to choose the correct function to model this data. Write your regression equation. Define the variables. Identify the correlation coefficient.**

   c. **Sketch the function on the same graph as your scatter plot.**

2. Naasira used an exponential function to model the situation. Brendan used a linear function to model the situation. Who is correct? Explain your reasoning.

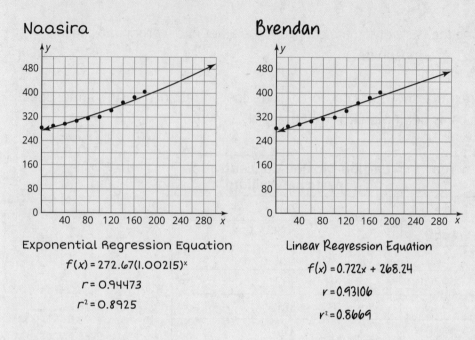

Naasira

Exponential Regression Equation

$f(x) = 272.67(1.00215)^x$

$r = 0.94473$

$r^2 = 0.8925$

Brendan

Linear Regression Equation

$f(x) = 0.722x + 268.24$

$r = 0.93106$

$r^2 = 0.8669$

3. What other information would help you to make the decision as to whether a linear or exponential function is best to model this context and data?

4. Why does the exponential function look very similar to the linear function?

5. Use each function to predict the concentration of carbon dioxide for each given year.

   a. During 2160

   b. During 2500

6. According to the data, the concentration of carbon dioxide has been increasing over the past 157 years. What factors could have contributed to this behavior?

TALK the TALK 💬

Making a List, Checking It Twice

Reflect on the exponential situations and graphs you have encountered in past lessons.

1. Consider the contexts.

   a. Describe the contexts that can be modeled by an exponential function.

   b. What do the contexts have in common that identify them as being exponential functions?

2. Consider the graphs.

   a. How can you tell from a scatter plot that it can be modeled by an exponential function?

   b. Sketch four different possible graphs of an exponential function of the form $y = a \cdot b^x$. Describe the a-value and common multiplier in each.

Assignment

Write

Describe the information that can be used to determine whether a linear or exponential function is best to model a context and data.

Remember

You can use exponential functions to model scenarios that involve a percent increase or decrease, such as compound interest and population growth or decay.

Sometimes it may be difficult to determine whether a scatter plot is best modeled by a linear or exponential function. In these cases, sometimes knowing the scenario can help, while in other cases more data points or information may be needed.

Practice

1. The table shows the number of U.S. Post Offices at the beginning of each decade from 1900 to 2000.
   a. Create a scatter plot of the data.
   b. Determine the exponential regression equation and the value of the correlation coefficient, r. Then graph the equation on the grid with the scatter plot.
   c. Predict the number of U.S. Post Offices in the year 2050.
   d. Predict when the number of U.S. Post Offices will reach 20,000.
   e. What do you think is causing the decline in the number of U.S. Post Offices?

Year	Number of U.S. Post Offices
1900	76,688
1910	59,580
1920	52,641
1930	49,063
1940	44,024
1950	41,464
1960	35,238
1970	32,002
1980	30,326
1990	28,959
2000	27,876

Stretch

1. The number of fixed landline phone subscribers in the U.S. has been declining. The bar graph shows the decrease in the number of subscribers from 2010 to 2015.

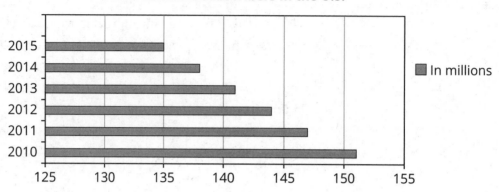

Fixed Landline Subscribers in the U.S.

■ In millions

a. To estimate the number of subscribers per year, create a scatter plot of the ordered pairs, with *x* representing the number of years since 2010 and *y* representing the number of subscribers in millions.

b. Determine both an exponential and a linear regression function to model the situation.

c. Which model would you use from part (b)? Explain your reasoning.

Review

1. Given $f(x) = 2^x$, graph $g(x) = -f(x - 1) + 2$.

2. Given $a(x) = \frac{1}{2}^x$, graph $b(x) = a(-x) - 1$.

3. An experiment begins with 400 bacteria. The bacteria population doubles each day. Write an equation in function notation to represent the number of bacteria as a function of the day number, *x*. Explain how you determined the equation.

4. Write the absolute value function for the graph shown.

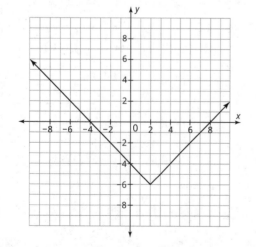

5. Write the piecewise function for the graph shown.

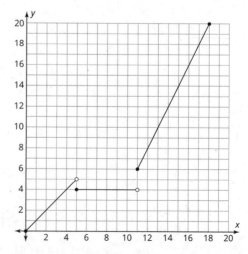

4

BAC Is BAD News

Choosing a Function to Model Data

Warm Up

1. Is the scatter plot shown best represented by a linear or exponential function? Explain your answer.

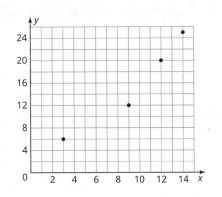

2. Determine a regression equation that best fits this data.

Learning Goals

- Determine the appropriate regression equation for a data set.
- Solve a complex problem using the mathematical modeling process.
- Reflect upon the mathematical modeling process.

You can determine a regression equation for a data set. How can you use this knowledge to solve a real-world problem?

Drinking and Driving Don't Mix

> A BAC of 0.08 means that 0.08% of a person's blood is alcohol.

Blood Alcohol Content (BAC) is a way of measuring the amount of alcohol in a person's blood stream. BAC levels are measured in percentages.

A recent study shows that a person with no alcohol in the blood system has a 1.8% chance of causing a car accident.

There is a relationship between the relative probability of a driver causing a car accident and a driver's BAC. The relative probability is the number of times more likely a driver with alcohol in their blood system is to cause a car accident than a driver with no alcohol in their blood system. For example, a relative probability of 2 for a driver with a BAC of 0.06% means that a car accident is twice as likely to occur as for a driver with a BAC of 0.00.

1. **Explain the difference in meaning between probability and relative probability using the values in this scenario.**

> It is illegal for anyone over the age of 21 to drive once their BAC reaches 0.08. For drivers under 21, any BAC level above 0.00 is illegal!

2. **Use the likelihood of a person with no alcohol in their blood system causing a car accident to answer each question.**

   a. **There is a relative probability of 2 that a person with a BAC of 0.06% causes an accident. What is the probability that this person will cause a car accident?**

b. There is a relative probability of 5 that a person with a BAC of 0.10% causes an accident. What is the probability that this person will cause a car accident?

c. There is a relative probability of 25 that a person with a BAC of 0.16% causes an accident. What is the probability that this person will cause a car accident?

3. Examine your answers from Question 2. What do you notice about the rate at which alcohol affects a person's ability to drive?

Analyzing and Using Data to Make Predictions

Different factors affect a person's BAC, including weight, gender, the duration of consuming alcohol, and the amount of food the person eats. According to the Virginia Tech Alcohol Abuse Prevention website, a typical 140-pound male who has one drink over a 40-minute period will have a BAC of 0.03%. If he has another drink over the next 40 minutes, his BAC rises to 0.05%. If he has one more drink over the next 40-minute period, his BAC rises to 0.08%, which means he legally cannot drive.

BAC Level (percent)	Relative Probability of Causing an Accident (percent)
0.02	1
0.06	2
0.10	5
0.16	25

Create a model to predict the likelihood of a person causing an accident based on their BAC. Include a table, a graph, and an equation in your model. Be sure to define your variables.

Include these elements in your analysis.

- Describe why the function type you chose is appropriate for this situation. How do you know that it's a good fit?
- Predict the probability that drivers with different BACs will cause an accident. Show all your work.
- How can your graph be used to write guidelines around when a person is safe to drive, even if they can legally drive?

Write an article to report your conclusions for the newsletter of the local chapter of S.A.D.D. (Students Against Destructive Decisions) that stresses the seriousness of drinking and driving. Include tables and/or graphs to help the reader make sense of the issue. You may want to include facts about the rate at which a driver's probability of causing an accident increases as their BAC increases, the definitions of legal limits in your state, and how a driver's motor skills are affected by alcohol.

TALK the TALK

What Have I Done?

By solving the problem in this lesson, you intuitively engaged in the mathematical modeling process.

1. **Reflect on your process by referencing the diagram and noting the type of thinking and work you engaged in next to each step.**

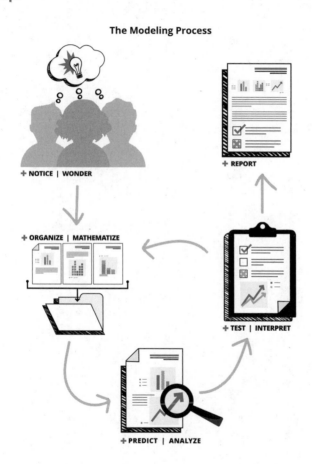

The Modeling Process

+ NOTICE | WONDER

+ ORGANIZE | MATHEMATIZE

+ PREDICT | ANALYZE

+ TEST | INTERPRET

+ REPORT

2. **Were there instances where you looped back in the process? Explain how you knew you needed to loop back and how you changed the direction in your thinking.**

Assignment

Write

Describe the mathematical modeling process in your own words.

Remember

Determining and using a regression equation is sometimes a step in the process of solving a more complex mathematical problem, rather than the final solution.

Practice

The table shows the purchasing value of the dollar, or the consumer price index, for consumers in the United States from 1955 to 2010. The table uses the year 1982 as a base period, so the consumer price index written in dollars and cents in 1982 is 1.00. For instance, in 1955 the consumer price index was 3.73. This means that a dollar in 1955 was worth 3.73 times what it was worth in 1982. Similarly, a dollar in 2010 was worth 0.46 times what it was worth in 1982.

Year	Consumer Price Index	Year	Consumer Price Index
1955	3.73	1985	0.93
1960	3.37	1990	0.77
1965	3.17	1995	0.66
1970	2.57	2000	0.58
1975	1.86	2005	0.51
1980	1.22	2010	0.46

The scatter plot shows the data in the table where x represents the number of years since 1955 and y represents the consumer price index.

1. Describe how the consumer price index changes over time.
2. What type(s) of function(s) model this situation? Explain your reasoning.

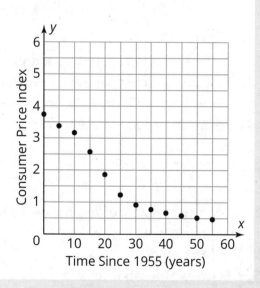

3. Analyze the data and scatter plot.

    a. Determine the regression equation for the model that best represents the data. Explain how you determined your answer. Then, graph the model on the same grid as the scatter plot.

    b. Predict the consumer price index in 2025. Explain what your answer means in terms of the problem situation.

    c. Mr. Kratzer asks his students to calculate what the consumer price index was in 1950. Melina says that you must evaluate the function at $x = 5$ to determine the consumer price index in 1950. Dominque argues you must evaluate the function at $x = -5$ to determine the consumer price index in 1950. Who is correct? Explain your reasoning.

    d. Calculate the consumer price index for 1950. Show your work.

    e. The consumer price index in 1950 was actually 4.15. Compare this to the answer you calculated in part (d). Explain why these answers differ.

Stretch

1. Analyze the scatter plot shown.

    a. Determine the function that best models the graph.

    b. Plot the point (8, 6) on the graph. Does your answer to part (a) change? Why or why not?

    c. If you were doing research and a situation arose in which a data point that gets added to the graph changes the model, what is one thing you might do to investigate further?

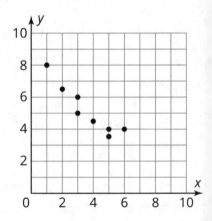

Review

1. A home recently experienced an infestation of insects. The insect population over time is shown in the table. Write the function that represents the insect population over time.

Insect Population	
Day	Number of Insects
1	240
2	360
3	540
4	810

2. Solve each system of linear equations.

    a. $\begin{cases} 2x - 3y = 4 \\ 4x + y = 8 \end{cases}$
                    b. $\begin{cases} -5x + 6y = 10 \\ 2x - 3y = 15 \end{cases}$

3. Solve each equation for x.

    a. $8^{3x} = 262{,}144$
                                  b. $2^{-x} = 1{,}048{,}576$

Using Exponential Equations Summary

KEY TERMS

- simple interest
- compound interest
- exponential growth function
- exponential decay function

LESSON 1	Uptown and Downtown

In a **simple interest** account, a percent of the starting balance is added to the account at each interval. The formula for simple interest is $I = Prt$, where P represents the starting amount, or principal, r represents the interest rate, t represents time, and I represents the interest earned.

In a **compound interest** account, the balance is multiplied by the same amount at each interval. Because the entire balance is multiplied by the same percent for each interval, the formula is represented by an exponential equation: $I = P \cdot (1 + r)^t$.

The rate of change for a simple interest account is constant. The rate of change between the values for the compound interest account is increasing as t becomes larger. A constant rate of change means that the graph of the linear equation is a straight line. An increasing rate of change means that the graph of the exponential function is a smooth curve.

For example, consider two accounts that each have an initial balance of $500. One account earns 3% simple interest each year while the other earns 3% compound interest each year.

Time (years)	Simple Interest Balance (dollars)	Compound Interest Balance (dollars)
0	500	500
1	515	515
2	530	530.45
10	650	671.96
100	2000	9609.32

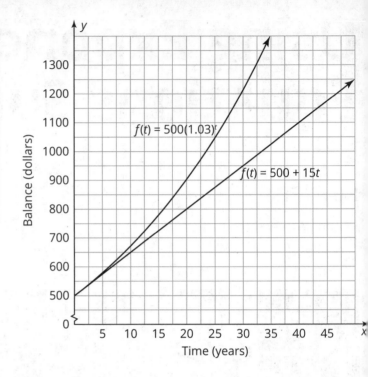

An **exponential growth function** has a b-value greater than 1 and is of the form $y = a(1 + r)^x$, where r is the rate of growth. An **exponential decay function** has a b-value greater than 0 and less than 1 and is of the form $y = a(1 - r)^x$, where r is the rate of decay.

For example, consider a population that starts at 50,000 and grows at a rate of 2% every year. The scenario can be modeled by the function $f(x) = 50{,}000 \cdot (1.02)^x$. The a-value of the exponential function is the initial population and since the population grows, the b-value is $(1 + 0.02)$ or 1.02.

LESSON 2

Powers and the Horizontal Line

Graphs can be used to solve exponential equations by estimating the intersection point of the graph of an exponential function with a constant function.

For example, to determine the solution to $125 \cdot (0.8)^x = 50$, graph each side of the equation on the same coordinate plane.

The solution to the equation is $x \approx 4$.

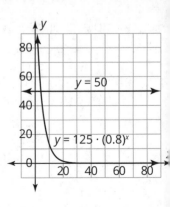

Savings, Tea, and Carbon Dioxide

Technology can be used to determine which exponential regression equation best models real-world data. This regression equation can be used to predict future values.

For example, the table shows the weight of a golden retriever puppy as recorded during her growth. A scatter plot and regression equation of the data are shown.

The exponential regression equation for this scenario is $f(x) = 3.31(1.025)^x$. The correlation coefficient, r, is 0.9999.

Age (days)	Weight (pounds)
0	3.25
10	4.25
20	5.5
30	7
40	9
50	11.5
60	15
70	19

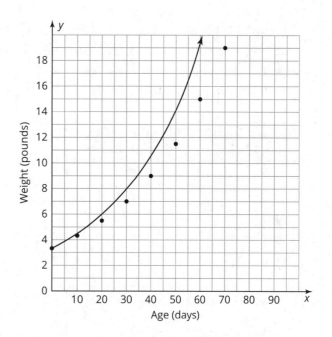

The equation can be used to predict the puppy's weight at 80 days.

$f(80) = 3.3(1.03)^{80}$
$f(80) = 35.1$

The puppy's weight will be approximately 35.1 pounds on day 80.

LESSON 4

BAC is BAD News

You can determine a regression equation for a data set. Then you can you use this knowledge to solve a real-world problem.

It is often difficult to tell the type of regression that best fits a data set. Calculating and graphing the regression equation can help determine which type of regression is the best fit.

For example, the cell phone use of Americans has increased dramatically since 1985. The data table shows the number of cell phone subscribers in the small town of Springfield.

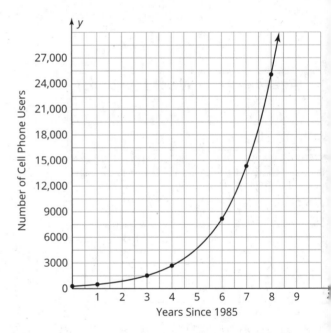

Year Since 1985	Number of Cell Phone Users
0	285
1	498
3	1527
4	2672
6	8186
7	14,325
8	25,069

The number of cell phone users increases with the increase of each year. Increasing functions can be modeled by a linear or exponential function. However, because the number of cell phone users does not increase at a constant rate, the data cannot be modeled by a linear function. The exponential regression equation for the data is $f(x) = 285(1.75)^x$. This function, when graphed, closely models the data.

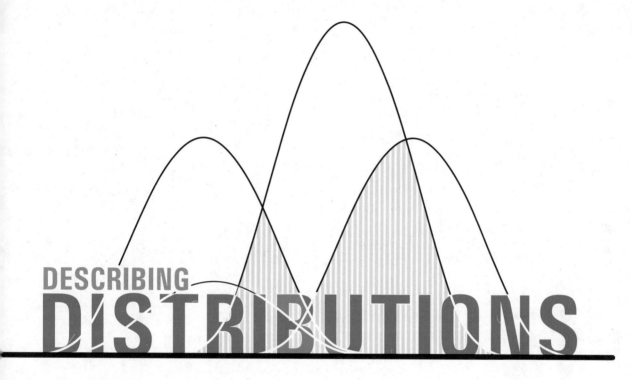

DESCRIBING DISTRIBUTIONS

The lessons in this module build on your experiences with collecting, displaying, and analyzing data. You will use the shape, center, and spread of data sets to make comparisons and decisions. You will organize two-variable categorical data into two-way frequency tables and look for trends in the data.

One-Variable Statistics

In a fishing contest, participants will catch varying numbers of fish. There are many ways to represent their catch graphically!

Module 4: Describing Distributions

TOPIC 1: ONE-VARIABLE STATISTICS

In this topic, students begin by representing data in dot plots, histograms, and box-and-whisker plots and think about when these data displays are helpful for a given data set. Students are then introduced to more formal notation for mean: $\bar{x} = \frac{\Sigma x}{n}$. This notation is important as it prepares students to make sense of the formula for standard deviation that they encounter later in the lesson. Students learn to identify outliers and recognize that median and interquartile range (IQR) are not greatly affected by outliers in a data set. By the end of the topic, students know when and how to describe a data set with mean and standard deviation vs. median and IQR. The final lesson provides students with opportunities to practice comparing two data sets and making a decision based on the comparison.

Where have we been?

Throughout elementary school, students have displayed data using line plots and pictographs. In middle school, students represented data using histograms, dot plots, stem-and-leaf plots, and box-and-whisker plots. They described the shape of the graph in terms of symmetry and skew. They calculated the mean and median to represent the central tendency of the a data set; they calculated the interquartile range (IQR) and mean absolute deviation (MAD) to represent the spread of the data. Students also compared two data sets using these same displays and the corresponding measures of center and spread.

Where are we going?

This topic develops students' statistical literacy as they increase their knowledge of, and the level of complexity of their engagement with, the statistical problem solving process. Students are prepared for the use of the standard normal distribution for calculating the likelihood of a specific outcome, which leads students to significance test, margin of error, and confidence intervals.

Sample Standard Deviation Formula

The formula to compute the sample standard deviation can be read as a step-by-step process:

$$S = \sqrt{\frac{\sum_{i=1}^{n}(x_i - \bar{x})^2}{n-1}}$$

1. $(x_i - \bar{x})^2$: Subtract the mean from each data value and square the result.

2. $\sum_{i=1}^{n}$:   Add up all of the results from Step 1, for data values x_1 to x_n.

3. $(n-1)$:   Divide the result from Step 2 by 1 less than the sample size, n.

4. $\sqrt{}$:   Take the square root of the result from Step 3.

The Latest Gallup Poll Shows . . .

Should you believe the results of polls reported in the news? Absolutely not—at least, not without researching the information presented. Even though most polls are conducted properly, the results are often not reported properly.

Look closely for the margin of error reported along with poll results. (If there isn't one, it may not be a scientific poll.) If, for example, a political candidate is leading 50% to 47%, and the margin of error is ±3%, that means that the 50% could be as low as 47% and the 47% could be as high as 50%.

News organizations will often report this result as though the candidate with 50% is leading, but according to the margin of error, it is not possible to actually make an accurate conclusion like this. The leading candidate may actually be behind!

Talking Points

Statistics is an important topic to know about for college admissions tests.

Here is a sample question:

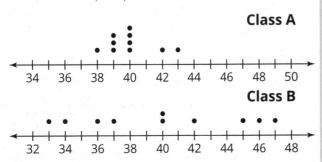

The dot plots show quiz scores for students in Class A and B. Each dot represents 2 students and each class has 20 students. Which data set has a smaller standard deviation?

To solve this, students should know that standard deviation is a measure of how far data are spread out from the mean. So, Class A has a smaller standard deviation, because the data are all closer to the mean.

Key Terms

interquartile range
The interquartile range, IQR, measures how far the data are spread out from the median. It is calculated by subtracting Q3 − Q1 in the five-number summary.

outlier
An outlier is a data value that is significantly greater or lesser than other data values in a data set.

standard deviation
Standard deviation is a measure of how spread out data are from the mean.

1

Way to Represent!

Graphically Representing Data

Warm Up

Consider the data set: 0.3, 0.7, 1.5, 1.9, 2.4, 3.0, 3.2, 5.3, 5.6, 5.8, 6.6, 7.5, 8.0, 9.1.

Determine which histogram best represents the data. Explain your reasoning.

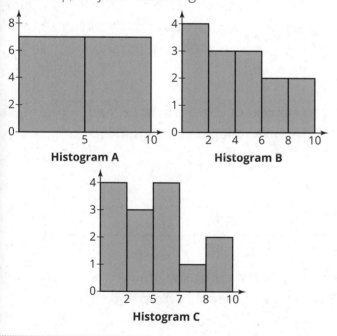

Learning Goals

- Represent and interpret data displayed on dot plots, histograms, and box-and-whisker plots.
- Determine whether a dot plot, histogram, or box-and-whisker plot is the best way to display a data set.
- Compare the box-and-whisker plots of two different data sets.

Key Terms

- dot plot
- histogram
- bin
- frequency
- box-and-whisker plot
- five-number summary

You know how to represent and interpret data using dot plots, histograms, and box-and-whisker plots. How can you determine which representation is most appropriate given a data set?

Ask yourself:

How is the statistical process similar to the modeling process?

Get the Lead Out

Recall that there are four components of the statistical process:
- Formulating a statistical question.
- Collecting appropriate data.
- Analyzing the data graphically and numerically.
- Interpreting the results of the analysis.

An issue of concern for many cities is the level of lead found in the drinking water. Lead concentrations in drinking water should be less than 15 parts per billion (ppb). The system that supplies water to a city is required to collect samples of tap water from sites it services. A water system technician took samples of the amounts of lead in the water in one neighborhood of the city of Greenville and recorded the data in the table shown.

Site Number	Amount of Lead in Water (ppb)
1	11
2	22
3	6
4	10
5	8
6	3
7	12
8	5
9	10
10	4
11	4
12	7
13	7
14	11
15	7
16	5
17	1
18	13
19	4
20	7

1. **Analyze the data collected using only the table. What conclusions can you draw about the amount of lead in the water at the different sites?**

One way to better organize data in a table is to create a *dot plot*. A **dot plot** is a graph that shows how discrete data, or data that can be "counted," are distributed using a number line. Dot plots are best used to organize and display a small number of data points.

2. **Construct a dot plot to represent the amount of lead in the water at each site. Make sure to label your dot plot.**

←--+--→

3. **What conclusions can you draw about the amount of lead in the water of the neighborhood in Greenville from your dot plot?**

According to the Environmental Protection Agency, if more than 10% of tap water samples are greater than or equal to 15 parts per billion (ppb), then action is required to reduce the levels.

1. **According to the data in the Getting Started, is action required to reduce the amount of lead in the water in the neighborhood? Justify your response.**

> The fourth part of the statistical process is to interpret the results of your analysis.

The mayor of Greenville wants to analyze the lead levels for the water in the entire city. The frequency table displays the data for the amount of lead in drinking water samples taken from sites all over Greenville.

Amount of Lead in Water (ppb)	Frequency
0 up to 5	32
5 up to 10	48
10 up to 15	100
15 up to 20	47
20 up to 25	23

Another way to display quantitative data is to create a *histogram*. A **histogram** is a graphical way to display quantitative data using vertical bars. The width of a bar in a histogram represents an interval of data and is often referred to as a *bin*. The height of each bar indicates the **frequency**, which is the number of data values included in any given bin. Histograms are effective in displaying large amounts of continuous data, or data which can take any numerical value within a range.

> A **bin** represents an interval of data instead of individual data values. The value shown on the left side of the bin is the least data value in the interval.

2. **Construct a histogram to display the data in the table.**

3. What conclusions can you draw from the histogram about the amount of lead in the drinking water of Greenville?

4. Marcel created a histogram to display the same data and claimed that no action had to be taken to reduce lead levels in Greenville's drinking water.

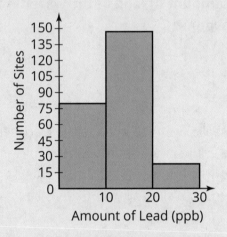

Ask yourself:

Do more than 10% of the samples have amounts of lead greater than or equal to 15 ppb?

Is Marcel correct? Explain why or why not.

5. Does the water system management of Greenville need to take action to reduce the amount of lead in the water? Explain your reasoning.

6. Do you think a histogram is a good representation of the data? Explain your reasoning.

Box-and-Whisker Plots

The governor wants to compare the amount of lead in the drinking water of different cities in her state to see where improvements in the water systems should be made.

You can visually compare two large data sets at a glance using *box-and-whisker plots*. A **box-and-whisker plot** is a graphical representation that displays the distribution of quantitative data based on a *five-number summary*. The **five-number summary** consists of the minimum value, the first quartile (Q1), the median, the third quartile (Q3), and the maximum value.

Worked Example

The five-number summary is used to create a box-and-whisker plot. Each vertical line of the box-and-whisker plot represents a value from the summary.

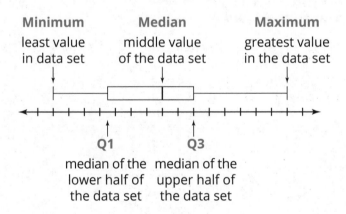

Minimum
least value in data set

Median
middle value of the data set

Maximum
greatest value in the data set

Q1
median of the lower half of the data set

Q3
median of the upper half of the data set

There are four sections of the graphical display: minimum to Q1, Q1 to median, median to Q3, and Q3 to maximum. Each section of the box-and-whisker plot represents 25 percent of the data set.

The five-number summaries of the data for the amount of lead in drinking water samples taken from the cities of Greenville and Oaktown are given.

Five-Number Summary	
Greenville	Oaktown
minimum = 1	minimum = 2
Q1 = 8	Q1 = 6
median = 12	median = 8
Q3 = 16	Q3 = 9
maximum = 22	maximum = 15

1. **Construct a box-and-whisker plot of the data for each city on the same number line using the five-number summaries.**

2. **Suppose you work in the governor's office. Compare the data displayed in your box-and-whisker plots and write an analysis to present to the governor.**

TALK the TALK

Dots, Bins, or Boxes?

Analyze each situation. Describe which representation you would use (dot plot, histogram, or box-and-whisker plot) to display and analyze the data set. Explain your reasoning.

1. **Nick collects data about the one hundred tallest buildings in the United States. He wants to quickly determine between which two heights the top 25% of the data fall.**

2. **Lily conducted a school survey to determine how many problems each math teacher assigned for homework on Friday.**

3. **The migration ranges of the white deer and mule deer populations in Montana are recorded and compared.**

4. **A school district wanted to determine how many students in the entire district scored above 70 on a standardized test.**

5. What conclusions can you draw from each display?

Participants Who Won Gold Medals at the Special Olympics

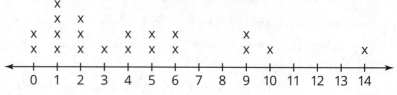

Number of Gold Medals Won

Rain in Collinsburg

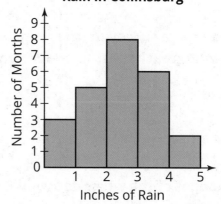

Volunteers Hours at the Local Animal Shelter

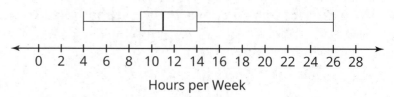

Hours per Week

Assignment

Write

Complete each statement.

1. A _____ is a graphical way to display quantitative data using vertical bars.
2. A _____ displays the data distribution based on a five number summary.
3. A _____ is a graph that shows how data are distributed using a number line.
4. For a set of data, the _____ consists of the minimum value, the first quartile, the median, the third quartile, and the maximum value.
5. The number of data values included in a given bin of a data set is called the _____.
6. The bar width in a histogram that represents an interval of data is often referred to as a _____.

Remember

A dot plot is useful for organizing a small number of data points. A histogram is effective in displaying large amounts of data. Box-and-whisker plots are effective for visually comparing two data sets.

Practice

1. Mr. Follweiller finished grading the quizzes for one of his Algebra 1 classes. The table shown is the recorded grades of the class.

   a. Mr. Follweiller is worried that his students may not have understood the material covered on the quiz. He would like to get a better idea of how the class did as a whole. Would you recommend that he make a dot plot, a box-and-whisker plot, or a histogram to display this data? Explain your reasoning.

   b. Construct a dot plot and histogram of the data in the table.

   c. What information does the dot plot provide that the histogram does not?

   d. The students argue that more than half the students failed the quiz, so they think Mr. Follweiller should let them retake it. A grade of 56 is failing. Construct a box-and-whisker plot of the data. Are the students correct? Explain your reasoning.

Student	Grade	Student	Grade
A	85	N	53
B	89	O	71
C	66	P	90
D	74	Q	65
E	77	R	55
F	72	S	98
G	64	T	53
H	55	U	62
I	61	V	55
J	52	W	64
K	81	X	62
L	61	Y	56
M	71	Z	87

Stretch

George bowls in tournaments on the weekends. He recorded the scores of each game for his last two tournaments. A perfect score is 300.

Tournament 1: 182, 197, 178, 272, 180, 188, 202, 179, 191
Tournament 2: 188, 195, 177, 192, 180, 187, 201, 183, 197

Calculate the five-number summary and IQR for the two tournaments. Interpret your findings.

Review

1. The table shows an example of a rabbit population.

Year	0	1	2	3	4	5	6
Population	4	11	29	79	213	577	1557

   a. Create a scatter plot of the data.
   b. What is the regression equation? Graph the equation on the grid with the scatter plot.
   c. How did you determine what type of function to use?
   d. What do you predict the rabbit population will be in the 20th year? Explain your reasoning.
2. Rewrite the expression $7^{\frac{3}{4}}$ using a radical.
3. Rewrite the expression $(\sqrt[6]{16})^5$ using a rational exponent.

A Skewed Reality

Determining the Better Measure of Center and Spread for a Data Set

Warm Up

Calculate the mean of each data set.

1. 4, 4, 7, 7, 7, 8, 8, 8, 8, 9, 9, 9, 12, 12

2. 0, 2, 10, 10, 11, 11, 11, 12, 12, 12, 13, 13

3. 40, 60, 60, 70, 70, 70, 80, 80, 100

4. 20, 20, 22, 23, 23, 24, 24, 24, 42, 50

Learning Goals

- Calculate and interpret the mean and median of a data set.
- Determine which measure of central tendency is best to use for a data set.
- Calculate and interpret the interquartile range (IQR) of a data set.
- Determine whether a data set contains outliers.
- Calculate and interpret the standard deviation of a data set.
- Determine which measure of spread is best to use for a data set.

Key Terms

- statistics
- measure of central tendency
- interquartile range (IQR)
- data distribution
- outlier
- lower fence
- upper fence
- standard deviation

You have displayed and interpreted data sets using the statistical process. How can you further describe a data set using center, shape, and spread?

Make Your Mark

Consider each data display.

Heights of Home Team Basketball Players

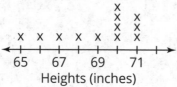

Heights (inches)

Amount of Grocery Purchases by Customer

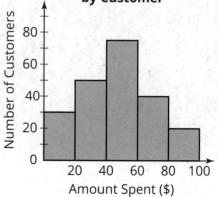

Daily Rainfall Amounts for Seattle April 2017

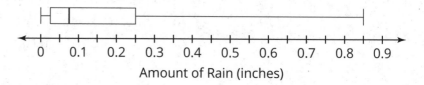

1. **Without doing any calculations, predict whether the mean or median will be greater for the data set represented by each display. Indicate your predictions by marking and labeling each measure of center on the number lines of the dot plot and the box-and-whisker plot, and within one or more bins of the histogram. Explain your reasoning.**

Median and IQR

You can analyze a data set by describing numerical characteristics, or **statistics**, of the data. A statistic that describes the "center" of a data set is called a *measure of central tendency*. A **measure of central tendency** is the numerical value used to describe the overall clustering of data in a set. Two measures of central tendency that are typically used to describe a set of data are the mean and the median.

A gym surveys its members about the average number of hours they spend at the gym each week. The data are recorded in the dot plot shown.

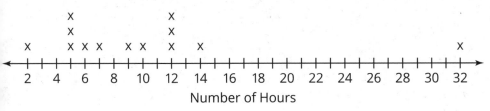

Average Number of Hours Spent in Gym Each Week

Number of Hours

To describe the mean of a data set you need to calculate $\bar{x}$, which is read as "*x* bar."

Think about:

Just as you analyze data presented in a scatter plot to determine which type of regression equation best fits the data, you can analyze data in a display to determine which measure of center best fits the data.

Worked Example

The formula shown represents the mean of a data set.

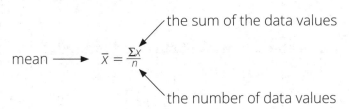

mean ⟶ $\bar{x} = \frac{\Sigma x}{n}$

the sum of the data values

the number of data values

The mean of the data set 5, 10, 9, 7, 5 can be written using this formula.

$$\bar{x} = \frac{5 + 10 + 9 + 7 + 5}{5}$$

$$\bar{x} = 7.2$$

The mean of this data set is 7.2.

The E-like symbol is actually the Greek letter sigma and in mathematical terms it means the "summation" or "sum of."

The median of the data set from the worked example is 7, because the data in order from least to greatest are 5, 5, 7, 9, 10.

To describe the median of a data set, determine the middle number in a data set when the values are placed in order from least to greatest or greatest to least.

1. Analyze the data collected from the gym members in the dot plot.

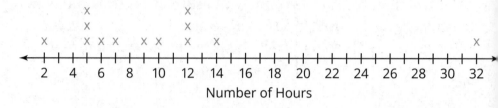

Average Number of Hours Spent in Gym Each Week

Number of Hours

   a. Calculate the five-number summary for the data. Construct a box-and-whisker plot that displays the same data on top of the dot plot.

   b. Calculate the mean of the data. Mark $\bar{x}$ above the point on the number line.

   c. What do you notice about how the data are clustered?

The overall shape of a graph is called the **data distribution**. Remember, there are three common distributions of data: skewed left, skewed right, and symmetric. The distribution of data can help you determine whether the mean or median is a better measure of center. Examine the diagrams shown.

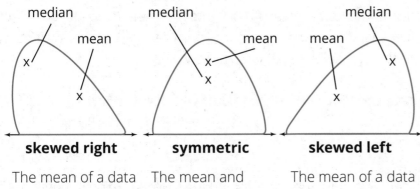

| skewed right | symmetric | skewed left |

skewed right	symmetric	skewed left
The mean of a data set is greater than the median when the data are skewed to the right. The median is the best measure of center because the median is not affected by very large data values.	The mean and median are equal when the data are symmetric.	The mean of a data set is less than the median when the data are skewed to the left. The median is the best measure of center because the median is not affected by very small data values.

2. **Which measure of central tendency would you choose to represent the data set? Explain your reasoning.**

Another characteristic to consider when analyzing a graphical display is the spread, or variability, of the data. One common measure of spread is the *interquartile range* or *IQR*. The **interquartile range, IQR**, measures how far the data are spread out from the median. It is calculated by subtracting Q3 − Q1 in the five-number summary.

If the median is the better measure of center to use to describe a data set, then the IQR should be used to describe the spread. A box-and-whisker plot provides both of these pieces of information.

3. Calculate the IQR of the data displayed in Question 1.

Remember:

An **outlier** is a data value that is significantly greater or lesser than other data values in a data set.

Another useful statistic when analyzing data is to determine if there are any *outliers*. It is important to identify outliers because outliers can often affect the other statistics of the data set, such as the mean.

An outlier is typically calculated by multiplying the IQR by 1.5 and then determining if any data values are greater or lesser than that calculated distance away from Q1 or Q3. The value of Q1 − (IQR · 1.5) is known as the **lower fence** and the value of Q3 + (IQR · 1.5) is known as the **upper fence**. Any value outside these limits is an outlier.

Let's analyze the data set from Question 1 to see how outliers can be represented on a box-and-whisker plot.

2, 5, 5, 5, 6, 7, 9, 10, 12, 12, 12, 14, 32

Given this data set, the five-number summary is:

Minimum = 2, Q1 = 5, Median = 9, Q3 = 12, Maximum = 32

IQR = 7

Using the five-number summary and IQR, calculate the upper and lower fence to determine if there are any outliers in the data set.

Lower Fence:	Upper Fence:
= Q1 − (IQR · 1.5)	= Q3 + (IQR · 1.5)
= 5 − (7 · 1.5)	= 12 + (7 · 1.5)
= −5.5	= 22.5
There are no values less than −5.5.	The value 32 is greater than 22.5.

If there are outliers, the whisker will end at the lowest or highest value that is not an outlier. Since 32 is an outlier, 14 is the greatest data value that is not an outlier.

Once the outlier is removed, the five-number summary is:

Minimum = 2, Q1 = 5, Median = 8, Q3 = 12, Maximum = 14

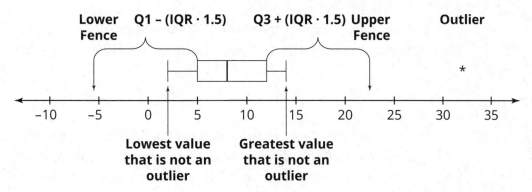

On a box-and-whisker plot, it is common to denote outliers with an asterisk.

4. Recalculate the IQR of the data from Question 1 with the outlier removed.

5. Was the IQR affected by the outlier? Do you think this is true in all cases?

Points Scored (2016)	Points Scored (2017)
10	0
13	7
17	17
20	17
22	18
24	24
24	24
27	24
28	25
29	27
35	45

Coach Petersen's Middletown High School football team is struggling to win games this season. He is trying to determine why his team has won only a few times this year. The table shows the points scored in games in 2016 and 2017. The box-and-whisker plots represent and compare the data in the table.

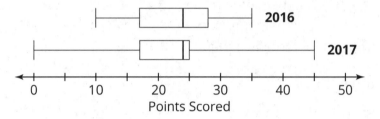

Points Scored by Middletown High School's Football Team

1. **Which year do you think was better in terms of points scored?**

When comparing two data sets, if one data set appears symmetric and the other appears skewed, the median and IQR should be used to compare both data sets.

2. **Calculate and interpret the IQR for the points scored each year. What does the IQR tell you about which year was better?**

3. **Remove any outliers for the data sets and, if necessary, reconstruct and label the box-and-whisker plot(s). Compare the IQR of the original data to your new calculations. What do you notice?**

4. **Analyze the box-and-whisker plots with the outliers removed and compare the number of points scored each year.**

Mean and Standard Deviation

Ms. Webb is determining which student she should add to the spelling bee roster that will represent Tyler High School. The chart shows the 10 most recent scores for three students.

Jack	Aleah	Tymar
33	20	5
32	42	10
30	45	12
50	51	40
49	49	45
50	47	55
35	58	88
73	53	60
71	55	90
77	80	95

The box-and-whisker plots display each of the student's spelling bee scores.

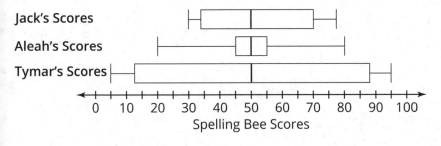

1. **Describe the shape of each student's data set.**

The reason why $n - 1$ is used in the formula is that statisticians have determined that it calculates a statistic that more closely represents the population.

You have learned about the spread of data values from the median, or the IQR. If you know the mean of a data set, you can calculate the spread using *standard deviation*. **Standard deviation** is a measure of how spread out the data are from the mean.

The formula to determine the standard deviation of a sample of a population is represented as:

$$s = \sqrt{\frac{\sum_{i=1}^{n}(x_i - \overline{x})^2}{n - 1}}$$

where s is the standard deviation, x_i represents each individual data value, $\overline{x}$ represents the mean of the data set, and n is the number of data points.

Let's look at each part of the standard deviation formula separately.

Worked Example

Follow the steps to determine the standard deviation. Let's use the data set 6, 4, 10, 8, where $\overline{x} = 7$.

First, think of each data value as its own term labeled as x_1, x_2, and so on.

$x_1 = 6$
$x_2 = 4$
$x_3 = 10$
$x_4 = 8$

The first part of the formula identifies the terms to be added. Since n represents the total number of values and $i = 1$, add all the values that result from substituting in the first term to the fourth term.

$$\sum_{i=1}^{n}$$

Next, evaluate the expressions to be added. Subtract $\overline{x}$ from each term and then square each difference.

$(x_1 - \overline{x})^2$
$(6 - 7)^2 = 1$
$(4 - 7)^2 = 9$
$(10 - 7)^2 = 9$
$(8 - 7)^2 = 1$

Now determine the sum of the squared values and divide the sum by the number one fewer than the number of data values.

$\dfrac{1 + 9 + 9 + 1}{4 - 1} = \dfrac{20}{3} \approx 6.7$

Finally, calculate the square root of the quotient.

$s = \sqrt{6.7}$
$s \approx 2.6$

So the standard deviation for the given data set is approximately 2.6. It is important to note that if the data values have a unit of measure, the standard deviation of the data set also used the same unit of measure.

2. Do you think the standard deviation for each student's spelling bee scores will be the same? If yes, explain your reasoning. If no, predict who will have a higher or lower standard deviation.

Think about:

The whole purpose of statistics is to make sense of a population using a sample. What is the sample in Ms. Webb's data? What is the population?

Each student's data set shows a symmetric distribution, so the mean is the better measure of center. Therefore, the standard deviation is the better measure to use to describe the spread.

3. Use the standard deviation formula to determine the standard deviation of Jack's spelling bee scores.

   a. Determine the $\bar{x}$ value.

b. **Complete the table. The data values have been put in ascending order.**

x_i	$x_i - \bar{x}$	$(x_1 - \bar{x})^2$
30		
32		
33		
35		
49		
50		
50		
71		
73		
77		
Sum		

Think

about:

The mean represents the balance point of the data values in the set. What sum should you expect to get when you add all the values for $x_i - \bar{x}$?

c. **Determine the standard deviation for Jack's spelling bee scores and interpret the meaning.**

4. **Complete each table for Aleah's and Tymar's spelling bee scores.**

a. **Aleah**

x_i	$x_i - \bar{x}$	$(x_1 - \bar{x})^2$
20		
42		
45		
47		
49		
51		
53		
55		
58		
80		
Sum		

b. Tymar

x_i	$x_i - \overline{x}$	$(x_1 - \overline{x})^2$
5		
10		
12		
40		
45		
55		
60		
88		
90		
95		
Sum		

5. **Determine the standard deviation of Aleah's and Tymar's spelling bee scores.**

6. **Was the prediction you made in Question 2 correct? What do the standard deviations tell you about each student's spelling bee scores?**

To calculate the standard deviation:
- Calculate the mean of the data set.
- Calculate the deviations from the mean.
- Add up the squared deviations.
- Divide by $n - 1$.
- Take the square root.

7. **Which student do you think Ms. Webb should add to the spelling bee roster? Use the mean and standard deviation for the student you recommend to add to the roster to justify your answer.**

The Mountain View High School basketball team has its first game of the season and Coach Maynard is comparing the heights of the home team's top ten players to the heights of the visiting team's top ten players. The dot plots of the data are given.

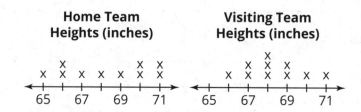

1. **Predict which team has the greatest standard deviation in their heights. Explain how you determined your answer.**

You can use technology to calculate the standard deviation of the data values for the sample of the population.

2. **Determine the standard deviation of the heights of each team. Describe what this means in terms of this problem situation. How does this information help Coach Maynard?**

TALK the TALK

Data on Display

Consider the dot plot from the Getting Started.

**Heights of Home Team
Basketball Players**

```
                    x
                    x   x
                    x   x
    x  x  x  x  x   x   x
    +--+--+--+--+--+--+--+-->
    65     67     69     71
         Heights (inches)
```

1. **Calculate the mean and median heights for the basketball players on the home team. Was your prediction correct?**

Consider the histogram from the Getting Started.

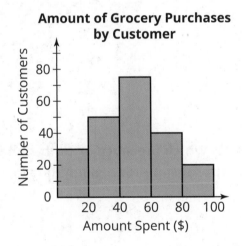

**Amount of Grocery Purchases
by Customer**

2. **The mean of the data set is 51 and the median of the data set is 50. How do these values compare to your prediction?**

Consider the box-and-whisker plot from the Getting Started.

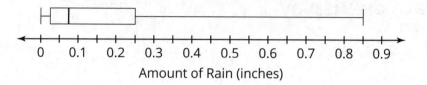

Daily Rainfall Amounts for Seattle April 2017

Amount of Rain (inches)

3. The median of the data set is 0.07 and the mean of the data set is 0.16. How do these values compare to your prediction?

4. Determine which measure of center and which measure of spread would be most appropriate to use to describe each data set. Explain your reasoning.

5. How do you know which measure of center and measure of spread is most appropriate for a given data set?

Assignment

Write

Match each definition to its corresponding term.

1. interquartile range (IQR)
2. standard deviation
3. lower fence
4. upper fence
5. statistic
6. measure of central tendency
7. outlier

a. a value calculated using the formula $Q1 - (IQR \cdot 1.5)$
b. numeric characteristics of a data set
c. a value that is much greater or lesser than other values in a data set
d. a value calculated using the formula $Q3 + (IQR \cdot 1.5)$
e. a measure of spread from the mean
f. a value used to describe the overall clustering of data in a set
g. a measure of spread from the median

Remember

The median is the better measure of central tendency and the IQR is the better measure of spread to use to describe a data set that is skewed. The mean is the better measure of central tendency and the standard deviation is the better measure of spread to use to describe a data set that is symmetric. Outliers in a data set are calculated using the formula $Q1 - (IQR \cdot 1.5)$ to determine a lower fence and $Q3 + (IQR \cdot 1.5)$ to determine an upper fence. Any value outside these limits is an outlier.

Practice

1. Consider each data set. Calculate the median, mean, IQR, and standard deviation of each set. Then, determine which measure of central tendency and which measure of spread is the most appropriate to use to describe the data set. Explain your reasoning.

   a. 1, 2, 2, 4, 8, 8, 8, 9, 9, 9, 10, 10, 10

   b. 5, 5, 6, 6, 6, 7, 7, 7, 8, 8, 8, 9, 9

   c. 0, 1, 2, 10, 12, 12, 16, 16, 16, 16, 18, 18, 20

   d. 2, 2, 2, 3, 3, 4, 4, 8, 9, 9, 10, 10, 10

2. The five number summaries for the average monthly precipitation in millimeters during the summer for the Western and Midwestern states are provided.

   a. Construct box-and-whisker plots of each area's monthly precipitation using the same number line for each.

   b. Describe the distribution of both box-and-whisker plots and explain what they mean in terms of the problem situation.

   c. Determine if there are outliers in either data set. Show your work and explain how you determined your answer.

   d. Chen is considering a long camping trip this summer and hopes to avoid the rain. Would you recommend that he camp in the West or the Midwest? Explain your reasoning.

West	Midwest
Min = 7	Min = 68
Q1 = 22	Q1 = 81.5
Med = 33	Med = 99.5
Q3 = 49	Q3 = 102.5
Max = 107	Max = 111

Stretch

Create a data set of 15 numbers where the mean and median are both 59 and the standard deviation is between 10 and 11. Then, add an outlier to your data set. How are the mean and standard deviation affected?

Review

1. Alejandra has $900 to open a bank account. She wants to put her money in the bank where she will earn the most money over time. Alejandra has a choice between the Platinum Bank that offers an account with 3% compound interest and the Diamond Bank that offers an account with 4% simple interest.

   a. What is the function used to calculate the balance in each account based on the year, t? Describe each function.

   b. In which bank should Alejandra deposit her money? Explain your reasoning.

2. The following is a list of seconds it takes swimmers to swim 50 yards freestyle.

   29, 27, 28, 24, 32, 30, 28, 29, 32, 26, 34, 30, 25, 27, 30, 29, 25, 28, 29, 32

   a. Construct a box-and-whisker plot based on the list of swimmers' times.

   b. What does the distribution of the box-and-whisker plot mean in terms of the swimmers' times?

3. Solve for x in each equation.

   a. $6^{5x-4} = 6^{4x}$ b. $9^x = 3^{3x+2}$

Dare to Compare

Comparing Data Sets

Warm Up

Determine if the distribution of each data set is symmetric, skewed left, or skewed right.

1. 4, 4, 7, 7, 7, 8, 8, 8, 8, 9, 9, 9, 12, 12

2. 0, 2, 10, 10, 11, 11, 11, 12, 12, 12, 13, 13

3. 40, 60, 60, 70, 70, 70, 80, 80, 100

4. 20, 20, 22, 23, 23, 24, 24, 24, 42, 50

Learning Goals

- Compare the standard deviation of data sets.
- Analyze and interpret data graphically and numerically.
- Determine which measure of central tendency and spread is most appropriate to describe a data set.

You know how to determine the most appropriate measure of center and spread to describe a data set based on its distribution. How can you use what you know to compare data sets in problem situations?

Stats on Cats

The Humane Society records the number of different visits from potential families a sample of 25 cats from each of their two locations received before being adopted. The box-and-whisker plots display the collected data

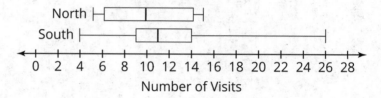

Visits to Cats Before Being Adopted

1. **Yumi, Mia, and Sloane are trying to determine which shelter's cats receive fewer visits before being adopted. Yumi says the mean and standard deviation of the data for the North shelter should be compared to the median and IQR of the data from the South shelter. Mia says the median and IQR of the data from each shelter should be compared. Sloane says the mean and standard deviation of the data from each shelter should be compared. Who's correct? Explain your reasoning.**

Ms. Webb, the spelling bee coach, is preparing her class for their first spelling bee scrimmage. She needs to determine which student should be the spelling bee captain. The two top spelling bee students' scores are recorded in the table. Ms. Webb analyzes the scores and calculates the approximate mean score and standard deviation for each student.

1. **Advise Ms. Webb whom she should choose to captain the spelling bee team. Explain your reasoning.**

Maria	Heidi
81	81
73	68
94	60
86	109
70	82
68	88
97	60
93	102
81	78
67	69
85	84
77	103
79	92
103	60
90	108

ACTIVITY

3.2 | Comparing Airlines

Data were collected from two rival airlines measuring the difference in the stated departure times and the times the flights actually departed. The average departure time differences were recorded for each month for one year. The results are shown in the table given.

Differences in Departure Times (minutes)	
My Air Airlines	**Fly High Airlines**
26	14
15	32
40	29
0	8
20	24
33	45
20	7
5	30
19	15
34	49
11	16
33	27

1. **You are scheduling a flight for an important meeting and you must be there on time. Which airline would you schedule with? Explain your reasoning.**

ACTIVITY 3.3 · Comparing Garages

Brenda needs to get the oil changed in her car, but she hates to wait! Quick Change and Speedy Oil are two garages near Brenda's house. She decides to check an online site that allows customers to comment on the service at different local businesses and record their wait times. Brenda chooses 12 customers at random for each garage. The wait times for each garage are shown.

Wait Times (minutes)	
Quick Change	**Speedy Oil**
10 60 22 15	5 60 45 24
12 24 20 18	40 26 55 30
16 23 22 15	32 85 45 30

1. **Based on the data gathered, which garage should Brenda choose if she is in a hurry?**

TALK the TALK

Which Came First—the Data or the Display?

1. Analyze the box-and-whisker plots shown.

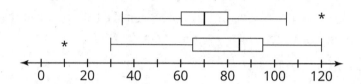

a. Create a possible data set for each box-and-whisker plot.

b. Create a possible scenario that compares the two data sets.

c. Write at least two questions that could be answered using your scenario and data sets.

2. A data set ranges from 10 to 20. A value of 50 is added to the data set.

   a. Explain how the mean and median are affected by this new value.

   b. Which measure of central tendency and spread would you use to describe the original data set before the new value is added? Explain your reasoning.

   c. Which measure of central tendency and spread would you use to describe the data set after the new value is added? Explain your reasoning.

Assignment

Write

Describe in your own words how to compare two data sets.

Remember

When comparing two data sets, if at least one of the data sets is skewed, you should use the median and IQR to compare the data.

Practice

1. Dannette and Alphonso work for a computer repair company. They must include the time it takes to complete each repair in their repair log book. The dot plots show the number of hours each of their last 12 repairs took.

Dannette's Repair Times

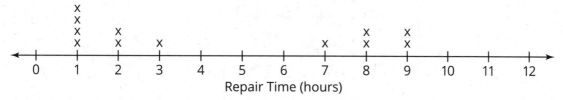

Repair Time (hours)

Alphonso's Repair Times

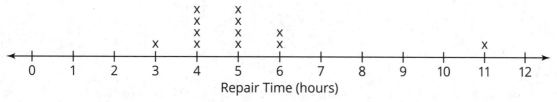

Repair Time (hours)

a. Calculate the median, mean, IQR, and standard deviation of each data set.

b. Which measure of central tendency and spread should you use to compare the two data sets? Explain your reasoning.

c. Determine whether there are any outliers in either data set and recalculate the IQR, if necessary.

d. Which repair person would you ask to fix your computer if you were in a hurry to have it repaired? Explain your reasoning.

Stretch

A normal curve is a bell-shaped curve that is symmetric about the mean of the data.

Normal curves A, B, and C represent the battery lives of a population of cell phones of comparable models from three different companies. The normal curves represent distributions with standard deviations of 0.1, 0.4, and 0.5.

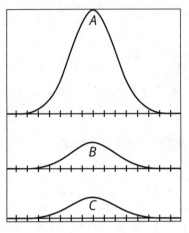

1. Match each standard deviation value with one of the normal curves and explain your reasoning.

Review

1. Consider the data set: 6, 7, 7, 10, 12, 16, 16, 17, 20, 22, 22, 22, 23, 24, 24, 24, 24, 24, 25, 40.
   a. What is the five number summary and the IQR for the data set?
   b. Are there outliers for the data set? If so, what are they?

2. Solve each equation for x.

   a. $\frac{1}{5^{x-3}} = 25^{2x}$

   b. $16^{-2x} = \left(\frac{4}{64}\right)^{x+6}$

3. Determine whether the expressions are equivalent. If they are not equivalent, write an expression equivalent to each of the expressions provided.

   a. $2 + (6^3 \cdot 6^{10}) - 9^{\frac{1}{2}}$ and $1 + 6^{30}$

   b. $\frac{4^{(12 \cdot 2)}}{4^{(3 \cdot 9)}} + \frac{18^5}{9^5}$ and $4^{-3} + 2^5$

One-Variable Statistics Summary

KEY TERMS

- dot plot
- histogram
- bin
- frequency
- box-and-whisker plot

- five number summary
- statistic
- measure of central tendency
- interquartile range (IQR)

- outlier
- lower fence
- upper fence
- standard deviation

LESSON

1

Way to Represent!

Data sets presented as a table may be difficult to analyze. One way to better organize a data set is to create a graphical display. When you analyze a graphical display, you can draw conclusions from the shape, center, and spread of the graph.

A **dot plot** is a graph that shows how discrete data, or data that can be "counted," are distributed using a number line. Dot plots are best used to organize and display data sets with a small number of data points.

Heights of Home Team Basketball Players

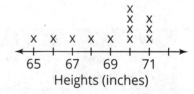

For example, the dot plot shown represents the heights in inches of 12 basketball players on the home team. The dot plot shows that there are 4 players that are 70 inches tall and only one player that is 67 inches tall.

Another way to display quantitative data is to create a **histogram**. A histogram is a graphical way to display quantitative data using vertical bars. The width of a bar in a histogram represents an interval of data and is often referred to as a **bin**. A bin represents an interval of data instead of individual data values. The value shown on the left side of the bin is the least data value in the interval. The height of each bar indicates the **frequency**, which is the number of data values included in any given bin. Histograms are effective in displaying large amounts of continuous data, or data that can take any numerical value within a range.

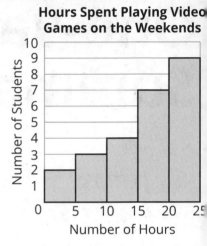

Hours Spent Playing Video Games on the Weekends

For example, the histogram shown represents the data distribution for the number of hours students spend playing video games on the weekends. The histogram shows that there are 4 students who spend between 10 and 15 hours playing video games on the weekends.

Another graphical representation that displays the distribution of quantitative data is a **box-and-whisker plot**. A box-and-whisker plot displays the data distribution based on a **five number summary**. The five number summary consists of the minimum value, the first quartile (Q1), the median, the third quartile (Q3), and the maximum value. Each vertical line of the box-and-whisker plot represents a value from the summary.

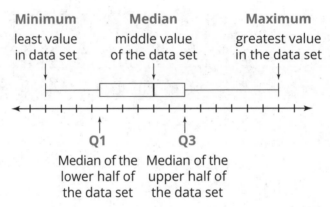

There are four sections of the graphical display: minimum to Q1, Q1 to median, median to Q3, and Q3 to maximum. Each section of the box-and-whisker plot represents 25% of the data set.

LESSON

2

A Skewed Reality

You can analyze a data set by describing numerical characteristics, or **statistics**, of the data. A statistic that describes the "center" of a data set is called a measure of central tendency. A **measure of central tendency** is a numerical value used to describe the overall clustering of data in a set. Two measures of central tendency that are typically used to describe a set of data are the mean and the median.

To determine the mean of a data set, which represents the sum of the data values divided by the number of values, you need to calculate $\bar{x}$, which is read as "x bar."

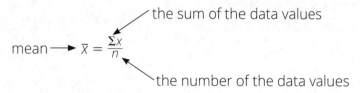

mean $\longrightarrow$ $\bar{x} = \dfrac{\Sigma x}{n}$ $\nearrow$ the sum of the data values

$\searrow$ the number of the data values

The median is the middle number in an ordered data set.

The overall shape of a graph is called the data distribution. There are three common distributions of data: skewed left, skewed right, and symmetric. The distribution of data can help you determine whether the mean or median is a better measure of center.

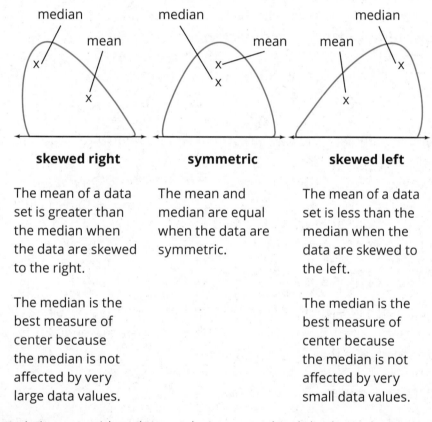

skewed right

symmetric

skewed left

The mean of a data set is greater than the median when the data are skewed to the right.

The median is the best measure of center because the median is not affected by very large data values.

The mean and median are equal when the data are symmetric.

The mean of a data set is less than the median when the data are skewed to the left.

The median is the best measure of center because the median is not affected by very small data values.

Another characteristic to consider when analyzing a graphical display is the spread, or variability, of the data. One common measure of spread is the *interquartile range* or *IQR*. The **interquartile range**, **IQR**, measures how far the data are spread out from the median. It is calculated by subtracting Q3 − Q1 in the five number summary. The IQR is the range of the middle 50% of the data. When the median is the best measure of center to describe the data set, the IQR is the best measure of spread to use.

For example, suppose that the number of home runs hit by each of the 12 batters for the York High School varsity baseball team is represented on the box-and-whisker plot.

Home Runs for York High School Varsity Baseball

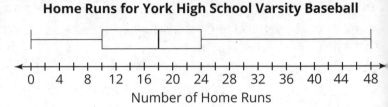

Number of Home Runs

The data are skewed right, so the median, 18, is the most appropriate measure of central tendency and the IQR, 14, is the most appropriate measure of spread.

An **outlier** is a data value that is significantly greater or lesser than other data values in a data set. It is important to identify outliers because outliers can often affect the other statistics of the data set such as the mean. An outlier is typically calculated by multiplying the IQR by 1.5 and then determining if any data values are greater or lesser than that calculated distance away from Q1 or Q3. The value of Q1 − (IQR · 1.5) is known as the **lower fence**, and the value of Q3 + (IQR · 1.5) is known as the **upper fence**. Any value outside these limits is an outlier.

Consider the data set given to see how outliers can be represented on a box-and-whisker plot.

2, 5, 6, 6, 7, 9, 10, 11, 12, 12, 14, 28, 30

Using the five number summary and IQR, calculate the upper and lower fence to determine if there are any outliers in the data set.

Minimum = 2	Lower Fence:	Upper Fence:
Q1 = 6	= Q1 − (IQR · 1.5)	= Q3 + (IQR · 1.5)
Median = 10	= 6 − (7 · 1.5)	= 13 + (7 · 1.5)
Q3 = 13	= −4.5	= 23.5
Maximum = 30		
IQR = 7		

There are no values less than −4.5. Both 28 and 30 are greater than 23.5. Since 28 and 30 are both outliers, 14 is the greatest data value that is not an outlier. If there are outliers, the whiskers will end at the **least** or **greatest** value that is not an outlier.

It is common to denote an outlier with an asterisk.

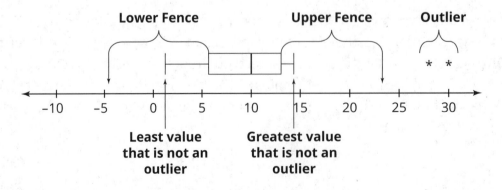

If you reanalyze the data with outliers removed, you will notice that the IQR does not change significantly, which is why it is the better measure of spread when data are skewed.

Standard deviation is a measure of how spread out the data is from the mean. The formula to determine the standard deviation of a sample is represented as:

$$s = \sqrt{\frac{\sum_{i=1}^{n}(x_i - \bar{x})^2}{n-1}}$$

where s is the standard deviation, x_i represents each individual data value, $\bar{x}$ represents the mean of the data set, and n is the number of data points.

For example, suppose 6, 4, 10, 8 represents a data sample from a population. Use the formula to calculate the standard deviation of the sample.

The mean of the data set is 7.

Calculate the deviations from the mean and the square of the deviations from the mean.

x_i	$x_i - \bar{x}$	$(x_i - \bar{x})^2$
4	$4 - 7 = -3$	$(-3)^2 = 9$
6	$6 - 7 = -1$	$(-1)^2 = 1$
8	$8 - 7 = 1$	$3^2 = 9$
10	$10 - 7 = 3$	$1^2 = 1$
Sum	$-3 + (-1) + 1 + 3 = 0$	$9 + 1 + 9 + 1 = 20$

Substitute the sum of the square of the deviations and the number of terms into the formula to calculate the standard deviation.

$$s = \sqrt{\frac{\sum_{i=1}^{n}(x_i - \bar{x})^2}{n-1}}$$
$$= \sqrt{\frac{20}{4-1}} = \sqrt{\frac{20}{3}}$$
$$= \sqrt{6.7} \approx 2.6$$

The standard deviation is approximately 2.6.

A smaller standard deviation represents data that are more tightly clustered. A larger standard deviation represents data that are more spread out from the mean.

When the mean is the most appropriate measure of center of a data set, the standard deviation is the most appropriate measure of spread.

When comparing data sets, you need to first analyze the distribution of each set. If both sets are symmetric, you should use the mean and standard deviation to compare the sets. If one or both sets are skewed, you need to use the median and IQR to compare the sets.

For example, consider the data displayed in the box-and-whisker plots representing the number of visits cats from two shelters received before being adopted.

Visits to Cats Before Being Adopted

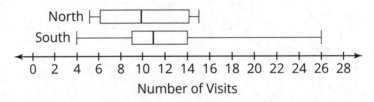

Number of Visits

The data for the North shelter is symmetric, and the data for the South shelter is skewed right. Therefore, the median and IQR of the sets should be compared when interpreting the data. The median number of visits at the North shelter is 10 and the median number of visits at the South shelter is 11. However, the North shelter has a greater IQR, so the middle 50 percent of the number of visits is more spread out from the median than at the South shelter.

Two-Variable Categorical Data

How many kindergartners vs. first graders want to play outside vs. fingerpaint?

Module 4: Describing Distributions

TOPIC 2: TWO-VARIABLE CATEGORICAL DATA

In this topic, students first learn how to create two-way frequency distributions to display two variables whose data can be grouped into categories and analyze the data for any possible trends or associations. However, because analyzing raw frequencies can lead to misinterpretations, students learn to display categorical data using a relative frequency distribution. Conditional relative frequency distributions organize categorical data so that students can determine the percent of occurrence of a category given the specific value of another category. Finally, students use all the tools that they have to analyze a set of categorical data and make recommendations based on their interpretation.

Where have we been?

Since middle school, students have collected, organized, and interpreted data using the statistical process. And in middle school, students were first introduced to bivariate categorical data. They have constructed and interpreted two-way frequency and relative frequency tables and used them to describe possible associations.

Where are we going?

As students increase their proficiency with the statistical process, they are able to perform more advanced analyses of complex data sets. Building on their deep understanding of how to use two-way tables to draw inferences about categorical data, they will be able to use the two-way table to decide if probabilistic events are independent and to approximate conditional probabilities.

Conditional Relative Frequency

A conditional relative frequency distribution is the percent or ratio of occurrences of a category given the specific value of another category.

This conditional relative frequency distribution gives the percent of participants with each handedness, given the type of sports they play.

Sports Participation

Hand Favored		Individual	Team	Does Not Play
	Left	$\frac{3}{10} = 30\%$	$\frac{13}{39} = 33\%$	$\frac{8}{14} = 57\%$
	Right	$\frac{6}{10} = 60\%$	$\frac{23}{39} = 59\%$	$\frac{4}{14} = 29\%$
	Mixed	$\frac{1}{10} = 10\%$	$\frac{3}{39} = 8\%$	$\frac{2}{14} = 14\%$
	Total	$\frac{10}{10} = 100\%$	$\frac{39}{39} = 100\%$	$\frac{14}{14} = 100\%$

Blinded Me with Science!

In the Age of Enlightenment, which took place in the 17th and 18th centuries, there was rapid scientific advancement where scientists such as Descartes and Newton confirmed scientific thinking with experiments and mathematics. Today there are two major groups of sciences: natural sciences and social sciences. The natural sciences include topics such as astronomy, biology, chemistry, physics, and earth science. The social sciences include topics dealing with society and human behavior such as economics, linguistics, and psychology.

Both the natural sciences and the social sciences make heavy use of statistics and statistical analysis.

Talking Points

Categorical data is an important topic to know about for college admissions tests.

Here is a sample question:

At a diner, each meal comes with a free appetizer or dessert. Data were collected regarding the choice of the past 500 customers based on age. Out of a group of 10 high school students who just entered the diner, use the data to predict how many will order a free appetizer.

	Appetizer	Dessert
Ages 10–24	70	100
Ages 25–39	135	50
Ages 40–64	50	95

High school students would be in the 10–24 year age range. According to the data for that age range, $\frac{70}{170}$ or 41.1% chose an appetizer. So, for 10 students, 10 × 0.41, or about 4 of them would probably order a free appetizer.

Key Terms

categorical data
Categorical data are data that can be grouped into categories, unlike numerical data that can be placed on a numerical scale and compared.

marginal frequency distribution
A marginal frequency distribution displays the total of the frequencies of the rows or columns of a frequency distribution.

relative frequency distribution
A relative frequency distribution provides the ratio of occurrences in each category to the total number of occurrences.

It Takes Two

Creating and Interpreting Frequency Distributions

Warm Up

1. Create a bar graph to display the data in the frequency table.

Favorite School Subjects in Mr. Luft's Class	
Subject	**Frequency**
Math	IIII III
History	IIII
Science	IIII I
Art	IIII II

Learning Goals

- Construct and interpret frequency and marginal frequency distributions displayed in two-way tables for two-variable categorical data.
- Create and interpret graphs of frequency distributions displayed in two-way tables.

Key Terms

- categorical data
- two-way frequency table
- frequency distribution
- joint frequency
- marginal frequency distribution

You have explored the relationship between two variables of numerical data. How can you follow the statistical process to determine whether there are any associations between two variables of categorical data?

Survey Says . . .

Recall that the first step of the statistical process is to formulate a question. A statistical question anticipates an answer based on data that vary.

Cut out the survey questions located at the end of the lesson. Read each question and consider how you and other people might answer it. Sort the questions into groups based on the types of answers that could be given for each.

1. **Record your groups and the questions in each group.**

2. **What observations can you make about the types of data that can be collected by the questions?**

Two types of variable data that can be collected from a statistical question are numerical and *categorical data*. **Categorical data** are data that can be grouped into categories. Numerical data are data that can be placed on a numerical scale and compared.

3. **For the survey questions that have categorical answers, is there a way to group the data collected by the question into more than one category? Explain your reasoning.**

Categorical Data in Two Variables

Ms. Seymour is the school cafeteria supervisor at Williams High School. She has been asked to cut her food budget for the upcoming school year. One idea she has is to cut the number of meal choices during the week. Ms. Seymour decides to survey the students in Mr. Kolbe's gym class, which consists of 9th and 10th graders. She recorded the results of her survey in the table shown.

The first step of the statistical process is to formulate a statistical question. The second step is to collect the data.

1. Consider the table.

  a. What type of collection method did Ms. Seymour use?

  b. What question(s) did she ask the students?

  c. Describe the data she collected as either numerical or categorical. Explain your reasoning.

Grade	Favorite Meal
9	Salad bar
10	Burgers
10	Pizza
10	Chicken nuggets
10	Chicken nuggets
9	Burgers
10	Salad bar
9	Salad bar
10	Chicken nuggets
9	Burgers
10	Pizza
9	Salad bar
9	Burgers
10	Burgers
9	Chicken nuggets
9	Salad bar
10	Chicken nuggets
10	Chicken nuggets
10	Salad bar
10	Burgers
10	Salad bar
9	Burgers
9	Pizza
10	Chicken nuggets
10	Salad bar
9	Salad bar
10	Pizza
9	Pizza
10	Chicken nuggets
9	Pizza

The third step of the statistical process is to analyze the data.

2. Analyze Ms. Seymour's data table. Can you see any trends in the data just by looking at her data table? Explain why or why not.

Frequency Distribution Tables

Previously, you analyzed two-variable data sets that were quantitative, or numerical. You displayed those as a scatter plot and modeled them with a regression curve. In this topic you will explore the relationship between two-variable data sets that are qualitative, or categorical.

> Categorical data can also be called qualitative data.

One method of organizing categorical data is to use a *two-way frequency table*. A **two-way frequency table** displays categorical data by representing the number of occurrences that fall into each group for two variables. On the table, one variable is divided into rows and the other is divided into columns.

Consider the favorite meal data collected by Ms. Seymour in the previous activity.

1. **The first variable is the grade level. Identify the groups for this variable.**

Remember:

There is a difference between the variables in a data set and the groups in a data set.

2. **The second variable is the favorite meal. Identify the groups for this variable.**

Grade	Favorite Meal
9	Salad bar
10	Burgers
10	Pizza
10	Chicken nuggets
10	Chicken nuggets
9	Burgers
10	Salad bar
9	Salad bar
10	Chicken nuggets
9	Burgers
10	Pizza
9	Salad bar
9	Burgers
10	Burgers
9	Chicken nuggets
9	Salad bar
10	Chicken nuggets
10	Chicken nuggets
10	Salad bar
10	Burgers
10	Salad bar
9	Burgers
9	Pizza
10	Chicken nuggets
10	Salad bar
9	Salad bar
10	Pizza
9	Pizza
10	Chicken nuggets
9	Pizza

The third step of the statistical process is to analyze the data numerically and graphically. Creating a two-way frequency table helps to organize the data so that they can be analyzed numerically.

3. **Create a two-way frequency table of the data.**

   a. **Enter the name of each group.**

   b. **Record the favorite meal for each student in the appropriate row using tally marks. Then, write the frequency of each meal for each grade level.**

Favorite Meals

4. **Are there any associations between grade level and favorite meal? If so, explain what trends you think exist in these data.**

The table you created is a *frequency distribution*. A **frequency distribution** displays the frequencies for categorical data in a two-way table. Each time you determined the frequency of one favorite meal of one of the grade levels, you recorded a *joint frequency*. Any frequency you record within the body of a two-way frequency table is known as a **joint frequency**.

A two-way frequency table is helpful in organizing each group's frequency in an efficient way. However, it is common to determine the total number of people surveyed just to ensure that a good survey was taken. Determining this total is also helpful to ensure that you recorded the data accurately within the table. For example, if you know 50 people took part in the survey, and the sum of the joint frequencies is 47, then you know that you are missing three data points from the data set.

5. Use the data from your frequency distribution to determine the total number of 9th graders and 10th graders, and to determine the total number of frequencies for each favorite meal category.

Favorite Meals

Grade Level	Burgers	Chicken Nuggets	Pizza	Salad Bar	Total
9th grade					
10th grade					
Total					

You just created a *marginal frequency distribution* of the data by determining the totals for each group.

> A **marginal frequency distribution** displays the total of the frequencies of the rows or columns of a frequency distribution.

6. Analyze the marginal frequency distribution to answer each question.

   a. How many 9th graders participated in the survey?

   b. How many students prefer burgers?

   c. How many students prefer chicken nuggets?

   d. How many 10th graders participated in the survey?

   e. How many students prefer the salad bar?

7. How can you use the totals to determine whether you correctly created the frequency distribution?

8. Use the marginal frequency distribution to answer each question.

   a. Which meal did the least number of students say was their favorite meal?

   b. Which meal did the least number of ninth grade students say was their favorite meal?

   c. Which meal is the most favorite of all students?

   d. Which meal is the most favorite of the 10th graders?

Representing Data

While a two-way table shows a numerical summary of the data, a graph can help relay information about a survey in a visual way. Remember, every graph tells a story.

Recall that Ms. Seymour is trying to determine ways to cut the cafeteria budget for the upcoming school year. She would like to use a graph to visually display the ideas she has for cutting the cafeteria budget.

Ms. Seymour has gathered her data and organized them in the frequency distribution table shown.

Favorite Meals

		Burgers	Chicken Nuggets	Pizza	Salad Bar
Grade Level	9th grade	4	1	3	5
	10th grade	3	7	3	4

1. **Analyze the frequency distribution table.**

   a. **Determine which graphical display(s) would be appropriate to represent Ms. Seymour's data. Justify your response.**

   > You are still completing the third step of the statistical process, but now you are analyzing the data graphically by creating a display.

   b. **Determine which graphical display(s) would not be appropriate to represent Ms. Seymour's data. Justify your response.**

2. **Construct two bar graphs of the frequencies. Be sure to include a key to identify what each bar represents.**

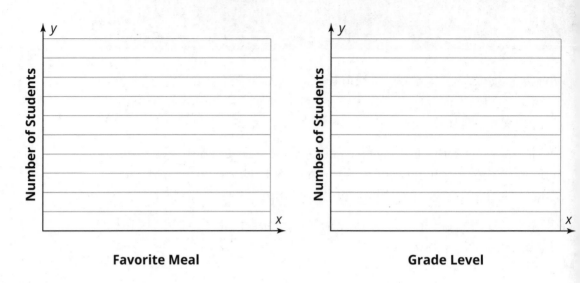

Favorite Meal   **Grade Level**

3. **What conclusions can you draw by examining the graphs?**

4. **Use the graphs to determine whether you represented the data from the frequency distribution table accurately. Explain how you verified that the data in the graphs match the data in the frequency distribution table.**

5. **Does it matter which graph Ms. Seymour's uses to display her survey data? Explain your reasoning.**

Ms. Seymour must decide on a plan for the upcoming school year. The principal of the school would like Ms. Seymour to present her data and a graph to justify her decision to cut costs.

6. **Which meal choice would you cut according to the data? Explain why you would discontinue that meal choice. Then explain which graph you would recommend Ms. Seymour use when she presents her plan.**

> The fourth step of the statistical process is to interpret the data.

Ms. Seymour just thought of an idea, and she thinks it will help cut the cafeteria costs. She is recommending that two lunch periods be created: one for the 9th graders and one for the 10th graders. She thinks that if two lunch periods exist, she can keep all four meal choices, but just cook a lesser amount of certain choices; thus cutting costs.

7. **Do you think Ms. Seymour should present this idea to the principal? Use the data to justify your reasoning.**

8. **Which graph would you recommend Ms. Seymour use to justify her solution? Explain your reasoning.**

Frequent Favorites

An art teacher asks his students what their favorite color is and records the results in the table shown.

Student	Favorite Color
Paul	red
Rachel	blue
Jennifer	blue
Sean	red
Adam	green
Vicki	blue
Spencer	red
Josh	red
Katie	green
Gina	green
Matt	red
James	blue
Corinne	red
Ben	red
Troy	blue
Zach	blue

1. **Explain how the art teacher can represent these data in a way that others could interpret it.**

2. **List some advantages and disadvantages of using a table, a marginal frequency distribution, and a graphical display to represent categorical data.**

   table:

   marginal frequency distribution:

   graphical display:

Survey Questions

A

How many pets do you own?

B

What is your favorite color?

C

What is your favorite sport?

D

What score did you earn on the last math test?

E

How many texts do you send per day?

F

What type of music do you prefer?

G

How many glasses of water do you drink each day?

H

How far do you live from school in miles?

I

What is your favorite snack?

J

How many hours do you watch television per day?

K

What mascot would you prefer for a sports team?

L

What grade are you in?

Assignment

Write

Match each definition to its corresponding term.

1. displays the total of the frequencies of the rows or columns of a frequency distribution
2. displays the frequencies for categorical data in a two-way table
3. non-numerical data that can be grouped into categories
4. displays categorical data by representing the number of occurrences that fall into each group for two variables
5. any frequency you record within the body of a two-way frequency table

a. categorical data
b. two-way frequency table
c. frequency distribution
d. joint frequency
e. marginal frequency distribution

Remember

A frequency distribution table is helpful in organizing categorical data in two variables in order to see any associations and trends in the data.

You can use a double bar graph to visually represent categorical data in two variables.

Practice

1. Forty workers arriving at an office building in a city were asked how they got to work that day. They were also asked if they were less than 40 years old or older. The survey results are shown in the table.

   a. Identify the variables for this survey. Are the variables categorical or quantitative? Explain your reasoning.

   b. Construct and analyze a marginal frequency distribution for the survey data. What was the most commonly used transportation method for each age group? Explain how you determined your answer.

   c. Construct two bar graphs of the frequencies. In one, let the x-axis represent the transportation method, and in the other, let the x-axis represent the age levels. Let the y-axis represent the number of workers in both graphs. What conclusion(s) can you draw by examining each graph?

Age	Transportation Method	Age	Transportation Method
<40	Subway	<40	Bus
<40	Bus	<40	Bus
40+	Walk	<40	Subway
<40	Bus	40+	Car
<40	Subway	<40	Walk
40+	Car	40+	Taxi
40+	Car	40+	Walk
40+	Walk	<40	Subway
<40	Subway	40+	Car
40+	Taxi	<40	Taxi
<40	Walk	40+	Taxi
<40	Bus	<40	Bus
<40	Subway	<40	Bus
40+	Bus	<40	Subway
<40	Bus	40+	Walk
40+	Walk	40+	Car
40+	Taxi	40+	Subway
<40	Subway	40+	Bus
40+	Car	<40	Subway
<40	Car	40+	Taxi

d. The manager of a firm in the building where the survey was taken has noticed that a number of his employees have been coming in late. The late employees often say they are late because of subway problems, but he also notices it is mostly younger workers who are using this excuse. He thinks these employees may be irresponsible because most of his older employees are not coming in late. Which graph could be used to show the manager that his thinking may be wrong?

Stretch

1. Analyze the transportation survey data from the marginal frequency distribution in the Practice.

Percent Distribution		
	<40	40+
Subway		
Bus		
Walk		
Car		
Taxi		
Total	100%	100%

a. Complete the table to show the percent of the total in each category that used the different forms of transportation.

b. Construct a bar graph of the percentages. Let the x-axis represent the transportation method, and let the y-axis represent the percent of workers. What conclusions can you make based on the graph?

Review

1. A group of 45 adults were asked how many times they dined out the previous week. Their responses are shown in the dot plot.

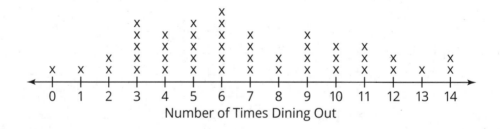

Number of Times Dining Out

a. Describe the distribution of the dot plot.
b. How do you think the mean and median of the data set compare? Explain your reasoning.
c. Calculate the mean and median. Explain what they mean in terms of the problem situation.
d. Which measure of center do you think best represents these data? Explain your reasoning.

2. A clothing store has two checkout methods. In Method A, the customer chooses a line at any of the cashiers' stations. In Method B, the customers wait in one line and then get called to the next available cashier. Data were collected for customers using both methods. The dot plots show the average wait times in minutes for 15 customers for each method of checkout.

a. Predict whether Method A or Method B has the greater standard deviation in wait times. Explain your reasoning.

b. Determine the standard deviation for Method A and Method B. Round your answers to the nearest tenth. Explain what the standard deviations mean in terms of the problem situation.

c. Which waiting line method would you prefer if you were in a big hurry to checkout? Explain your reasoning.

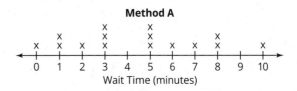

Method A

Wait Time (minutes)

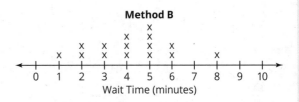

Method B

Wait Time (minutes)

3. Use the graph of the exponential function to determine the domain, whether it is increasing or decreasing, the y- and x-intercept, and the horizontal asymptote.

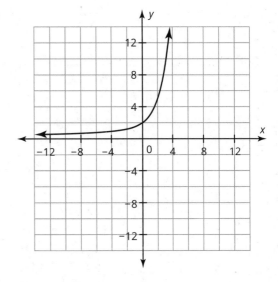

4. Is the graph of the function $f(x) = \left(\frac{1}{2}\right)^x$ increasing or decreasing? Explain your reasoning.

Relatively Speaking

Relative Frequency Distribution

Warm Up

Convert each ratio to a percent.

1. $\frac{39}{100}$

2. $\frac{3}{8}$

3. $\frac{7}{12}$

4. $\frac{13}{25}$

5. $\frac{77}{80}$

Learning Goals

- Construct and interpret relative frequency distribution and marginal relative frequency distributions displayed in two-way tables for categorical data.
- Analyze and use marginal relative frequency distributions to make decisions for a problem situation.

Key Terms

- relative frequency distribution
- marginal relative frequency distribution

You have organized and analyzed data using marginal frequency distribution tables. How can you use percents to analyze the same data set?

Sour Statements

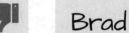

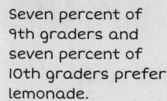

A sample of 9th and 10th grade students at Valley High School were surveyed about their favorite things to drink on a hot day. There were a total of five groups recorded for the variable *favorite drink*, including *water*, *sports drinks, iced coffee, lemonade,* and *iced tea*. The frequency distribution shows the results for the group *lemonade*.

Two students used the table to make the following statements.

Chris
Seven percent of 9th graders and seven percent of 10th graders prefer lemonade.

Brad
Since 7 = 7, the same percent of 9th and 10th graders prefer lemonade.

1. **Explain why each student is incorrect.**

The Northpointe community outreach director wants to plan special summer activities for the members of Northpointe. He selects a random sample of members of the community, and each of those members responds to his survey. Participants identify their age and then chose from four given activities. The responses gathered from the survey are shown.

Think about:

Is there an association between a person's age and their preferred activity?

Activities Preferred During Hot Weather

Age Group	Sports	Movies	Reading	Walking	Total
Students Age 18 Years Old and Under	20	30	22	8	80
Adults Age 19 Through 50 Years Old	10	32	25	43	110
Adults Over 50 Years Old	5	20	35	30	90
Total	35	82	82	81	280

While the raw data provide some information, it is often more efficient to use percents when analyzing data. The relative frequencies of each data entry can provide that information. Representing the relative frequencies for joint data displayed in a two-way table is called a *relative frequency distribution*. The **relative frequency distribution** provides the ratio of occurrences for each category to the total number of occurrences. Displaying the relative frequencies for the rows or columns is called a *marginal relative frequency distribution*. The **marginal relative frequency distribution** provides the ratio of total occurrences for each category to the total number of occurrences.

1. **Construct a marginal relative frequency distribution of the data. Represent each ratio as a percent.**

Activities Preferred During Hot Weather

	Sports	Movies	Reading	Walking	Total
Students Age 18 Years Old and Under					
Adults Age 19 Through 50 Years Old					
Adults Over 50 Years Old					
Total					

Age Group

2. **Five students in Mr. Thomas's class made the given statements. For each statement explain why the student is correct or incorrect. If the student is incorrect, tell what the correct statement should be.**

Isaac
58.6% of participants in the survey prefer watching movies or reading in the hot weather.

Shane
1.07% of adults over age 50 prefer walking in the hot weather.

Marie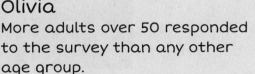
Out of all survey participants that prefer playing sports in the hot weather, 7.1% of those are students age 18 years old and under.

Olivia
More adults over 50 responded to the survey than any other age group.

Aaron
Playing sports is the least popular activity in the hot weather according to the survey results.

3. Which age group made up the smallest percent of people surveyed?

4. Which activity was preferred by the largest percent of people surveyed?

5. Does there appear to be an association between age and preferred activity? If so, explain what trends you notice in these data.

ACTIVITY

2.2 Analyzing Data Ratios

Previously, you have used a bar graph to visually represent data. Another way to represent data is to use a stacked bar graph in which the bars are stacked on top of each other as opposed to sitting next to each other. Consider the marginal relative frequency distribution from the previous activity. The stacked bar graph shown represents the activities preferred during hot weather by age group.

1. **Construct a stacked bar graph using the marginal relative frequency distribution by activities. Be sure to include a legend.**

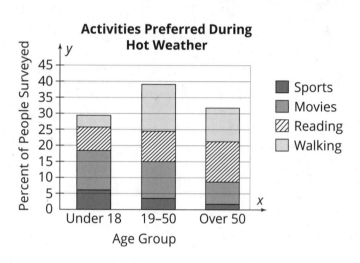

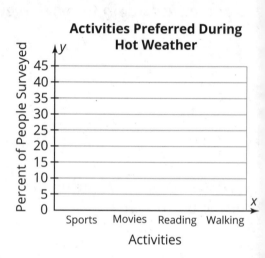

2. **How do the graphs compare to the relative frequency distribution table you completed in the previous activity?**

3. **What conclusions can you draw by examining the graphs?**

4. **Name some advantages of graphing the data by age group. Name some advantages of graphing the data by activity.**

Now that the community outreach director has gathered the data about preferred activities in hot weather, he wants to use them to plan different activities for the summer.

1. **Analyze each of the given activities. Determine whether you think the activity would be a good idea to have during the summer. Use the data to justify your answer.**

   a. **A walking club for community members aged 19 to 50**

   b. **A soccer tournament for community members over the age of 50**

   c. **An ultimate Frisbee league for community members aged 18 or younger**

The community outreach director wants to offer one summer activity each week that will appeal to all ages of the community.

2. **Write a letter to the community outreach director recommending one activity and tell why the other activities may not be the best activities during the summer. Use the data to support your idea.**

TALK the TALK 💬

A Hot Topic

Men and women were surveyed to determine their favorite drink on a cold day. The results are shown in the table.

Favorite Drink on a Cold Day

		Coffee	Tea	Hot Cocoa	Total
Gender	Men	10	2	4	16
	Women	5	7	4	16
	Total	15	9	8	32

1. **Construct a marginal relative frequency distribution of the data.**

Favorite Drink on a Cold Day

		Coffee	Tea	Hot Cocoa	Total
Gender	Men				
	Women				
	Total				

2. **Write a paragraph interpreting the marginal relative frequency distributions for the data.**

3. **Does there appear to be an association between gender and favorite drink on a cold day? Justify your answer.**

Assignment

Write

Write a brief explanation of the difference between a relative frequency distribution and a marginal relative frequency distribution.

Remember

A relative frequency distribution table provides the ratio of occurrences in each category to the total number of occurrences and allows you to use percents to analyze categorical data in two variables. You can use a stacked bar graph to visually represent the marginal relative frequencies of a data set.

Practice

1. The principal of Umber Elementary School (grades K – 4) would like to reward his students for recent good test scores on a standardized test. He thinks of four different types of assemblies. In order to please the most students, the principal asks his teachers to survey the students in their classes. The students from each grade are asked which assembly they would most want to see. The table shows the responses gathered from the surveys.

	Wild Animals	Hip Hop Show	Magic Show	Puppet Show
Kindergarten	18	5	8	33
Grade 1	26	10	21	15
Grade 2	21	19	17	12
Grade 3	22	28	20	8
Grade 4	19	44	7	2

a. Construct a marginal relative frequency distribution of the data.

b. The principal wants to choose one assembly that he can show to all of the students. Construct two stacked bar graphs of the marginal relative frequency distribution. Then tell which assembly he should choose for the students. Explain how you determined your answer.

c. The principal has come up with an idea to hold a hip hop assembly for Grades 1 through 4 and a puppet show for Kindergarten. Do you think this is a good idea? Explain your reasoning.

Stretch

1. A teacher at the Umber Elementary School decides to organize the data from the students differently. She decides to calculate percentages of the assembly types the students want within each grade, not out of the total.

a. Use the data from Umber Elementary School to show the percentages for each assembly type by grade.

	Wild Animals	Hip Hop Show	Magic Show	Puppet Show	Total
Kindergarten	$\frac{18}{64} \approx 28.1\%$				
Grade 1					
Grade 2					
Grade 3					
Grade 4					

b. Construct a stacked bar graph of the percentages for each grade. How does this graph compare to the stacked bar graph of the marginal relative frequency distribution that you constructed in the Practice to show the assembly choice by grade?

Review

1. A company conducts a study to find out how much time employees spend on their smart phones doing non-work related things doing work hours. The table displays the data collected from surveying 20 employees.

Create an appropriate data display. Use statistics appropriate to the shape of the data distribution to describe the measure of center and spread. Write a report to summarize your findings.

Employee	Time on Phone (minutes)	Employee	Time on Phone (minutes)
1	45	11	52
2	35	12	60
3	68	13	58
4	55	14	20
5	43	15	30
6	59	16	55
7	37	17	44
8	75	18	40
9	41	19	65
10	48	20	25

2. For each function $f(x)$, sketch a graph of the given transformation, $g(x)$, and describe the transformation from the graph of $f(x)$ to $g(x)$.

a. $g(x) = \frac{1}{3} \cdot f(x) - 1$

b. $g(x) = 2 \cdot f(x) + 4$

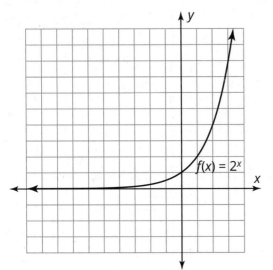

$f(x) = 2^x$

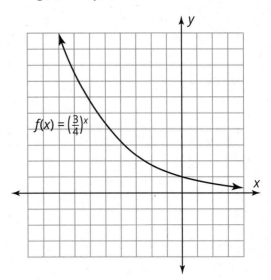

$f(x) = \left(\frac{3}{4}\right)^x$

On One Condition . . . or More

Conditional Relative Frequency Distribution

Warm Up

Identify which fraction is greater. Explain your reasoning.

1. $\frac{6}{55}$, $\frac{6}{19}$

2. $\frac{2}{12}$, $\frac{2}{5}$

3. $\frac{15}{23}$, $\frac{15}{91}$

4. $\frac{7}{9}$, $\frac{7}{8}$

5. $\frac{67}{100}$, $\frac{67}{200}$

Learning Goals

- Construct and interpret conditional relative frequency distributions displayed in two-way tables for categorical data.
- Recognize possible associations and trends in categorical data.

Key Term

- conditional relative frequency distribution

You have created and interpreted relative frequency distributions for categorical data in two variables. How can you compare relative frequencies within a single variable?

Did They Pass the Class?

Mr. Lewis teaches three science classes at Matthews High School. He wants to compare the grades of the three classes of his students. He creates the marginal frequency distribution table shown.

Grades of Mr. Lewis's Science Students

Science Classes	A	B	C	D	F	Total
Biology	6	6	5	1	2	20
Chemistry	4	8	12	4	2	30
Physics	2	5	6	1	1	15
Total	12	19	23	6	5	65

1. **Complete the marginal relative frequency distributions for the data. Round each percent to the nearest tenth of a percent.**

Grades of Mr. Lewis's Science Students

Science Classes	A	B	C	D	F	Total
Biology						
Chemistry						
Physics						
Total						

2. **Explain what each percent means in the marginal relative frequency distribution table.**

a. 18.5%   b. 23.1%

c. 29.2%

3. **Create a stacked bar graph to represent the percent of students passing in each class.**

> At Matthews High School, passing grades are As, Bs, or Cs.

Analyze the marginal relative frequency distribution table you completed in the Getting Started.

1. **Campbell claims that Mr. Lewis's chemistry class is the smartest because it has the greatest percent of students passing. Is Campbell's statement correct? Explain your reasoning.**

A **conditional relative frequency distribution** is the percent or ratio of occurrences of a category given the specific value of another category.

You can use a *conditional relative frequency distribution* to determine which class is doing the "best."

Let's construct a conditional relative frequency distribution of grades given the classes using the information from the Getting Started.

2. **Analyze the three conditional relative frequencies that have been completed for you. Describe why the denominator of each ratio is different.**

Grades of Mr. Lewis's Science Students

		A	B	C	D	F	Total
Science Classes	Biology	$\frac{6}{20} = 30\%$					
	Chemistry			$\frac{12}{30} = 40\%$			
	Physics				$\frac{1}{15} \approx 6.7\%$		

3. Complete the remaining conditional relative frequencies in the table.

4. Interpret the conditional relative frequency distributions of each class.

5. Use the conditional relative frequency distribution to answer each question.

   a. What percent of the biology students are passing?

   b. What percent of the chemistry students are passing?

   c. What percent of the physics students are passing?

   d. Which science class is doing the best according to their grades? Explain your reasoning.

   e. How does this compare to the statement Campbell made?

6. Which science class has the greatest percent of students failing?

Let's look at these data a different way. You can construct a different conditional relative frequency distribution for each class given the grades.

7. **Use the information from the Getting Started activity to determine the relative frequency for each class given that particular grade.**

Grades of Mr. Lewis's Science Students

Science Classes	A	B	C	D	F
Biology	$\frac{6}{12} = 50\%$				
Chemistry					$\frac{2}{5} = 40\%$
Physics			$\frac{6}{23} \approx 26.1\%$		
Total					

8. **Campbell claims that 80% of the students who received a grade of F were in biology and chemistry. Is Campbell's statement correct? Explain your reasoning.**

9. **Does there appear to be an association between the science class and the grades of Mr. Lewis's science students? Justify your answer.**

TALK the TALK

Down to a Science

Mr. Lewis also teaches two general science classes. He wants to teach his students about a topic they are most interested in. He surveys his students and records the data in the table shown.

Science Topics

Science Classes	Matter	Plants and Animals	Astronomy	Anatomy	Genetics	Total
Class 1	5	3	10	3	4	25
Class 2	9	5	3	7	6	30
Total	14	8	13	10	10	55

1. **Mr. Lewis wants to teach the same topic to both classes. Which topic would you recommend Mr. Lewis teach? Use conditional relative frequencies to explain why you made your suggestion to Mr. Lewis.**

Assignment

Write

How does a marginal relative frequency compare to a conditional relative frequency?

Remember

A conditional relative frequency distribution is the percent or ratio of occurrences of a category given the specific value of another category.

Practice

1. Angie is taking a broadcast communications class at her local college. The professor presents the students with the results of a survey that was conducted to determine where different age groups of people get their news. The table shows the results of the survey.

News Source

Age Group	Local TV	National TV	Radio	Newspaper	Internet	Total
Under 35	95	72	74	53	110	404
35–49	110	107	100	78	84	479
50+	136	129	111	106	71	553
Total	341	308	286	237	265	1436

   a. Angie claims that overall more people get their news from local TV than any other source. Is she correct? Explain your reasoning.

   b. Angie's classmate claims that the under 35 age group must use local TV less than the 35 to 49 age group because 95 is less than 110. Is she correct? Explain your reasoning.

   c. Construct a conditional relative frequency distribution of news source given the age group. Then, construct a conditional relative frequency distribution of age group given the news source.

   d. Which age group has the fewest number of people who receive their news from local TV? How does this compare to the claim made in part (b)?

   e. A company wants to make sure their ad reaches as many people under the age of 50 as possible. What news source would you suggest they use? Explain your reasoning.

Stretch

A study is done to see if there is a difference between the colors of cars that men and women prefer to drive. The colors in the study are black, white, gray, red, and blue. The researcher receives this incomplete information about the 100 total people that were surveyed. The ratio of the number of males who prefer red to the number of males is $\frac{15}{57}$. The ratio of the number of men who prefer white cars to the number of white cars is $\frac{3}{20}$. The ratio of the number of women who prefer black to the number of women is $\frac{6}{43}$. The ratio of the number of women who prefer blue cars to the number of people who prefer blue cars is $\frac{8}{10}$. A total of 37 males and females prefer black cars. A total of 17 males and females prefer red cars. Use the information to construct a two-way frequency table.

Review

1. The five number summaries for the heights in inches of male soccer and basketball players for a school district are provided.

   a. Construct box-and-whisker plots of each type of player's heights using a single number line.

   b. Describe each distribution and explain what they mean in terms of the problem situation.

   c. Determine if there are outliers in either data set. Explain how you determined your answer.

Soccer Players	Basketball Players
Min = 61	Min = 65
Q1 = 63	Q1 = 69
Med = 66	Med = 71
Q3 = 68	Q3 = 73
Max = 71	Max = 78

2. A grocery store surveys customers by age group to determine what is most important to them when shopping. The table shows the customer responses.

	Self-Checkout Option	Good Customer Service	Good Selection of Produce	Butcher Available
20–29	52	8	20	14
30–39	44	11	23	16
40–49	34	15	26	17
50–59	25	31	32	2
60–69	5	35	27	25

   a. Construct a marginal relative frequency distribution of the data.

   b. The manager wants to concentrate on one area of the store to improve customer satisfaction. In which area should the manager concentrate? Explain your reasoning.

3. For each function $f(x)$, sketch a graph of the given transformation, $g(x)$, and describe the transformation from the graph of $f(x)$ to $g(x)$.

   a. $g(x) = -f(x)$

   b. $g(x) = f(-x)$

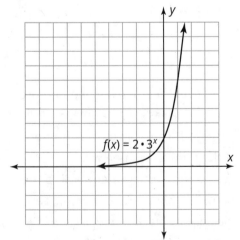

$f(x) = 2 \cdot 3^x$

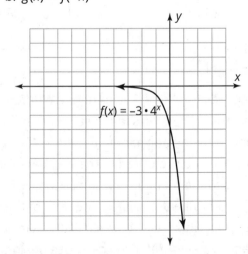

$f(x) = -3 \cdot 4^x$

Data Jam

Drawing Conclusions from Data

Warm Up

Consider the scatter plot shown.

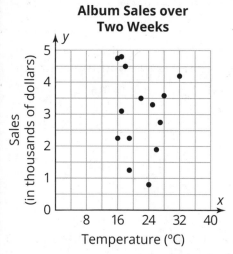

Album Sales over Two Weeks

The weather forecast for the following week shows that temperatures will be over 24°C each day.

1. Should the owner of the music store plan to spend extra money on advertising during the week of higher temperatures? Explain your reasoning.

Learning Goals

- Recognize possible associations and trends in categorical data.
- Use categorical data to make decisions.
- Recognize possible associations and trends in data sets.

You have analyzed categorical data in two variables by creating marginal frequency distributions, stacked bar graphs, and conditional relative frequency distributions. How can you use these representations to make decisions in a problem situation?

I'm a Little Bit Country

A survey was conducted at Rawlings High School and 38 students in one 9th-grade classroom were asked two questions about their musical preferences: "Do you like country?" and "Do you like rock?" The responses are summarized in the marginal frequency distribution shown.

	Likes Country	Doesn't Like Country	Total
Likes Rock	18	7	25
Doesn't Like Rock	5	8	13
Total	23	15	38

1. **What percentage of the students in the classroom like rock?**

2. **Does there appear to be an association between liking country and liking rock? Use the data to justify your response.**

3. **Is this a random sample that fairly represents the opinions of all students at Rawlings High School? Explain your reasoning.**

ACTIVITY 4.1

Interpreting a Whole Data Set

Andres is a new radio station general manager at KYWN. Currently, the station features country music. However, Andres is considering changing the genre of music to make the station more popular. He wants to target one of the highest demographics in radio listening—teenagers—so he decides to sponsor the next dance at Rawlings High School. Prior to the dance, Andres surveys the students. The survey results are located at the end of this lesson. He will use these data to determine the new genre of KYWN.

1. **Organize the data in a table and represent them using a graph to help Andres determine which music genre is most popular at Rawlings High School according to the survey he conducted.**

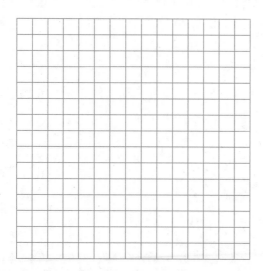

2. Analyze the table you created to organize Andres's data.

   a. How many students did Andres survey for the dance? How did you determine that you organized the data correctly?

   b. Can you determine which genre of music was the most popular from the representations you created? Explain why or why not.

   c. Do you think the results might be the same or different if Andres conducted another random survey at Rawlings High School? Explain your reasoning.

   d. Based on the data you have analyzed, would you advise Andres to change the format of his station? If so, explain why. If not, explain why not.

Andres knows that one of the most sought-after age groups is the age 18 to 35 group. If KYWN can target and successfully attract listeners in this age range, it can then lure advertisers to buy more air time. Knowing this, Andres decides to use only the data he gathered from the seniors he surveyed at Rawlings High School.

1. **Analyze the tables and graphs you created in the previous activity and predict which music genre is the most popular for the Rawlings High School seniors. Explain how you came to your conclusion.**

Ask
yourself:

Is there only one way to analyze and interpret data?

Suppose Andres decides to suggest a music format change for KYWN to dance music.

2. **What information would you advise Andres use to strengthen his suggestion? Use any of the data and supply any graphs you think may strengthen Andres's suggestion. Finally, explain why you chose the information.**

3. **Based on the information you analyzed regarding the seniors, would you change KYWN's music format to match the Rawlings High School seniors' survey results? If yes, use the data to explain why. If not, explain why not.**

TALK the TALK

Pass the Aux Cord

1. **Construct a marginal relative frequency distribution of the data using the bar graph provided.**

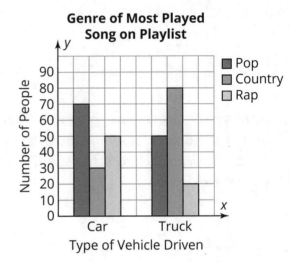

Genre of Most Played Song on Playlist

Genre of Most Played Song on Playlist			
Type of Vehicle Driven			

2. **Write a paragraph interpreting the relative frequency distributions and marginal relative frequency distributions for the data. Include an explanation of whether or not there appears to be an association between the genre of the most played song on someone's playlist and the type of vehicle they drive.**

Music Genre					
Grade Level	Rock (Classic/Alternative)	Classical	Hip-Hop/Rap	Dance	Country
12				X	
9		X			
10				X	
10					X
9					X
11			X		
12		X			
10	X				
9					X
9				X	
10		X			
12				X	
11	X				
12				X	
11			X		
9	X				
9	X				
10					X
11	X				
9	X				
12				X	
12			X		
11			X		
10		X			
9			X		
12			X		
11				X	
9			X		
10	X				
10	X				
12					X
9				X	
9				X	
9					X
10		X			
12	X				
12	X				
12		X			

(*Continued*)

Music Genre					
Grade Level	Rock (Classic/ Alternative)	Classical	Hip-Hop/ Rap	Dance	Country
10		X			
10			X		
10				X	
11			X		
9				X	
9					X
10		X			
10		X			
12				X	
11	X				
12	X				
11	X				
11		X			
12				X	
12				X	
12		X			
11			X		
11					X

Assignment

Write

Describe how you can determine whether there is an association between two-variable categorical data.

Remember

For categorical data in two variables, organizing and representing data in frequency distributions, marginal relative frequency distributions, conditional relative frequency distributions, and bar graphs are useful in formulating conclusions and using statistics to support your conclusions.

Practice

Men and women were surveyed to determine their favorite vehicle. The results are shown in the table.

Favorite Vehicle

Gender	Sedan	SUV	Convertible	Total
Men	88	115	34	237
Women	73	62	102	237

Suppose you were the general sales manager of a car dealership and you were planning a big car sale. Use the information in the frequency table to answer each question. Support your answers with tables and/or graphs.

1. Which type of car would you have on display in the showroom if you anticipate that most people shopping for a car would be women?

2. Which type of car would you have on display in the showroom if you anticipate that most people shopping for a car would be men?

3. Which type of car would you have on display in the showroom if you want to promote sales of cars that appeal to both men and women?

Stretch

In statistics, the frequencies in two-way tables can be used to help determine if the frequency counts are distributed identically across populations. Using probability theory, expected frequencies can be determined if the counts are distributed identically. These frequencies are calculated for each cell by multiplying the row total by the column total and dividing by the grand total of frequencies.

1. Complete the table of expected frequencies for gender and favorite vehicle.

Expected Frequencies	Sedan	SUV	Convertible	Row Total
Men	$\frac{(237)(161)}{474} \approx 80.5$			237
Women				237
Column Total	161	177	136	474

2. Does there seem to be a difference between the frequencies that were observed in the survey and those that would be expected if counts are distributed identically? What conclusion can you make?

Review

1. A realtor recorded the number of homes she sold each month for a year. Her numbers are shown in the dot plot.

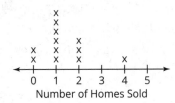

Number of Homes Sold

a. Describe the distribution of the dot plot.

b. Calculate the mean and median. Explain what they mean in terms of the problem situation.

c. Which measure of center do you think best represents these data? Explain your reasoning.

2. Two hundred residents of Grapeville City are asked in a survey where they get their prescription medicine filled. The residents are categorized by age group: young adult, adult, and senior. The results from the survey are shown in the table.

Prescription Source

Age Group	Drugstore	Grocery Store	Big Box Store	Online	Total
Young Adult	2	4	15	44	65
Adult	18	25	19	10	72
Senior	26	22	10	5	63
Total	46	51	44	59	200

a. Construct a conditional relative frequency distribution of age group given source of prescription.

b. A lot of young adults are currently moving to the city. Which prescription source should be most concerned? Explain your reasoning.

Two-Variable Categorical Data Summary

KEY TERMS

- categorical data
- two-way frequency table
- frequency distribution
- joint frequency

- marginal frequency distribution
- relative frequency distribution
- marginal relative frequency distribution
- conditional relative frequency distribution

LESSON 1

It Takes Two

Two types of variable data that can be collected from a statistical question are numerical and categorical data. **Categorical data** are data that can be grouped into categories. Numerical data are data that can be placed on a numerical scale and compared.

One method of organizing categorical data is to use a two-way frequency table. A **two-way frequency table** displays categorical data by representing the number of occurrences that fall into each group for two variables. On the table, one variable is divided into rows and the other is divided into columns.

A **frequency distribution** displays the frequencies for categorical data in a two-way table. Any frequency you record within the body of a two-way frequency table is known as a **joint frequency**.

The frequency distribution shown displays the favorite colors of a sample of boys and girls.

<table>
<tr><th colspan="2"></th><th colspan="4">Favorite Colors</th></tr>
<tr><th colspan="2"></th><th>Blue</th><th>Red</th><th>Yellow</th><th>Green</th></tr>
<tr><td rowspan="2">Gender</td><td>Girls</td><td>#### //

7</td><td>//

2</td><td>////

4</td><td>///

3</td></tr>
<tr><td>Boys</td><td>//

2</td><td>#### ///

8</td><td>///

3</td><td>/

1</td></tr>
</table>

You can see on the frequency distribution that more girls liked the color blue than any other option, and fewer girls liked red. More boys liked red than any other option, and fewer boys liked green.

A **marginal frequency distribution** displays the total of the frequencies of the rows or columns of a frequency distribution.

Favorite Colors

	Blue	Red	Yellow	Green	Total
Girls	7	2	4	3	16
Boys	2	8	3	1	14
Total	9	10	7	4	30

(Gender)

Thirty children participated in the survey. Ten children liked red best; it is the most popular favorite color of those polled. Four children liked green best; it is the least popular favorite color of those polled.

A graph can help relay information from a two-way frequency table in a visual way. Bar graphs and stacked bar graphs are all good choices for displaying this type of data. Remember, a key is necessary to identify what each bar represents.

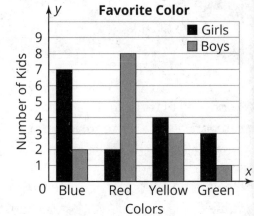

Red appears to be the most preferred by boys and blue is the most preferred by girls. Green appears to be the least favorite overall.

Representing the relative frequencies for joint data displayed in a two-way table is called a **relative frequency distribution**. The relative frequency distribution provides the ratio of occurrences in each category to the total number of occurrences. The ratio is generally represented as a percent.

Displaying the relative frequencies for the rows or columns is called a **marginal relative frequency distribution**. The marginal relative frequency distribution provides the ratio of total occurrences for each category to the total number of occurrences.

Preferred Movie Genre

Age Range of Movie Viewers	Animation	Comedy	Drama	Horror	Total
Movie Viewers ages 8 years and younger	$\frac{40}{240} \approx 16.7\%$	$\frac{18}{240} = 7.5\%$	$\frac{2}{240} \approx 0.8\%$	$\frac{0}{240} = 0\%$	$\frac{60}{240} = 25\%$
Movie Viewers ages 9 thru 16 years old	$\frac{20}{240} \approx 8.3\%$	$\frac{42}{240} = 17.5\%$	$\frac{13}{240} \approx 5.4\%$	$\frac{5}{240} \approx 2.1\%$	$\frac{80}{240} \approx 33.3\%$
Movie Viewers ages 17 and older	$\frac{5}{240} \approx 2.1\%$	$\frac{35}{240} \approx 14.6\%$	$\frac{32}{240} \approx 13.3\%$	$\frac{28}{240} \approx 11.7\%$	$\frac{100}{240} \approx 41.7\%$
Total	$\frac{65}{240} \approx 27.1\%$	$\frac{95}{240} \approx 39.6\%$	$\frac{47}{240} \approx 19.5\%$	$\frac{33}{240} \approx 13.8\%$	$\frac{240}{240} = 100\%$

Viewers ages 8 years and younger made up the smallest percent of participants. Horror movies are the least popular type of movie overall. Comedies are preferred by about 39.6% of participants.

You can use a stacked bar graph to visually represent the relative frequencies of a data set. A stacked bar graph is a graph in which the bars are stacked on top of each other as opposed to sitting next to each other.

Animation appears to be the favorite genre of participants ages 8 and younger. Comedy appears to be the favorite genre of participants ages 9 to 16. Comedy, drama, and horror seem to be fairly evenly favored for participants ages 17 and older.

LESSON 3

On One Condition . . . or More

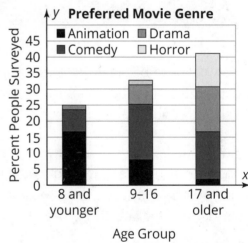

A **conditional relative frequency distribution** shows the percent or ratio of occurrences of a category given the specific value of another category. A conditional relative frequency distribution can be used to answer questions related to the given situation.

For example, the data shown below can be used to determine the preferred movie genre of viewers in several age groups, as well as the preference of all of the survey participants.

Preferred Movie Genre

	Animation	Comedy	Drama	Horror	Total
Movie Viewers ages 0–8	$\frac{40}{60} \approx 66.7\%$	$\frac{18}{60} = 30\%$	$\frac{2}{60} \approx 3.3\%$	$\frac{0}{60} = 0\%$	$\frac{60}{60} = 100\%$
Movie Viewers ages 9–16	$\frac{20}{80} = 25\%$	$\frac{42}{80} = 52.5\%$	$\frac{13}{80} = 16.25\%$	$\frac{5}{80} = 6.25\%$	$\frac{80}{80} = 100\%$
Movie Viewers ages 17+	$\frac{5}{100} = 5\%$	$\frac{35}{100} = 35\%$	$\frac{32}{100} = 32\%$	$\frac{28}{100} = 28\%$	$\frac{100}{100} = 100\%$

Of participants ages 8 and younger, only 3.3% preferred dramas. Of participants ages 9 to 16, 52.5% preferred comedies. Of participants ages 17 and older, only 5% preferred animated films.

LESSON

4

Data Jam

Raw data can be organized into a marginal relative frequency distribution table and graph. To further examine the trends within certain categories instead of the overall group, a conditional relative frequency distribution table and graph can be used.

For example, suppose a hardware store chain collected some data on the departments within their store that are most frequented by different types of customers so they could target their advertising. They can use a conditional relative frequency distribution to determine if there is an association between the types of customers and the departments they frequent.

Department

		Garden	Lumber	Paint	Tools	Total
	Homeowner	$\frac{83}{205} \approx 40\%$	$\frac{12}{205} \approx 6\%$	$\frac{65}{205} \approx 32\%$	$\frac{45}{205} \approx 22\%$	$\frac{205}{205} = 100\%$
Type of Customer	**Contractors/ Professionals**	$\frac{25}{250} = 10\%$	$\frac{95}{250} = 38\%$	$\frac{85}{250} = 34\%$	$\frac{45}{250} = 18\%$	$\frac{250}{250} = 100\%$
	Landlords	$\frac{25}{160} \approx 16\%$	$\frac{25}{160} \approx 16\%$	$\frac{65}{160} \approx 41\%$	$\frac{45}{160} \approx 28\%$	$\frac{160}{160} = 100\%$

The conditional relative frequency distribution displays the department frequented given the type of customer. From the table, there appears to be an association between the variables: the homeowners tend to shop in the Garden department, while the contractors/professionals frequent the Lumber department and the landlords frequent the Paint department.

MODULE 5

MAXIMIZING & MINIMIZING

The lessons in this module build on your experience analyzing functions, solving equations, and operating with polynomials. You will investigate situations that can be modeled by quadratic functions to learn about the different algebraic and graphical representations. You will transform quadratic functions and learn various strategies to solve quadratic equations. You will solve systems made up of quadratics and determine quadratic regressions that best model data sets.

Introduction to Quadratic Functions

A parabola is U-shaped, though it may open up or down.

Module 5: Maximizing and Minimizing

TOPIC 1: INTRODUCTION TO QUADRATIC FUNCTIONS

In this topic, students begin by exploring 4 scenarios that can be represented with quadratic functions. Students then represent each situation with an equation, a graph, and a table of values and explore the characteristics of the functions represented by each situation and different forms of a quadratic function. They use what they have learned about function transformations and apply this knowledge to transforming quadratic functions. Finally, students summarize the key characteristics and attributes of the different forms of quadratic functions.

Where have we been?

Students have had a brief introduction to a few scenarios that can be modeled using quadratic functions. In a previous topic, students created a graphic organizer that highlighted the form of a quadratic function, a few sample graphs, and the key characteristics that can define a quadratic function.

Where are we going?

In this topic, students will solidify their knowledge of function transformations. Understanding how to sketch a quadratic is the underpinning for sketching more complicated polynomials in higher levels of mathematics.

Second Differences

Linear functions have a constant rate of change, so their first differences are constant: for each increase or decrease of 1 in the x-value, the y-value of a linear function goes up or down the same amount. But quadratic functions are different.

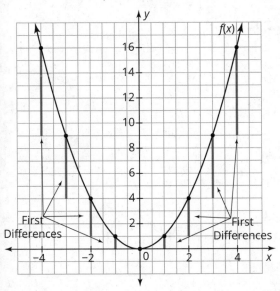

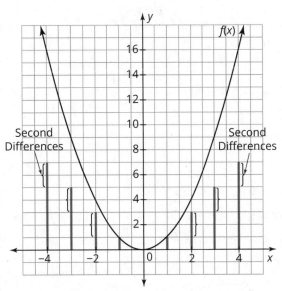

The first differences of a quadratic function are not constant. But the second differences—the differences between the first differences—are constant.

Punkin' Chunkin'

Every year the county of Sussex, Delaware, holds a competition called the Punkin' Chunkin' World Championships, which is a pumpkin-throwing competition. Participants build machines that hurl pumpkins great distances. The winner is the person whose machine hurls the pumpkin the farthest. There are different divisions based on the type of machine used.

- The Air Cannon Division includes machines that use compressed air to fire pumpkins.
- In the Catapult Division, catapults are composed of cords, springs, rubber, weights, or other mechanisms that create and store energy.
- The Centrifugal Division includes machines that have devices that spin at least one revolution before firing pumpkins.
- There is also the Trebuchet Division. Trebuchets are machines that have swinging or fixed counterweights that can fling pumpkins up and through the air.

Talking Points

Recognizing functions from a table of values is an important topic to know about for college admissions tests.

Here is a sample question:

What type of function models this table of values?

x	f(x)
0	1
1	−2
2	−1
3	4
4	13

Because the x-values are consecutive, analyze consecutive f(x)-values. First differences are −3, 1, 5, and 9. *Second differences*, the difference between first differences, are 4, 4, and 4. Because second differences are equal, the function is quadratic.

Key Terms

parabola
The shape that a quadratic function forms when graphed is called a parabola.

roots
The roots of an equation indicate where the graph of the equation crosses the x-axis.

vertex form
A quadratic function written in the form $f(x) = a(x - h)^2 + k$, where $a \neq 0$, is in vertex form.

general form
A quadratic function written in the form $f(x) = ax^2 + bx + c$, where $a \neq 0$, is in general form, or standard form.

factored form
A quadratic function written in the form $f(x) = a(x_1 - r)(x_2 - r)$, where $a \neq 0$, is in factored form.

Up and Down or Down and Up

Exploring Quadratic Functions

Warm Up

Consider $f(x) = x^2 + 3x + 4$.
Evaluate the function for each given value.

1. $f(1)$

2. $f(-1)$

3. $f(2)$

4. $f(-2)$

Learning Goals

- Write quadratic functions to model contexts.
- Graph quadratic functions using technology.
- Interpret the key features of quadratic functions in terms of a context.
- Identify the domain and range of quadratic functions and their contexts.

Key Terms

- parabola
- vertical motion model
- roots

You have used linear functions to model situations with constant change, and you have used exponential functions to model growth and decay situations. What type of real-world situations can be modeled by quadratic functions?

Squaring It Up

Maddie is using pennies to create a pattern.

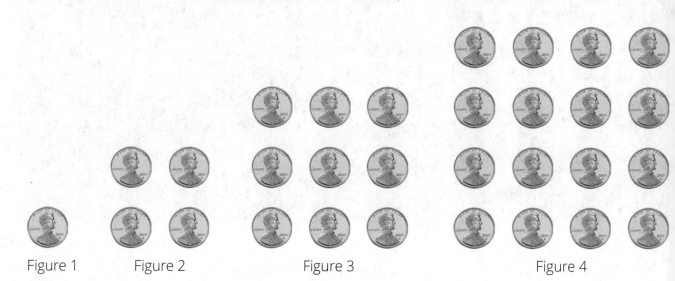

Figure 1   Figure 2   Figure 3   Figure 4

1. **Analyze the pattern and explain how to create Figure 5.**

2. **How many pennies would Maddie need to create Figure 5? Figure 6? Figure 7?**

3. **Which figure would Maddie create with exactly $4.00 in pennies?**

4. **Write an equation to determine the number of pennies for any figure number. Define your variables.**

5. **Describe the function family to which this equation belongs.**

A dog trainer is fencing in an enclosure, represented by the shaded region in the diagram. The trainer will also have two square-shaped storage units on either side of the enclosure to store equipment and other materials. She can make the enclosure and storage units as wide as she wants, but she can't exceed 100 feet in total length.

100 ft

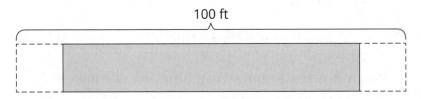

1. Let *s* represent a side length, in feet, of one of the storage units.

   a. Label the length and width of the enclosure in terms of *s*.

   b. Write the function $L(s)$ to represent the length of the enclosure as a function of side length, *s*.

   c. Sketch and label a graph of the function on the given coordinate plane. Identify any key points.

Ask yourself:

To identify key points on the graph, think about the function you are representing. Are there any intercepts? Are there any other points of interest?

2. Describe the domain and range of the context and of the function.

3. Identify each key characteristic of the graph. Then, interpret the meaning of each in terms of the context.

   a. slope

   b. *y*-intercept

   c. increasing or decreasing

   d. *x*-intercept

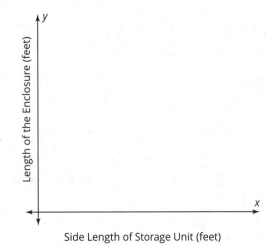

The progression of diagrams below shows how the area of the enclosure, A(s), changes as the side length, s, of each square storage unit increases.

4. **Write the function $A(s)$ to represent the area of the enclosure as a function of side length, s.**

5. **Describe how the area of the enclosure changes as the side length increases.**

6. **Consider the graph of the function, $A(s)$.**

   a. **Predict what the graph of the function will look like.**

   b. **Use technology to graph the function $A(s)$. Then sketch the graph and label the axes.**

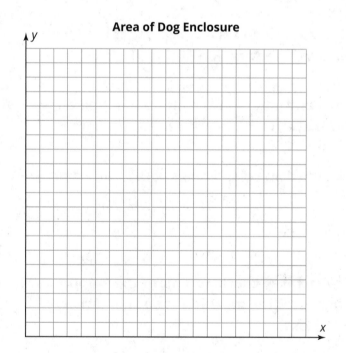

Area of Dog Enclosure

7. **Describe what all the points on the graph represent.**

The function $A(s)$ that you wrote to model area is a quadratic function. The shape that a quadratic function forms when graphed is called a **parabola**.

8. Think about the possible areas of the enclosure.

   a. Is there a maximum area that the enclosure can contain? Explain your reasoning in terms of the graph and in terms of the context.

   b. Use technology to determine the maximum of $A(s)$. Describe what the x- and y-coordinates of the maximum represent in this context.

   c. Determine the dimensions of the enclosure that will provide the maximum area. Show your work and explain your reasoning.

9. Identify the domain and range of the context and of the function.

10. Identify each key characteristic of the graph. Then, interpret the meaning of each in terms of the context.

   a. y-intercept

   b. increasing and decreasing intervals

   c. symmetry

   d. x-intercepts

Think about:

Quadratic functions model area because area is measured in square units.

ACTIVITY 1.2

Writing and Interpreting a Quadratic Function

Suppose that there is a monthly meeting at CIA headquarters for all employees. How many handshakes will it take for every employee at the meeting to shake the hand of every other employee at the meeting once?

1. **Use the figures shown to determine the number of handshakes that will occur between 2 employees, 3 employees, and 4 employees.**

2 employees   3 employees   4 employees

2. **Draw figures to represent the number of handshakes that occur between 5 employees, 6 employees, and 7 employees and determine the number of handshakes that will occur in each situation.**

Ask yourself:

Can you tell what shape the graph will be?

3. **Enter your results in the table.**

Number of Employees	2	3	4	5	6	7	n
Number of Handshakes							

4. **Write a function to represent the number of handshakes given any number of employees. Enter your function in the table.**

5. **Use technology to graph the function you wrote in Question 4. Sketch the graph and label the axes.**

Handshake Problem

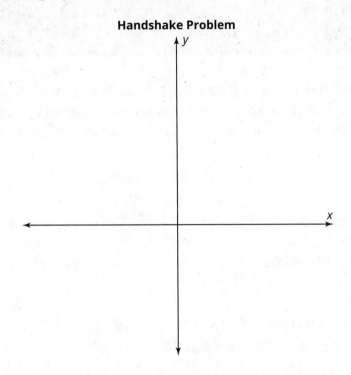

Ask yourself:

What do all the points on this graph represent?

6. **How is the orientation of this parabola different from the parabola for the area of the dog enclosure? How is this difference reflected in their corresponding equations?**

7. **Determine the minimum of your function. Then, describe what the x- and y-coordinates of this minimum represent in this problem situation.**

8. **Identify the domain and range of the problem situation and of the function.**

ACTIVITY

1.3

Using a Quadratic Function to Model Vertical Motion

You can model the motion of a pumpkin released from a catapult using a vertical motion model. A **vertical motion model** is a quadratic equation that models the height of an object at a given time. The equation is of the form shown.

$$y = -16t^2 + v_0t + h_0$$

In this equation, y represents the height of the object in feet, t represents the time in seconds that the object has been moving, v_0 represents the initial vertical velocity (speed) of the object in feet per second, and h_0 represents the initial height of the object in feet.

1. **What characteristics of this situation indicate that it can be modeled by a quadratic function?**

Suppose that a catapult hurls a pumpkin from a height of 68 feet at an initial vertical velocity of 128 feet per second.

2. **Write a function for the height of the pumpkin, $h(t)$, in terms of time, t.**

3. **Does the function you wrote have a minimum or maximum? How can you tell from the form of the function?**

4. **Use technology to graph the function. Sketch your graph and label the axes.**

Punkin' Chunkin'

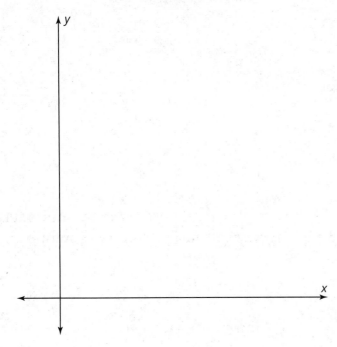

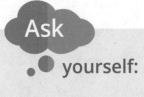

Ask yourself:

What do all the points on this graph represent?

5. **Use technology to determine the maximum or minimum and label it on the graph. Explain what it means in terms of the problem situation.**

6. **Determine the *y*-intercept and label it on the graph. Explain what it means in terms of the problem situation.**

7. Use a horizontal line to determine when the pumpkin reaches each height after being catapulted. Label the points on the graph.

   a. 128 feet

   b. 260 feet

   c. 55 feet

8. Explain why the *x*- and *y*-coordinates of the points where the graph and each horizontal line intersects are solutions.

9. When does the catapulted pumpkin hit the ground? Label this point on the graph. Explain how you determined your answer.

Remember:

The zeros of a function are the *x*-values when the function equals 0.

The time when the pumpkin hits the ground is one of the *x*-intercepts, (*x*, 0). When an equation is used to model a situation, the *x*-coordinate of the *x*-intercept is referred to as a root. The **root** of an equation indicates where the graph of the equation crosses the *x*-axis.

<table>
<tr>
<td>

ACTIVITY

1.4

</td>
<td>

Expressing a Quadratic Function as the Product of Two Linear Functions

</td>
<td></td>
</tr>
</table>

The Jacobson brothers own and operate their own ghost tour business. They take tour groups around town on a bus to visit the most notorious "haunted" spots throughout the city. They charge $50 per tour. Each summer, they book 100 tours at that price. The brothers are considering a decrease in the price per tour because they think it will help them book more tours. They estimate that they will gain 10 tours for every $1 decrease in the price per tour.

1. **According to the scenario, how much money do the Jacobson brothers currently generate each summer with their ghost tour business?**

Revenue is the amount of money regularly coming into a business. In the ghost tour business, the revenue is the number of tours multiplied by the price per tour. Your response to Question 1 can be referred to as revenue. Because the Jacobson brothers are considering different numbers of tours and prices per tour, the revenue can be modeled by a function.

2. **Write a function, $r(x)$, to represent the revenue for the ghost tour business.**

    a. **Let x represent the decrease in the price per tour. Write an expression to represent the number of tours booked if the decrease in price is x dollars per tour.**

    b. **Write an expression to represent the price per tour if the brothers decrease the price x dollars per tour.**

c. Use your expressions from parts (a) and (b) to represent the revenue, $r(x)$, as the number of tours times the price per tour.

Revenue = Number of Tours • Price per Tour

$r(x)$ = _____ • _____

3. Use technology to graph the function $r(x)$. Sketch your graph and label the axes.

Ghost Tour

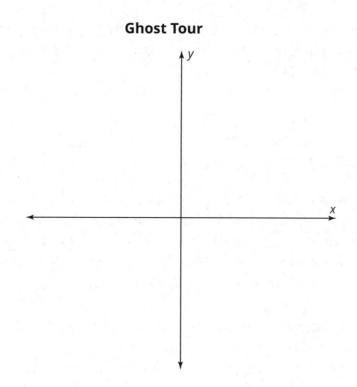

4. Assume that the Jacobson brothers' estimate that for every \$1 decrease in the price per tour, they will gain 10 tours is accurate.

a. What is the maximum revenue that the Jacobson brothers could earn for the summer?

b. Katie and Bryce are calculating the number of tours that would yield the maximum revenue.

Katie said that according to the graph, a tour should cost $20. Since $9000 ÷ $20 = 450, the number of tours would be 450.

Bryce said that the cost of a tour should be $30, and $9000 divided by $30 per tour is 300 tours.

Who is correct? Explain your reasoning.

c. Would you advise the Jacobson brothers to adjust their cost per tour to make the maximum revenue? Why or why not?

5. Identify each key characteristic of the graph. Then, interpret its meaning in terms of the context.

a. *x*-intercepts

b. *y*-intercept

c. increasing and decreasing intervals

TALK the TALK

Making Connections

Analyze the graphs of the four quadratic functions in this lesson.

1. **Summarize what you know about the graphs of quadratic functions. Include a sketch or sketches and list any characteristics.**

2. **Compare your sketch or sketches and list with your classmates. Did you all sketch the same parabola? Why or why not?**

Assignment

Write

Fill in the blank.

1. The *x*-intercepts of a graph of a quadratic function are also called the _____ of the quadratic function.
2. A quadratic equation that models the height of an object at a given time is a _____.
3. The shape that a quadratic function forms when graphed is called a _____.
4. The _____ of an equation indicate where the graph of the equation crosses the *x*-axis.

Remember

The graph of a quadratic function is called a parabola. Parabolas are smooth curves that have an absolute maximum or minimum, both increasing and decreasing intervals, up to two *x*-intercepts, and symmetry.

Practice

1. The citizens of Herrington County have an existing dog park for dogs to play, but have decided to build another one so that one park will be for small dogs and the other will be for large dogs. The plan is to build a rectangular fenced in area that will be adjacent to the existing dog park, as shown in the sketch. The county has enough money in the budget to buy 1000 feet of fencing.

   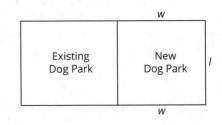

   a. Determine the length of the new dog park, *l*, in terms of the width, *w*.
   b. Write the function *A(w)* to represent the area of the new dog park as a function of the width, *w*. Does this function have a minimum or a maximum? Explain your answer.
   c. Determine the *x*-intercepts of the function. Explain what each means in terms of the problem situation.
   d. What should the dimensions of the dog park be to maximize the area? What is the maximum area of the park?
   e. Sketch the graph of the function. Label the axes, the maximum or minimum, the *x*-intercepts, and the *y*-intercept.
   f. Use the graph to determine the dimensions of the park if the area was restricted to 105,000 square feet.

Stretch

1. Sketch a graph of a quadratic function that has a maximum value of (0, 2) and x-intercepts when $x = \pm 2$.
2. What is the quadratic function of your graph? Explain your reasoning.

Review

People who prefer cats or dogs were surveyed to find out what their favorite season is.

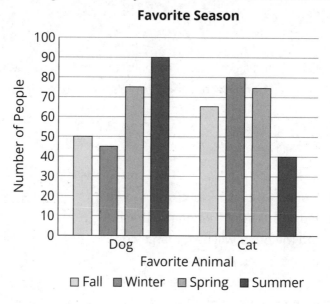

1. Construct a marginal relative frequency table from the bar graph provided and answer each question.
   a. Which season would a cat lover most likely prefer? Justify your response.
   b. Is there a season a dog and cat lover both prefer equally? If so, what season? Justify your response.
   c. What is the total percentage of people that like the fall?
2. If the basic function $f(x) = x^2$ is translated 3 units to the right and 4 units up, what is the transformed equation?
3. If the basic function $f(x) = 4^x$ is vertically stretched by a factor of 2 and translated 5 units down, what is the transformed equation?

Endless Forms Most Beautiful

Key Characteristics of Quadratic Functions

Warm Up

Determine the slope and
y-intercept of each linear function.

1. $h(x) = 3x$

2. $g(x) = \frac{1}{2}(x - 5)$

3. $k(x) = x - 2$

4. $m(x) = \frac{8x}{4} + 1$

Learning Goals

- Identify the factored form and general form of an equation for a quadratic function.
- Determine the equation for the axis of symmetry of a quadratic function, given the equation in general form or factored form.
- Determine the absolute minimum or absolute maximum point on the graph of a quadratic function and identify this point as the vertex.
- Describe intervals of increase and decrease in relation to the axis of symmetry on the graph of a quadratic function.
- Use key characteristics of the graph of a quadratic function to write an equation in factored form.

Key Terms

- second differences
- concave up
- concave down
- general form of a quadratic function
- factored form
- vertex of a parabola
- axis of symmetry

You have identified key characteristics of linear and exponential functions. What are the key characteristics of quadratic functions?

Dogs, Handshakes, Pumpkins, Ghosts

Consider the four quadratic models you investigated in the previous lesson. There are multiple equivalent ways to write the equation to represent each situation and a unique parabola to represent the equivalent equations. You can also represent the function using a table of values.

Area of Dog Enclosure

$$A(s) = -2s^2 + 100s$$
$$= -2(s)(s - 50)$$

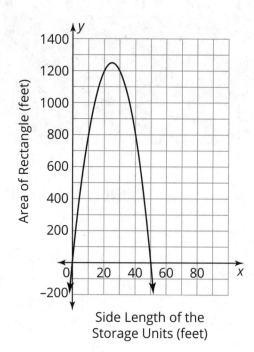

s	A(s)
0	0
1	98
2	192
3	282
4	368

Side Length of the Storage Units (feet)

Handshake Problem

$$f(n) = \frac{1}{2}n^2 - \frac{1}{2}n$$
$$= \frac{1}{2}(n)(n - 1)$$

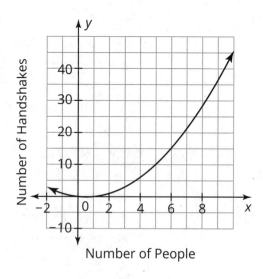

n	f(n)
0	0
1	0
2	1
3	3
4	6

Number of People

Punkin' Chunkin'

$h(t) = -16t^2 + 128t + 68$

$ = -16(t - \frac{17}{2})(t + \frac{1}{2})$

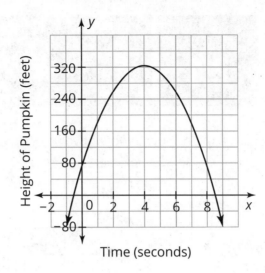

Height of Pumpkin (feet)

Time (seconds)

t	h(t)
0	68
1	180
2	260
3	308
4	324

Ghost Tour

$r(x) = -10(x + 10)(x - 50)$

$ = -10x^2 + 400x + 5000$

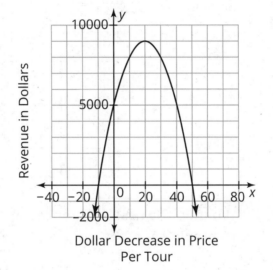

Revenue in Dollars

Dollar Decrease in Price
Per Tour

x	r(x)
0	5000
1	5390
2	5760
3	6110
4	6440

1. **Consider each representation.**

   a. **How can you tell from the structure of the equation that it is quadratic?**

   b. **What does the structure of the equation tell you about the shape and characteristics of the graph?**

   c. **How can you tell from the shape of the graph that it is quadratic?**

   d. **How can you tell from the table that the relationship is quadratic?**

ACTIVITY 2.1

Second Differences

Let's explore how a table of values can show that a function is quadratic. Consider the table of values represented by the basic quadratic function. This table represents the first differences between seven consecutive points.

x	f(x)
−3	9
−2	4
−1	1
0	0
1	1
2	4
3	9

First Differences

$4 - 9 = -5$

$1 - 4 = -3$

$0 - 1 = -1$

$1 - 0 = 1$

$4 - 1 = 3$

$9 - 4 = 5$

1. **What do the first differences tell you about the relationship of the table of values?**

Let's consider the *second differences*. The **second differences** are the differences between consecutive values of the first differences.

2. **Calculate the second differences for $f(x)$. What do you notice?**

You know that with linear functions, the first differences are constant. For quadratic functions, the second differences are constant.

Let's consider the graph of the basic quadratic function, $f(x) = x^2$ and the distances represented by the first and second differences. Graph 1 shows the distances between consecutive values of $f(x)$. The colored line segments are different lengths because the first differences are not the same.

Graph 1

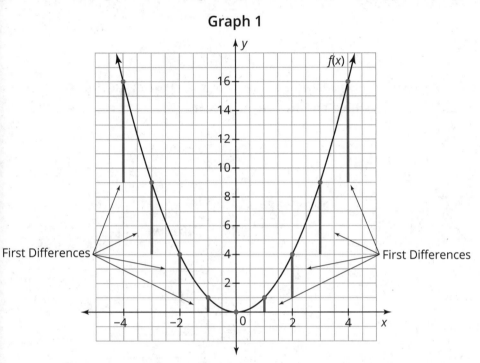

Graph 2 shows the lengths of the first differences positioned along the x-axis. By comparing these lengths, you can see the second differences.

Graph 2

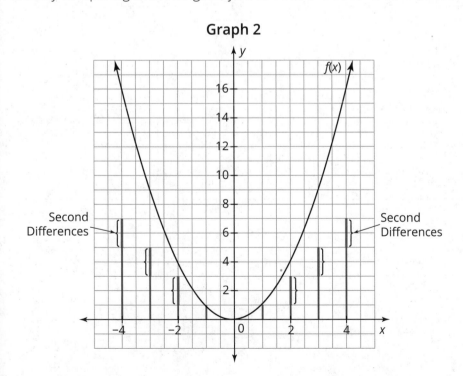

Think about:

Quadratic equations are polynomials with a degree of 2. Their second differences are constant. Linear functions are polynomials with a degree of 1, and their first differences are constant.

3. How does the representation in Graph 1 support the first differences calculated from the table of values?

4. How does the representation in Graph 2 support the second differences you calculated in the table?

5. Identify each equation as linear or quadratic. Complete the table to calculate the first and second differences. Then sketch the graph.

a. $y = 2x$ _____

x	y	First Differences	Second Differences
−3	−6		
−2	−4		
−1	−2		
0	0		
1	2		
2	4		
3	6		

b. $y = 2x^2$ _____

x	y	First Differences	Second Differences
−3	18		
−2	8		
−1	2		
0	0		
1	2		
2	8		
3	18		

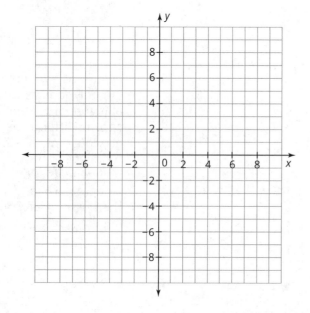

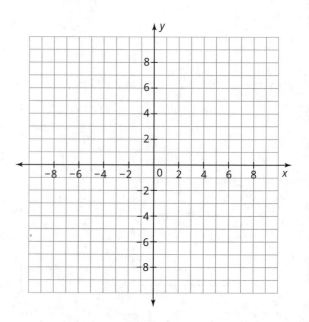

c. $y = -x + 4$ _____

x	y	First Differences	Second Differences
−3	7		
−2	6		
−1	5		
0	4		
1	3		
2	2		
3	1		

d. $y = -x^2 + 4$ _____

x	y	First Differences	Second Differences
−3	−5		
−2	0		
−1	3		
0	4		
1	3		
2	0		
3	−5		

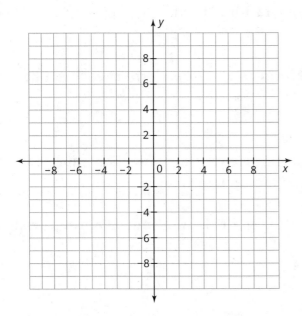

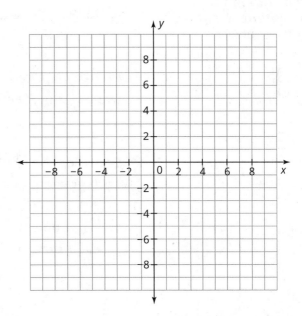

6. Compare the signs of the first and second differences for each function and its graph.

> A graph that opens upward is identified as being **concave up**. A graph that opens downward is identified as begin **concave down**.

a. How do the signs of the first differences for a linear function relate to the graph either increasing or decreasing?

b. How do the signs of the second differences for quadratic functions relate to whether the parabola is opening upward or downward?

You know that different forms of an equation can reveal different characteristics about functions. Quadratic functions can be written in different forms.

A quadratic function written in the form $f(x) = ax^2 + bx + c$, where $a \neq 0$, is in **general form**, or standard form. In this form, a and b are numerical coefficients and c is a constant.

A quadratic function written in **factored form** is in the form $f(x) = a(x - r_1)(x - r_2)$, where $a \neq 0$.

> **Remember:**
>
> The leading coefficient of an equation is the numeric coefficient of the term with the greatest power.

1. **Identify the general form and factored form of each equation in the Getting Started.**

2. **Consider the leading coefficient of each function equation in both general form and factored form.**

   a. **What does the leading coefficient tell you about the graph of each function?**

   b. **How is the leading coefficient related to the absolute minimum or absolute maximum of each function?**

   > The graph of a quadratic function has either an absolute maximum or absolute minimum.

   c. **How can you determine the y-intercept of the graph using general form?**

3. Determine from the equation whether each quadratic function has an absolute maximum or absolute minimum. Explain how you know.

a. $f(n) = 2n^2 + 3n - 1$

b. $g(x) = -2x^2 - 3x + 1$

c. $r(x) = -\frac{1}{2}x^2 - 3x + 1$

d. $b(x) = -0.009(x + 50)(x - 250)$

e. $f(t) = \frac{1}{3}(x - 1)(x - 1)$

f. $j(x) = 2x(1 - x)$

ACTIVITY 2.3 | Axis of Symmetry

The vertex is identified as either the absolute minimum or absolute maximum.

The **vertex of a parabola** is the lowest or highest point on the graph of the quadratic function. The **axis of symmetry** or the line of symmetry of a parabola is the vertical line that passes through the vertex and divides the parabola into two mirror images. Because the axis of symmetry always divides the parabola into two mirror images, you can say that a parabola has reflectional symmetry.

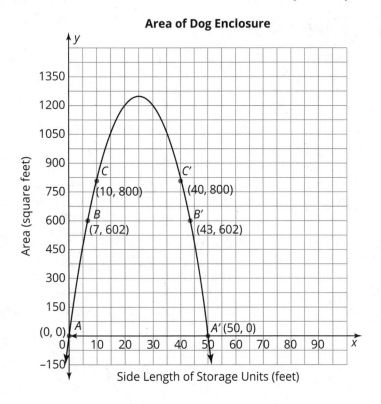

Area of Dog Enclosure

Area (square feet) vs. Side Length of Storage Units (feet)

1. **Use patty paper to trace the graph representing the area of the dog enclosure. Then fold the graph to show the symmetry of the parabola and trace the axis of symmetry.**

   a. **Place the patty paper over the original graph. What is the equation of the axis of symmetry?**

   b. **Draw and label the axis of symmetry on the graph from your patty paper.**

2. **Analyze the symmetric points labeled on the graph.**

   a. **What do you notice about the y-coordinates of the points?**

b. What do you notice about each point's horizontal distance from the axis of symmetry?

c. How does the *x*-coordinate of each symmetric point compare to the *x*-coordinate of the vertex?

For a function in factored form, $f(x) = a(x - r_1)(x - r_2)$, the equation for the axis of symmetry is given by $x = \frac{r_1 + r_2}{2}$. For a quadratic function in general form, $f(x) = ax^2 + bx + c$, the equation for the axis of symmetry is $x = \frac{-b}{2a}$.

3. Identify the axis of symmetry of the graph of each situation from the Getting Started using the factored form of each equation.

4. Describe the meaning of the axis of symmetry in each situation, if possible.

5. Describe how you can use the axis of symmetry to determine the ordered pair location of the absolute maximum or absolute minimum of a quadratic function, given the equation for the function in factored form.

As you analyze a parabola from left to right, it will have either an interval of increase followed by an interval of decrease, or an interval of decrease followed by an interval of increase.

6. How does the absolute maximum or absolute minimum help you determine each interval?

Consider the graph of the quadratic function representing the Punkin' Chunkin' problem situation.

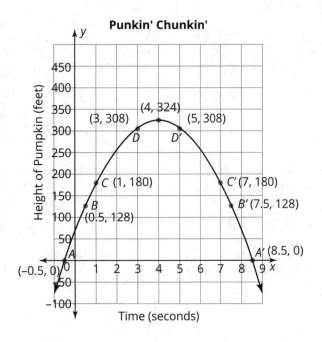

Punkin' Chunkin'

7. **Determine the average rate of change between each pair. Then summarize what you notice.**

   a. **points *A* and *B***

   b. **points *A'* and *B'***

   c. **points *B* and *C***

   d. **points *B'* and *C'***

The formula for the average rate of change is $\dfrac{f(b) - f(a)}{b - a}$.

e. **What do you notice about the average rates of change between pairs of symmetric points?**

8. For each function shown, identify the domain, range, *x*-intercepts, *y*-intercept, axis of symmetry, vertex, and interval of increase and decrease.

a. The graph shown represents the function $f(x) = -2x^2 + 4x$.

Domain: Range:

x-intercepts: *y*-intercept:

Axis of symmetry: Vertex:

Interval of increase: Interval of decrease:

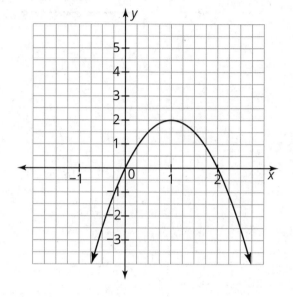

b. The graph shown represents the function $f(x) = x^2 + 5x + 6$.

Domain: Range:

x-intercepts: *y*-intercept:

Axis of symmetry: Vertex:

Interval of increase: Interval of decrease:

c. The graph shown represents the function $f(x) = x^2 - x - 2$.

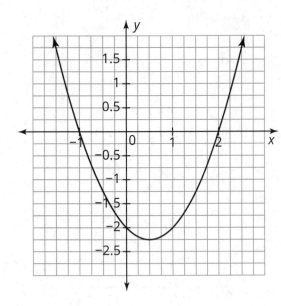

Domain: Range:

x-intercepts: *y*-intercept:

Axis of symmetry: Vertex:

Interval of increase: Interval of decrease:

d. The graph shown represents the function $f(x) = x^2 - 3x + 2$.

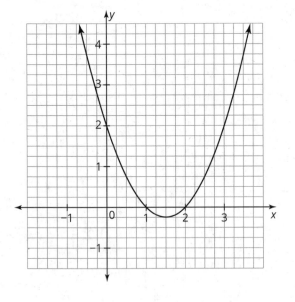

Domain: Range:

x-intercepts: *y*-intercept:

Axis of symmetry: Vertex:

Interval of increase: Interval of decrease:

Exploring Factored Form

You have analyzed quadratic functions and their equations. Let's look at the factored form of a quadratic function in more detail.

> If given a function $g(x)$ with a zero at $x = 4$, then $g(4) = 0$. This can also be interpreted as an x-intercept at $(4, 0)$.

1. **A group of students each write a quadratic function in factored form to represent a parabola that opens downward and has zeros at $x = 4$ and $x = -1$.**

Maureen
My function is
$k(x) = -(x - 4)(x + 1)$.

Tom
My function is
$g(x) = -2(x - 4)(x + 1)$.

Tim
My function is
$m(x) = 2(x - 4)(x + 1)$.

MiCHeAL
MY FUNCTioN iS
$F(x) = -(x + 4)(x - 1)$.

a. **Sketch a graph of each student's function and label key points. What are the similarities among all the graphs? What are the differences among the graphs?**

b. **What would you tell Tim and Micheal to correct their functions?**

c. How is it possible to have more than one correct function?

d. How many possible functions can represent the given characteristics? Explain your reasoning.

2. Consider a quadratic function written in factored form, $f(x) = a(x - r_1)(x - r_2)$.

a. What does the sign of the a-value tell you about the graph?

b. What do r_1 and r_2 tell you about the graph?

3. Use the given information to write a function in factored form. Sketch a graph of each function and label key points, which include the vertex, the x- and y-intercepts.

a. The parabola opens upward, and the zeros are at $x = 2$ and $x = 4$.

b. The parabola opens downward, and the zeros at $x = -3$ and $x = 1$.

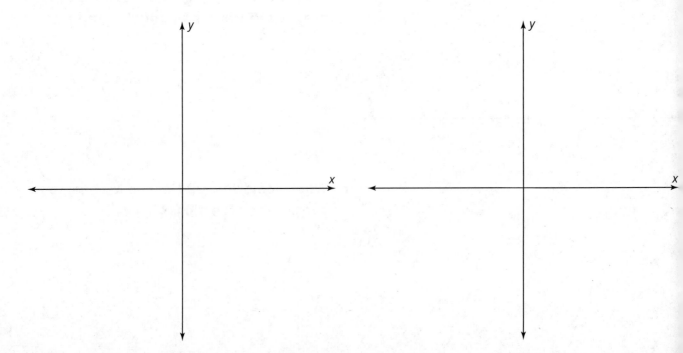

c. The parabola opens downward, and the zeros are at $x = 0$ and $x = 5$.

d. The parabola opens upward, and the zeros are at $x = -2.5$ and $x = 4.3$.

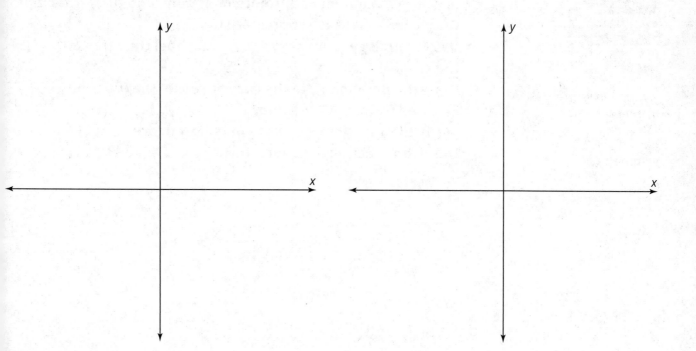

4. Compare your quadratic functions with your classmates' functions. How does the *a*-value affect the shape of the graph?

5. For each quadratic function,

- Use the general form to determine the axis of symmetry, the absolute maximum or absolute minimum, and the y-intercept. Graph and label each characteristic.
- Use technology to identify the zeros. Label the zeros on the graph.
- Draw the parabola. Use the curve to write the function in factored form.
- Verify the function you wrote in factored form is equivalent to the given function in general form.

Remember:

A function written in general form $f(x) = ax^2 + bx + c$ has an axis of symmetry at $x = \frac{-b}{2a}$.

a. $h(x) = x^2 - 8x + 12$

zeros: _____

factored form: _____

b. $r(x) = -2x^2 + 6x + 20$

zeros: _____

factored form: _____

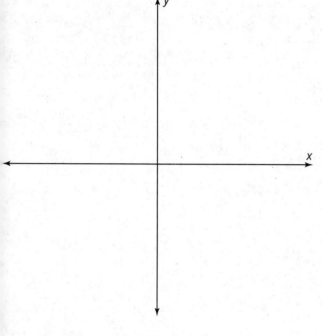

c. $w(x) = -x^2 - 4x$

zeros: _____

factored form: _____

NOTES

d. $c(x) = 3x^2 - 3$

zeros: ______________________

factored form: ______________________

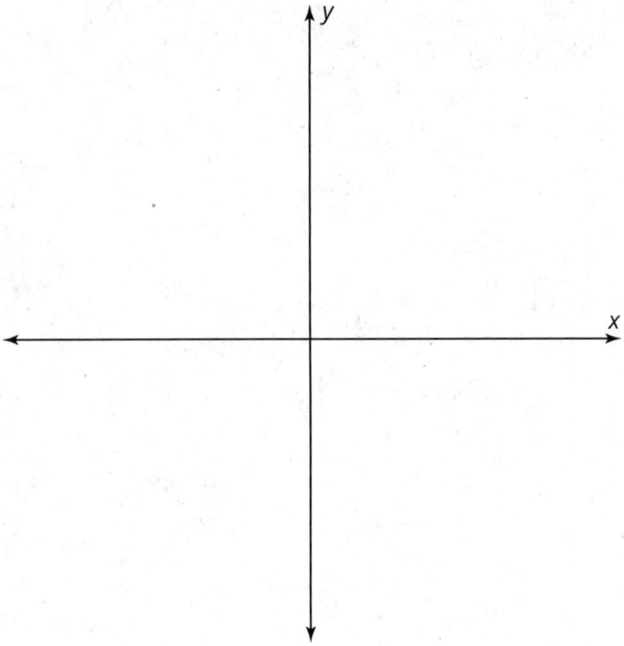

TALK the TALK

Quadratic Sleuthing

Use the given information to answer each question. Do not use technology. Show your work.

1. Determine the axis of symmetry of each parabola.

   a. The x-intercepts of the parabola are (1, 0) and (5, 0).

   b. The x-intercepts of the parabola are (−3.5, 0) and (4.1, 0).

   c. Two symmetric points on the parabola are (−7, 2) and (0, 2).

2. Describe how to determine the axis of symmetry given the x-intercepts of a parabola.

3. Determine the location of the vertex of each parabola.

   a. The function $f(x) = x^2 + 4x + 3$ has the axis of symmetry $x = -2$.

   b. The equation of the parabola is $y = x^2 - 4$, and the x-intercepts are (−2, 0) and (2, 0).

Think about:

Sketch a graph by hand if you need a model.

c. The function $f(x) = x^2 + 6x - 5$ has two symmetric points $(-1, -10)$ and $(-5, -10)$.

4. **Describe how to determine the vertex of a parabola given the equation and the axis of symmetry.**

5. **Determine another point on each parabola.**

   a. **The axis of symmetry is $x = 2$, and a point on the parabola is (0, 5).**

   b. **The vertex is (0.5, 9), and an x-intercept is (−2.5, 0).**

   c. **The vertex is (−2, −8), and a point on the parabola is (−1, −7).**

6. **Describe how to determine another point on a parabola if you are given one point and the axis of symmetry.**

Assignment

Write

1. Describe the characteristics of a quadratic function that you can determine from its equation in general form.

2. Describe the characteristics of a quadratic function that you can determine from its equation in factored form.

Remember

The sign of the leading coefficient of a quadratic function in standard form or factored form describes whether the function has an absolute maximum or absolute minimum.

A parabola is a smooth curve with reflectional symmetry. The axis of symmetry contains the vertex of the graph of the function, which is located at the absolute minimum or absolute maximum of the function.

Practice

1. Analyze each quadratic function.

$$g(x) = 12x - 4x^2 + 16 \qquad h(x) = -\tfrac{1}{4}(x - 3)(x + 2)$$

   a. Identify the quadratic function as general form or factored form.
   b. Does the quadratic function have an absolute maximum or absolute minimum?
   c. Does the graph open upward or downward?
   d. Determine any intercepts from the given form of the function.

2. Analyze each quadratic function.

$$f(x) = -\tfrac{2}{3}x^2 - 3x + 15 \qquad g(x) = \tfrac{3}{4}x^2 + 12x - 27$$

   a. Identify the axis of symmetry.
   b. Use the axis of symmetry to determine the ordered pair of the absolute maximum or absolute minimum value.
   c. Describe the intervals of increase and decrease.
   d. Sketch the graph based on the information you just calculated.
   e. Use technology to identify the zeros.
   f. Place two pairs of symmetric points on your graph. What is the average rate of change between these pairs of symmetric points?
   g. Write the function in factored form.

3. Given a parabola that opens downward and has zeros at $x = -2$ and $x = 3$.

   a. Represent it as a quadratic equation in factored form.
   b. Sketch a graph of the quadratic function.
   c. What is the axis of symmetry and y-intercept of the quadratic function?

Stretch

1. Sketch the graph $f(x) = -3x^2 - 4$. How could you change the quadratic function to make the graph open upward? Show the change on the graph.
2. How could you change the quadratic function $f(x) = -3x^2 - 4$ to shift the graph up or down? Show on the graph.
3. How could you change the quadratic function $f(x) = -3x^2 - 4$ to shift the graph right or left? Show the change on the graph.

Review

1. A camp wants to create a larger space for their albino rabbit, Clover. They want to reuse the materials from Clover's current enclosure in the construction of the new enclosure. The perimeter of Clover's current space is 6 feet. The perimeter of his new enclosure will be 3 times larger than his former enclosure.

   a. What is the area of the new enclosure $A(w)$ in terms of width, w?

   b. What is the maximum area of the new enclosure? What are the dimensions?

2. Is $7x^{2t} \cdot 5x^{2t}$ equivalent to $35x^{2t}$? Justify your answer.
3. Is $(16^{3z})^{6y}$ equivalent to 16^{18yz}? Justify your answer.
4. Use the marginal frequency distribution to answer each question.

Favorite Fruit				
	Apples	Oranges	Grapes	Total
Men	10	4	7	21
Women	11	9	8	28
Total	21	13	15	49

   a. Which fruit do men and women prefer overall? Justify your response.

   b. Is the fruit that the men and women like the least also the fruit that just women like the least? Justify your response.

More Than Meets the Eye

Transformations of Quadratic Functions

Warm Up

Write the equation for the axis of symmetry given each quadratic function.

1. $f(x) = -3x^2 - 4x + 5$

2. $f(x) = \frac{1}{4}(x - 1)(x + 2)$

3. $f(x) = -x^2 + 3$

Learning Goals

- Translate, reflect, and dilate quadratic functions horizontally and vertically.
- Write equations of quadratic functions given multiple transformations.
- Graph quadratic functions given multiple transformations.
- Identify multiple transformations of quadratic functions given equations.
- Understand the form in which a quadratic function is written can reveal different key characteristics.
- Write quadratic equations in vertex and factored form.

Key Term
- vertex form

You know how to transform linear, absolute value, and exponential functions. How can you apply what you know about the transformation form of a function, $g(x) = A \cdot f(B(x - C)) + D$, to quadratic functions?

Quadratics and Absolutes

The coordinate plane shows the graph of the absolute value function $f(x) = |x - 4|$ and a quadratic function, $q(x)$.

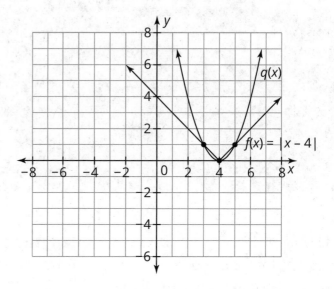

1. **How was the basic absolute value function $f(x) = |x|$ transformed to produce the graph shown?**

2. **Write an equation which can represent the quadratic function, $q(x)$. Test your equation with the graph to see if it is correct.**

3. **How does knowing that $1^2 = |1|$ and $(-1)^2 = |-1|$ explain the intersection points of the graph of the absolute value function and the graph of the quadratic function?**

Translations and Reflections of Quadratic Functions

Given $g(x) = f(x - C) + D$, consider how to transform the basic function, $f(x) = x^2$, to graph the transformed function.

1. Consider the four quadratic functions shown, where $f(x) = x^2$ is the basic function.

   - $c(x) = x^2 + 3$
   - $d(x) = x^2 - 3$
   - $j(x) = (x + 3)^2$
   - $k(x) = (x - 3)^2$

   Ask
   yourself:

   How do you think translating quadratics may be similar to translating other functions?

   a. Write the functions $c(x)$, $d(x)$, $j(x)$, and $k(x)$ in terms of the basic function. For each, determine whether an operation is performed on the function or on the argument of the function. Describe the operation.

   b. Given the form $ax^2 + bx + c$, the functions $c(x)$ and $d(x)$ each have a b-value equal to 0. What does this tell you about the axis of symmetry of each graph? Explain your answer.

   c. Sketch a graph of each function. Label each graph and include key points.

   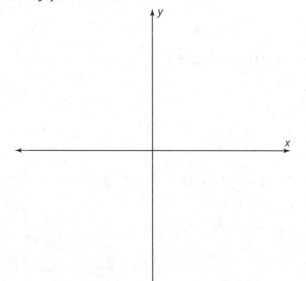

   d. Use coordinate notation to represent the vertical or horizontal translation of each function, c, d, j, and k. Each point (x, y) on the graph of $f(x)$:

   - becomes the point _____ on the graph of $c(x)$.

   - becomes the point _____ on the graph of $d(x)$.

   - becomes the point _____ on the graph of $j(x)$.

   - becomes the point _____ on the graph of $k(x)$.

You know that for any basic function, the C- and D-values describe translations of the function. The C-value defines an operation that is performed on the argument, and it describes a horizontal translation that affects the input values. The D-value defines an operation performed on the function, and it describes a vertical translation that affects the output values.

Now, let's consider reflections of graphs. You know that when a negative is on the outside of a function, the graph is reflected across a horizontal line of reflection. When a negative is on the inside of a function, the graph is reflected across a vertical line of reflection. Given $f(x) = x^2$, consider $g(x) = -f(x)$ and $h(x) = f(-x)$.

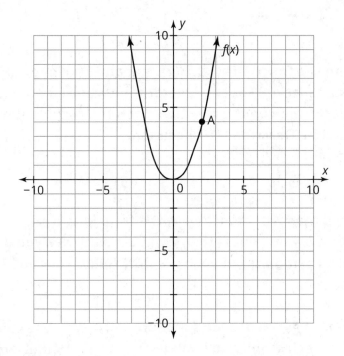

2. **Consider the placement of the negative sign in each function, $g(x)$ and $h(x)$.**

   a. **Sketch the graph and describe the line of reflection for $g(x)$. Label A' on your graph.**

   b. **Sketch the graph and describe the line of reflection for $h(x)$. Label A'' on your graph.**

c. Use coordinate notation to represent the reflection of each function. Each point (x, y) on the graph of f(x):

• becomes the point _____ on the graph of g(x).

• becomes the point _____ on the graph of h(x).

d. Given the basic quadratic function, $f(x) = x^2$, why does the graph of $f(-x)$ map onto itself?

3. Consider the graph of each given function. Sketch the result of the transformed function. Label A′ on your graph. Then describe the transformation you performed.

a. Given the graph of v(x), sketch $m(x) = v(-x)$.

b. Given the graph of w(x), sketch $z(x) = -w(x)$.

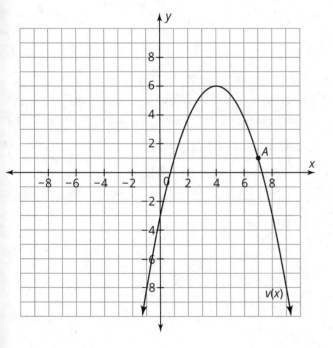

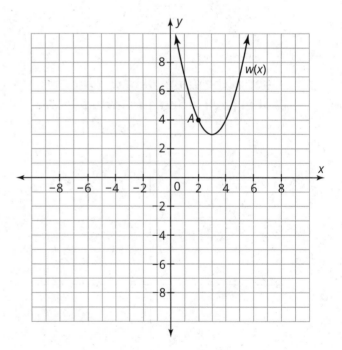

You can vertically and horizontally dilate quadratic functions just like other functions you have studied.

1. Consider the three quadratic functions shown, where $f(x) = x^2$ is the basic function.

   - $f(x) = x^2$

   - $n(x) = \frac{1}{2}x^2$

   - $p(x) = 2x^2$

   a. Write the functions $n(x)$ and $p(x)$ in terms of the basic function $f(x)$. For each, determine whether an operation is performed on the function $f(x)$ or on the argument of the function $f(x)$. Describe the operation.

   b. Sketch the graph of each function. Label each graph and include key points.

   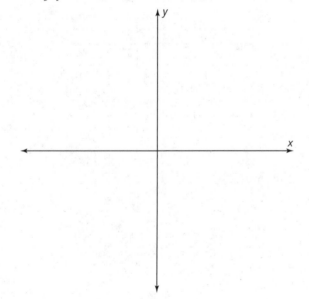

   c. Use coordinate notation to represent the dilation of each function. Each point (x, y) on the graph of $f(x)$:

   - becomes the point _____ on the graph of $n(x)$.

   - becomes the point _____ on the graph of $p(x)$.

2. Consider the three quadratic functions, where $f(x) = x^2$ is the basic function.

   - $f(x) = x^2$

   - $t(x) = (3x)^2$

   - $q(x) = \left(\frac{1}{3}x\right)^2$

   a. Write the functions $t(x)$ and $q(x)$ in terms of the basic function $f(x)$. For each, determine whether an operation is performed on the function $f(x)$ or on the argument of the function $f(x)$. Describe the operation.

   b. Sketch the graph of each function. Label each graph and include key points.

   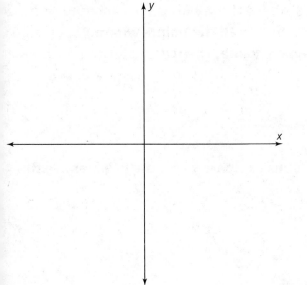

   c. Use coordinate notation to represent the dilation of each function. Each point (x, y) on the graph of $f(x)$:

      - becomes the point _____ on the graph of $t(x)$.

      - becomes the point _____ on the graph of $q(x)$.

Remember, a horizontal dilation is a type of transformation that stretches or compresses the entire graph. Horizontal stretching is the stretching of a graph away from the y-axis. Horizontal compression is the squeezing of a graph towards the y-axis.

3. Now, let's compare the graph of $f(x) = x^2$ with $r(x) = f\left(\frac{1}{2}x\right)$.

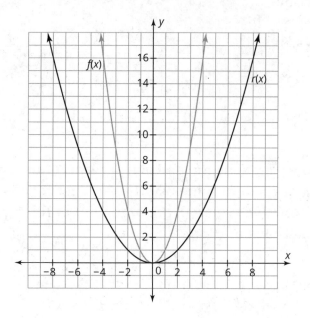

x	$f(x) = x^2$	$r(x) = p\left(\frac{1}{2}x\right)$
0	0	0
1	1	0.25
2	4	1
3	9	2.25
4	16	4
5	25	6.25
6	36	9

a. Analyze the table of values that correspond to the graph.

   Circle instances where the y-values for each function are the same. Then, list all the points where $f(x)$ and $r(x)$ have the same y-value. The first instance has been circled for you.

b. How do the x-values compare when the y-values are the same?

c. Complete the statement.

   The function $r(x)$ is a _____ of $f(x)$ by a factor of _____ .

d. How does the factor of stretching or compression compare to the B-value in $r(x)$?

Compared with the graph of $f(x)$, the graph of $f(Bx)$ is:

- horizontally compressed by a factor of $\frac{1}{|B|}$ if $|B| > 1$.
- horizontally stretched by a factor of $\frac{1}{|B|}$ if $0 < |B| < 1$.

Worked Example

You can use reference points to graph the function $q(x) = f(\frac{1}{3}x)$ when $f(x) = x^2$.

From $q(x)$ you know that $C = 0$, $D = 0$, and $B = \frac{1}{3}$. The vertex for $q(x)$ is $(0, 0)$.

Notice $0 < |B| < 1$, so the graph will horizontally stretch by a factor of $\frac{1}{\frac{1}{3}}$ or 3.

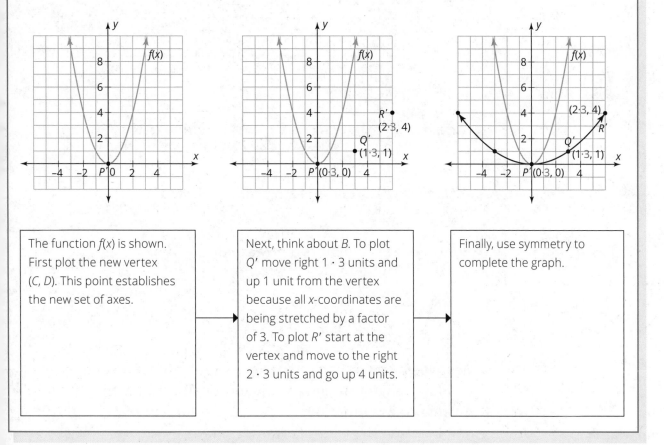

| The function $f(x)$ is shown. First plot the new vertex (C, D). This point establishes the new set of axes. | Next, think about B. To plot Q' move right $1 \cdot 3$ units and up 1 unit from the vertex because all x-coordinates are being stretched by a factor of 3. To plot R' start at the vertex and move to the right $2 \cdot 3$ units and go up 4 units. | Finally, use symmetry to complete the graph. |

4. **If you were asked to graph $p(x) = f(3x)$, describe how the graph would change. If (x, y) is any point on $f(x)$, describe any point on $p(x)$.**

5. Consider the graph showing the quadratic functions $k(x)$ and $m(x)$. Antoine and Xi Ling are writing the function $m(x)$ in terms of $k(x)$.

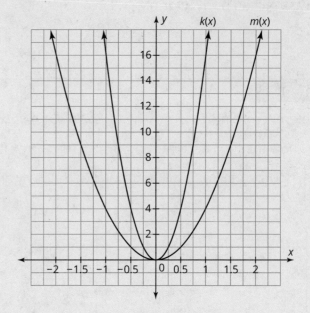

Antoine says that $m(x)$ is a transformation of the A-value.

$$m(x) = \tfrac{1}{4}k(x)$$

Xi Ling says that $m(x)$ is a transformation of the B-value.

$$m(x) = k(\tfrac{1}{2}x)$$

Who's correct? Justify your reasoning.

6. Describe how you can rewrite a quadratic function with a B-value transformation as a quadratic function with an A-value transformation.

7. Rewrite the function from the worked example, $q(x) = f(\tfrac{1}{3}x)$, without a B-value.

Consider the formula to calculate the area of a circle, $A = \pi r^2$. You can represent the area formula as the function $A(r) = \pi r^2$ and represent it on a coordinate plane.

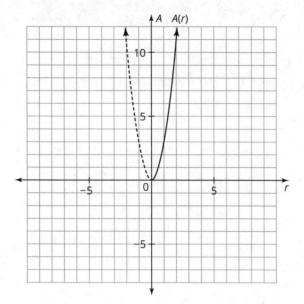

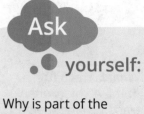

Ask
yourself:

Why is part of the graph represented with a dashed smooth curve?

8. **How is the area affected if you double the radius? Explain the change in area in terms of a transformation of the graph.**

Using Reference Points to Graph Quadratic Functions

Think

about:

What is the pattern of the *A*-value when transforming the basic quadratic function?

Given $y = f(x)$ is the basic quadratic function, you can use reference points to graph $y = Af(B(x - C)) + D$. Any point (x, y) on $f(x)$ maps to the point $(\frac{1}{B}x + C, Ay + D)$.

Worked Example

Given $f(x) = x^2$, graph the function $g(x) = 2f(x - 3) + 4$.

You can use reference points for $f(x)$ and your knowledge about transformations to graph the function $g(x)$.

From $g(x)$, you know that $A = 2$, $C = 3$, and $D = 4$.

The vertex for $g(x)$ will be at $(3, 4)$. Notice $A > 0$, so the graph of the function will vertically stretch by a factor of 2.

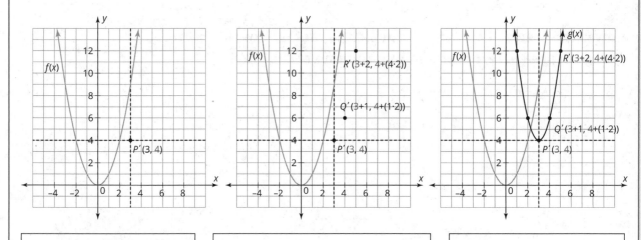

First, plot the new vertex, (C, D). This point establishes the new set of axes.	Next, think about the reference points for the basic quadratic function and that $A = 2$. To plot point Q' move right 1 unit and up, not 1, but 1×2 units from the vertex P' because all y-coordinates are being multiplied by a factor of 2. To plot point R' move right 2 units from P' and up, not 4, but 4×2 units.	Finally, use symmetry to complete the graph.

1. **Christian, Julia, and Emily each sketched a graph of the equation $y = -x^2 - 3$ using different strategies. Provide the step-by-step reasoning used by each student.**

Christian

$A = -1$ and $D = -3$

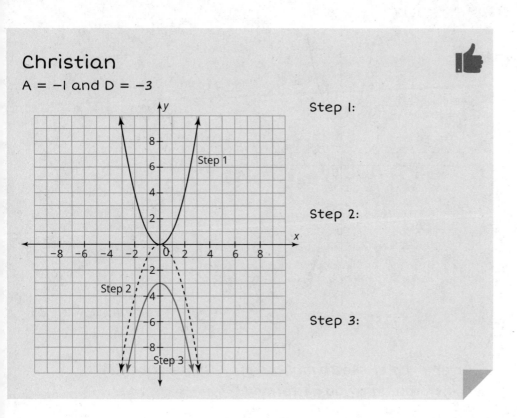

Step 1:

Step 2:

Step 3:

Julia

$D = -3$ and $A = -1$

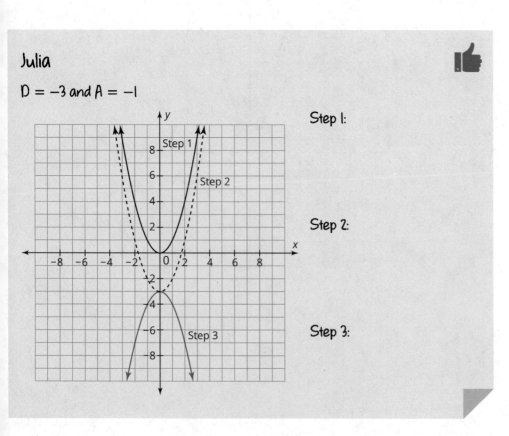

Step 1:

Step 2:

Step 3:

Emily

I rewrote the equation as $y = -(x^2 + 3)$.

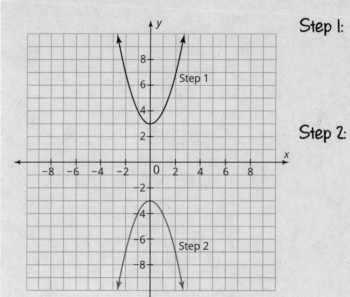

Step 1:

Step 2:

2. Given $y = p(x)$, sketch $m(x) = -p(x + 3)$. Describe the transformations you performed.

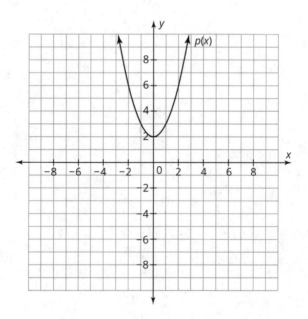

3. Given $f(x) = x^2$, graph each function. Then write each corresponding quadratic equation.

a. $f'(x) = \frac{1}{2}f(x - 2) + 3$

b. $f'(x) = -3f(x + 1) + 1$

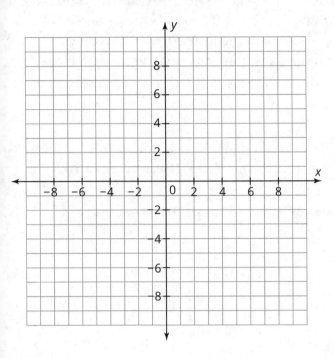

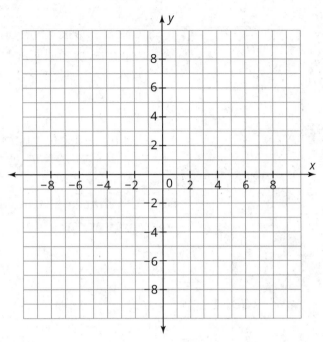

4. Write $n(x)$ in terms of $d(x)$. Then write the quadratic equation for $n(x)$.

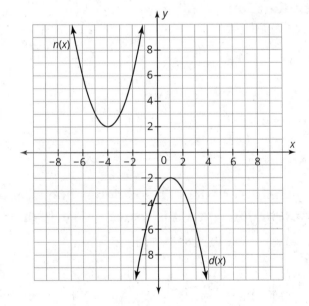

Given a basic function $y = f(x)$, you have learned how to identify the effects and graph a function written in the transformation form $g(x) = Af(x − C) + D$. For quadratic functions written in transformation form, $A \neq 0$.

For quadratic functions specifically, you will also see them written in the form $f(x) = a(x − h)^2 + k$, where $a \neq 0$. This is referred to as **vertex form**.

In vertex form, the coefficient of x is always 1. Therefore, the B-value in the transformation form in this case is also 1 and is left out of the expression.

1. **What does the variable h represent in the vertex form of a quadratic function?**

Think
about:

Do you see how this form of the function tells you about the vertex?

2. **What does the variable k represent in the vertex form of a quadratic function?**

3. **What key characteristics can you determine directly from the quadratic function when it is written in vertex form?**

4. Simone, Teresa, Jesse, Aricka, and Leon are working together to write a quadratic function to represent a parabola that opens upward and has a vertex at $(-6, -4)$.

Simone

My function is

$s(x) = 3(x + 6)^2 - 4.$

Teresa

My function is

$t(x) = \frac{1}{4}(x + 6)^2 - 4.$

Jesse

My function is

$j(x) = -3(x + 6)^2 - 4.$

ARiCKA

MY FUNCTioN iS

$D(x) = (x + 6)^2 - 4.$

Leon

My function is

$z(x) = 2(x - 6)^2 - 4.$

a. What are the similarities among all the graphs of the functions? What are the differences among the graphs?

b. How is it possible to have more than one correct function?

c. What would you tell Jesse and Leon to correct their functions?

d. How many possible functions can you write for the parabola described in this problem? Explain your reasoning.

5. Use technology to graph each function. Use the graph to rewrite the function in vertex form and in factored form.

a. $h(x) = x^2 - 8x + 12$

vertex: _____

vertex form: _____

zero(s): _____

factored form: _____

b. $r(x) = -2x^2 + 6x + 20$

vertex: _____

vertex form: _____

zero(s): _____

factored form: _____

c. $w(x) = -x^2 - 4x$

vertex: _____

vertex form: _____

zero(s): _____

factored form: _____

d. $c(x) = 3x^2 - 3$

vertex: _____

vertex form: _____

zero(s): _____

factored form: _____

6. Identify the form(s) of each quadratic function as either general form, factored form, or vertex form. Then state all you know about each quadratic function's key characteristics, based only on the given equation of the function.

a. $g(x) = -(x - 1)^2 + 9$

b. $g(x) = x^2 + 4x$

c. $g(x) = -\frac{1}{2}(x - 3)(x + 2)$

d. $g(x) = x^2 - 5$

You can write a quadratic function in vertex form if you know the coordinates of the vertex and another point on the graph.

Worked Example

Write an equation for a quadratic function with vertex (1, −2) that passes through the point (0, 1).

Step 1: Substitute the coordinates of the vertex into vertex form of a quadratic function.

$y = a(x - h)^2 + k$
$y = a(x - 1)^2 - 2$

Step 2: Substitute the coordinates of the other point on the graph for x and y.

$1 = a(0 - 1)^2 - 2$

Step 3: Solve for the value of a.

$1 = a(-1)^2 - 2$
$1 = a(1) - 2$
$1 = a - 2$
$3 = a$

Step 4: Rewrite the equation in vertex form, substituting the vertex and the value of a.

$f(x) = 3(x - 1)^2 - 2$

---

1. **How would you determine an equation of a quadratic function in factored form given the zeros and another point on the graph?**

2. **Dawson and Dave each wrote an equation for the function represented by the graph shown.**

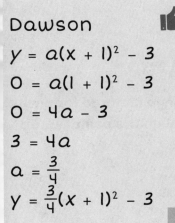

Dawson 👍

$y = a(x + 1)^2 - 3$

$0 = a(1 + 1)^2 - 3$

$0 = 4a - 3$

$3 = 4a$

$a = \frac{3}{4}$

$y = \frac{3}{4}(x + 1)^2 - 3$

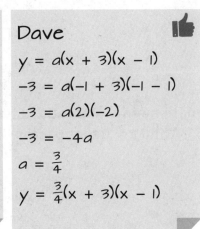

Dave 👍

$y = a(x + 3)(x - 1)$

$-3 = a(-1 + 3)(-1 - 1)$

$-3 = a(2)(-2)$

$-3 = -4a$

$a = \frac{3}{4}$

$y = \frac{3}{4}(x + 3)(x - 1)$

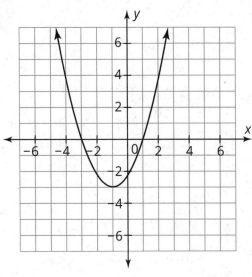

a. Explain Dawson's reasoning.

b. Explain Dave's reasoning.

c. Use technology to show that Dawson's equation and Dave's equation are equivalent.

3. Write an equation for a quadratic function in vertex form with vertex (3, 1) that passes through the point (1, 9).

4. Write an equation for a quadratic function in factored form with zeros at $x = -4$ and $x = 0$ that passes through the point (−3, 6).

5. Write an equation for a quadratic function in vertex form with vertex (−1, 6) that passes through the point (−3, 4).

6. Write an equation for a quadratic function $g(x)$ in vertex form given the graph of $g(x)$.

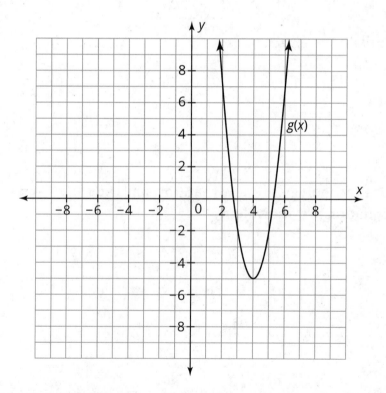

TALK the TALK

Show What You Know

1. **Based on the equation of each function, describe how the graph of each function compares to the graph of $f(x) = x^2$.**

   a. $z(x) = -(x - 1)^2 - 10$

   b. $r(x) = \frac{1}{2}(x + 6)^2 + 7$

   c. $m(x) = (4x)^2 + 5$

2. **Describe each transformation in relation to the basic function $f(x) = x^2$.**

   a. $h(x) = f(x) + D$ when $D > 0$

   b. $h(x) = f(x) + D$ when $D < 0$

c. $h(x) = f(x - C)$ when $C > 0$ **d.** $h(x) = f(x - C)$ when $C < 0$

e. $h(x) = Af(x)$ when $|A| > 1$ **f.** $h(x) = Af(x)$ when $0 < |A| < 1$

g. $h(x) = Af(x)$ when $A = -1$

Assignment

Write

Describe the connections between the vertex form of a quadratic function, $f(x) = a(x - h)^2 + k$, and the transformation form, $g(x) = A \cdot f(x - C) + D$, of the basic quadratic function, $y = f(x)$.

Remember

Transformations performed on any function $f(x)$ can be described by the transformation function $g(x) = Af(B(x + C)) + D$ where the C-value translates the function $f(x)$ horizontally, the D-value translates $f(x)$ vertically, the A-value vertically stretches or compresses $f(x)$, and the B-value horizontally stretches or compresses $f(x)$. When the A-value is negative the function $f(x)$ is reflected across a horizontal line of reflection and when the B-value is negative the function $f(x)$ is reflected across a vertical line of reflection.

Practice

1. Given $f(x) = x^2$, graph each function and write the corresponding quadratic equation.
   a. $g(x) = 3f(x - 1)$
   b. $g(x) = f(3x) - 1$
   c. $g(x) = \frac{1}{2}f(x) + 5$
   d. $g(x) = 2f(x - 3) + 1$

2. The graph shows the basic function $f(x) = x^2$, and also shows the function $h(x)$.
   a. Describe the types of transformations performed on $f(x)$ to result in $h(x)$.
   b. If the dilation factor is 16, write the function $h(x)$.

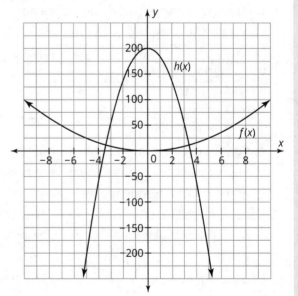

3. Use the given characteristics to write a function $R(x)$ in vertex form. Then, sketch the graph of $R(x)$ and the basic function $f(x) = x^2$.
   • The function has an absolute maximum.
   • The function is translated 70 units up and 100 units to the right.
   • The function is vertically dilated by a factor of $\frac{1}{5}$.

Stretch

Given $f(x) = x^2$. Sketch each function. Label point A' for each transformation.

1. $m(-x + 3)$
2. $n(-(x + 3))$
3. $r(-(x - 3))$
4. $t(-x - 3)$

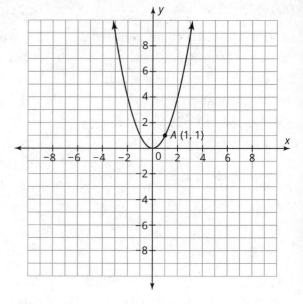

Review

1. Rupert owns a small store and he polled his customers to decide what type of bread he should be carrying. The table shows the results.

	White	Wheat	Rye
0–20 Years Old	15	5	3
21–30 Years Old	13	12	7
31–40 Years Old	6	16	9
41+ Years Old	8	21	5

   a. Construct a marginal relative frequency distribution of the data.

   b. Rupert wants to choose one type of bread to sell in his store. Construct a stacked bar graph of the relative frequency distribution. Which type of bread should he sell? Justify your response.

2. Use the equation $f(x) = \frac{1}{3}(x - 5)(x - 3)$ to determine each characteristic.

   a. axis of symmetry   b. x-intercepts

   c. Will the graph open upward or downward?

3. Use the equation $f(x) = 4x^2 + 3x - 10$ to determine each characteristic.

   a. axis of symmetry   b. y-intercept

You Lose Some, You Lose Some

Comparing Functions Using Key Characteristics and Average Rate of Change

Warm Up

Write the ordered pair for the y-intercept of each quadratic function.

1. $f(x) = 4(x - 2)(x - 3)$

2. $f(x) = -6x^2 + 9x - 5$

3. $f(x) = 5(x - 1)^2 + 14$

Learning Goals

- Understand the form in which a quadratic function is written can reveal different key characteristics.
- Show different rearrangements of quadratic functions in general form, factored form, and vertex form and analyze their properties.
- Compare properties of quadratic functions represented in different ways.
- Compare functions increasing linearly, quadratically, and exponentially by analyzing the average rate of change of the function.
- Use multiple representations of quadratic functions to identify key characteristics, such as the maximum, minimum, intercepts, and the axis of symmetry.

You have seen quadratic functions modeled using tables, equations, and graphs. How can you use the different representations of quadratic functions to analyze their key characteristics?

Function Form File Cabinet

1. Complete each graphic organizer located at the end of the lesson using the general form of the function given. For each form of the equation, check the box of any characteristic that can be identified in that form of the equation. Then, sketch a graph of the equation and identify key points.

ACTIVITY 4.1

Comparing Functions Increasing Linearly, Quadratically, and Exponentially

Think about the two functions you studied in the previous activity.

$$f(x) = x^2 + 2x - 3$$

$$g(x) = 2x^2 - 4x - 30$$

1. Compare the two functions. Show your work and explain your reasoning.

   a. Which function has the lowest minimum point?

   b. Which function has a greater value at $x = 8$?

   c. Which function has a greater value at $x = 9$?

2. **Complete the table to compare the average rate of change of the two functions on the given intervals. Show your work.**

Remember:

The average rate of change of any function over an interval is the slope of a linear function passing through the beginning and end points of the interval.

Interval	Average Rate of Change $f(x) = x^2 + 2x - 3$	Average Rate of Change $g(x) = 2x^2 - 4x - 30$
[0, 1]		
[0, 2]		
[0, 3]		
[4, 5]		

3. **The two functions you compared increase or decrease quadratically, but they do not have the same average rates of change on the given intervals. Explain why.**

Let's compare a quadratic function with other function types you have studied. You can say that a quadratic function increases or decreases quadratically, so a linear function increases or decreases linearly, and an exponential function increases or decreases exponentially.

4. **Consider the linear, exponential, and quadratic functions shown.**

$h(x) = 2x$

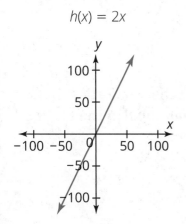

$j(x) = 2^x$

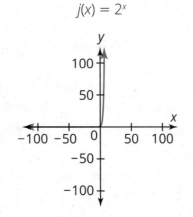

$k(x) = x^2$

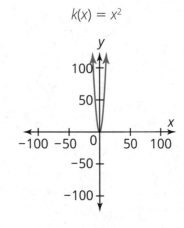

a. At what point do the three graphs intersect? Explain how you know.

b. Which function do you think has the greatest average rate of change from negative infinity to positive infinity? Explain your reasoning.

The table shown organizes the average rates of change of the three functions across different intervals of their domains. Some of the rates have been provided.

	[−10, 10]	[10, 100]	[100, 1000]
$h(x) = 2x$			
$j(x) = 2^x$		6.34×10^{27}	1.07×10^{298}
$k(x) = x^2$	0		

5. Consider the quadratic function.

a. Why is the average rate of change for the quadratic function 0 across the interval [−10, 10]? Use a calculation to explain your reasoning.

b. Enter the average rate of change for the quadratic function across the intervals [10, 100] and [100, 1000] in the table. Explain why your answers are correct.

6. Enter the average rate of change for the linear function across each of the three intervals in the table. Justify your answers.

7. Enter the average rate of change for the exponential function across the interval [−10, 10] in the table. Show your work.

8. Do the average rates of change for the exponential function in the table seem reasonable? Explain why or why not.

9. Compare the change in the average rates of change for the functions shown in the table across the different intervals. What do you notice?

10. Parker says that any function increasing exponentially will eventually have a greater value than any function increasing linearly or quadratically.

Is Parker correct? Explain why or why not.

Maya saved up some money and decided to take a risk and invest in some stocks. She invested her money in Doogle, a popular computer company. Unfortunately she lost it all in just 25 months. The change in her money during this time can be represented by the function $v(x) = 75 + 72x - 3x^2$, where v is the value of her investment and x is the time in months.

1. **Three quadratic functions are shown. Which of these models represents Maya's investment money over time? Explain your choice and why you eliminated the other model(s).**

Model 1

$$v(x) = -3(x + 1)(x - 25)$$

Model 3

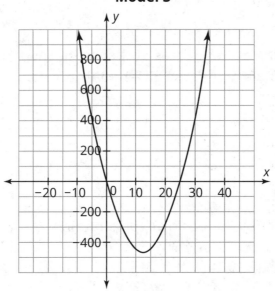

Model 2

x	y
0	0
3	197
15	450
25	0

2. **How much money did Maya initially invest? Explain how you determined your answer.**

3. The function that models Maya's investment over time has a maximum value.

   a. What was the greatest value of Maya's investment account over the time of her investment? Show your work.

   b. How much time did it take for Maya's account to reach its maximum value?

   c. On average, how much did Maya's account gain in value each month from the time she opened the account to the time it reached its maximum value?

Consider the quadratic function $h(t) = -5(t - 3)^2 + 60$.

1. **Sketch a graph of the function and label the vertex and the**
   y-intercept. Explain your work.

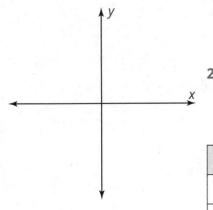

2. **Identify the table that represents the function. Explain why**
   you eliminated the other tables.

A

t	$h(t)$
−1	55
0	60
1	55
2	40

B

t	$h(t)$
0	45
1	20
4	5
5	20

C

t	$h(t)$
$-\sqrt{12} + 3$	0
0	15
3	60
$\sqrt{12} + 3$	0

D

t	$h(t)$
$-\sqrt{12} + 3$	−60
0	−45
3	0
$\sqrt{12} + 3$	−60

3. **Describe how the function $h(x)$ has been transformed from the**
   basic function $f(x) = x^2$.

Comparing Quadratics in Different Forms

In this activity, you will compare quadratic functions represented in different forms.

1. **Josiah compared the table of values for $f(x)$ and the graph of $g(x)$ to determine which quadratic function has the greater maximum.**

x	$f(x)$
-1	0
0	4.5
1	8
2	10.5
3	12

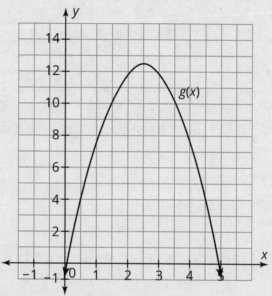

Josiah says that the function $g(x)$ has a greater maximum, because it has an output value greater than 12 at its maximum while the table for $f(x)$ shows a greatest output of 12. Is Josiah's reasoning correct? Explain your answer.

2. **Approximate the absolute maximum for each function. Show your work.**

Ben and Corinne are trying out their new drones, but they're not very good at flying them yet. The drones keep very precise records of their elevations.

3. **Compare these two drone flights, launched at the same time.**

The height in feet of Corinne's drone flight over time in seconds can be approximated by the function $c(x) = -3x^2 + 7x + 1$.	The table of values shows the height in feet of Ben's drone at different times.

x	$b(x)$
0	4
0.25	4.25
0.5	4
1	2
1.281	0

a. **Which flight began at a higher elevation? How do you know?**

b. **Which drone began descending first? Show your work.**

c. **Which of the drones had a greater average increase in height over time up to its maximum height? Explain your reasoning.**

TALK the TALK

More Ups and Downs

1. Analyze each pair of representations. Then, answer each question and justify your reasoning.

   a. Which function has a greater average rate of change for the interval (2, 4)?

A	B	
	x	**y**
$f(x) = (x + 1)^2 + 20$	0	4
	2	0
	4	4

   b. Which function has a greater absolute minimum?

   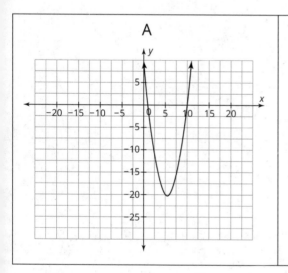

A	B	
	x	**y**
	0	4
	1	0
	4	0

c. **Which function's axis of symmetry has a greater *x*-value?**

A	B
$f(x) = 2x^2 + 4$	

x	y
−3	30
0	0
5	30

Graphic Organizer

General Form

Equation: $f(x) = x^2 + 2x - 3$

Select which key features of the graph can be identified from the general form of the equation.

☐ parabola opens up/down
☐ location of vertex
☐ zeros
☐ y-intercept

Factored Form

Equation: _____

Select which key features of the graph can be identified from the factored form of the equation.

☐ parabola opens up/down
☐ location of vertex
☐ zeros
☐ y-intercept

KEY CHARACTERISTICS OF A QUADRATIC FUNCTION

Equation: _____

Select which key features of the graph can be identified from the vertex form of the equation.

☐ parabola opens up/down
☐ location of vertex
☐ zeros
☐ y-intercept

Vertex Form

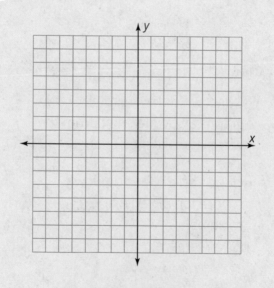

Graph of the Quadratic Function

Graphic Organizer

General Form

Equation: $g(x) = 2x^2 - 4x - 30$

Select which key features of the graph can be identified from the general form of the equation.

- ☐ parabola opens up/down
- ☐ location of vertex
- ☐ zeros
- ☐ y-intercept

Factored Form

Equation: _____

Select which key features of the graph can be identified from the factored form of the equation.

- ☐ parabola opens up/down
- ☐ location of vertex
- ☐ zeros
- ☐ y-intercept

KEY CHARACTERISTICS OF A QUADRATIC FUNCTION

Equation: _____

Select which key features of the graph can be identified from the vertex form of the equation.

- ☐ parabola opens up/down
- ☐ location of vertex
- ☐ zeros
- ☐ y-intercept

Vertex Form

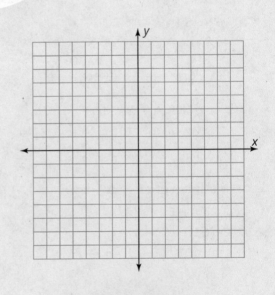

Graph of the Quadratic Function

Assignment

Practice

1. Analyze each pair of representations. Then, answer each question and justify your reasoning.

   a. Which function has a greater y-intercept?

   b. Which function has a greater average rate of change for the interval (1, 2)?

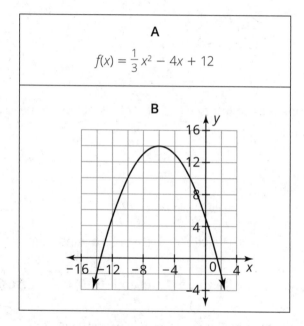

A

$f(x) = \frac{1}{3}x^2 - 4x + 12$

B

A

$f(x) = \frac{1}{2}x^2 + 9$

B

x	y
0	9
1	7
2	1

   c. Which function has an absolute maximum with a greater y-value?

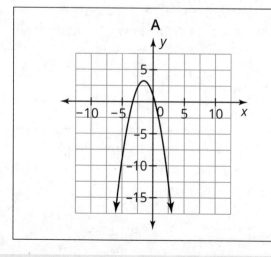

A

B

x	y
−1	0
0	0
0.5	−0.75

Stretch

Analyze each pair of representations.

A	B
$f(x) = x^2 + 2x - 3$	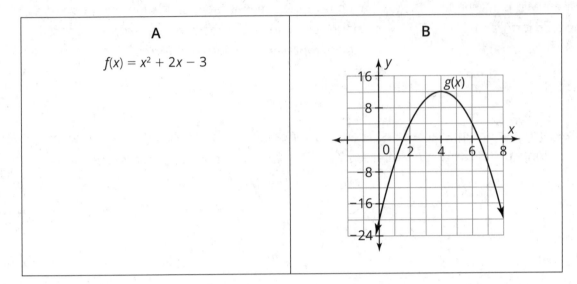

Write a function $m(x)$ that has an average rate of change for the interval (1, 2) that falls between the average rate of change for the same interval for $f(x)$ and $g(x)$.

Review

1. Write an equation for a quadratic function in vertex form with vertex (4, 9) that has a y-intercept of (0, 12.2).

2. Write an equation for a quadratic function in factored form with zeros (−7, 0) and (10, 0) that passes through the point (−4, −10).

3. The table shows the careers that students in grades 2, 6, and 12 would like to have when they are adults.

	Fire/Police	Doctor/Nurse	Teacher	Engineer	Veterinarian
2nd Graders	12	6	4	3	5
6th Graders	6	7	5	5	9
12th Graders	4	7	10	8	6

a. Construct a conditional relative frequency distribution of future careers by grade level.

b. What percent of 2nd graders want to be a doctor, nurse, or veterinarian?

c. What percent of 12th graders want to be something other than a teacher?

Introduction to Quadratic Functions Summary

KEY TERMS

- parabola
- vertical motion model
- roots
- second differences
- general form of a quadratic function
- factored form
- vertex
- axis of symmetry
- vertex form

LESSON 1

Up and Down or Down and Up

The shape that a quadratic function forms when graphed is called a *parabola*. A **parabola** is a smooth curve in a U-shape that has symmetry. The parabola can open upward, decreasing to a minimum point before increasing, or can open downward, increasing to a maximum point before decreasing. The domain of a quadratic function is all real numbers. The range of a quadratic function is all real numbers greater than or equal to the minimum *y*-value or less than or equal to the maximum *y*-value. The graph of a quadratic function has one *y*-intercept and, at most, 2 *x*-intercepts.

Quadratic functions model area because area is measured in square units.

For example, suppose you have 20 feet of fencing with which to enclose a rectangular area. The graph represents a quadratic function for the area of the rectangle given possible lengths of the rectangle. The maximum of the parabola is at the point (5, 25). It has x-intercepts at (0, 0) and (10, 0), and a y-intercept at (0, 0).

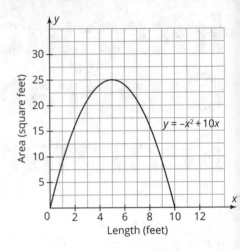

A **vertical motion model** is a quadratic equation that models the height of an object at a given time. The equation is of the form $y = -16t^2 + v_0t + h_0$, where y represents the height of the object in feet, t represents the time in seconds that the object has been moving, v_0 represents the initial vertical velocity of the object in feet per second, and h_0 represents the initial height of the object in feet.

For example, suppose a firework is launched into the air from the ground with a vertical velocity of 128 feet per second. The function that describes the height of the firework in terms of time is $g(t) = -16t^2 + 128t$.

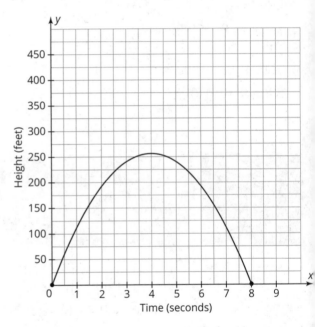

The x-intercepts of a graph of a quadratic function are also called the zeros of the quadratic function. The x-intercepts, or zeros, of $g(t) = -16t^2 + 128t$ are (0, 0) and (8, 0).

When an equation is used to model a situation, the x-intercepts are referred to as **roots**. The roots of an equation indicate where the graph of the equation crosses the x-axis.

LESSON

2 Endless Forms Most Beautiful

First differences are the differences between successive output values when successive input values have a difference of 1. **Second differences** are the differences between consecutive values of first differences. Linear functions have constant first differences and second differences of 0. Quadratic functions have changing first differences and constant second differences.

Linear function: $f(x) = -x + 2$

Quadratic function: $f(x) = 2x^2 - 3x$

x	$f(x)$	First Differences	Second Differences
0	2		
		−1	
1	1		0
		−1	
2	0		0
		−1	
3	−1		0
		−1	
4	−2		

x	$f(x)$	First Differences	Second Differences
0	0		
		−1	
1	−1		4
		3	
2	2		4
		7	
3	9		4
		11	
4	20		

A quadratic function written in standard form, which is also called the **general form of a quadratic function**, is in the form, $f(x) = ax^2 + bx + c$, where $a \neq 0$. In this form, a and b represent numerical coefficients and c represents a constant. A quadratic function written in factored form is in the form $f(x) = a(x - r_1)(x - r_2)$, where $a \neq 0$ and r_1 and r_2 represent the roots.

When the leading coefficient a is negative, the graph of the quadratic function opens downward and has a maximum. When a is positive, the graph of the quadratic function opens upward and has a minimum. When a quadratic function is written in general form, the constant c is the y-intercept.

The **vertex** of a parabola is the lowest or highest point on the graph of the quadratic function. The **axis of symmetry** of a parabola is the vertical line that passes through the vertex and divides the parabola into two mirror images.

For a quadratic function in factored form, the equation for the axis of symmetry is given by $x = \frac{r_1 + r_2}{2}$. For a quadratic function in general form, the equation for the axis of symmetry is $x = \frac{-b}{2a}$.

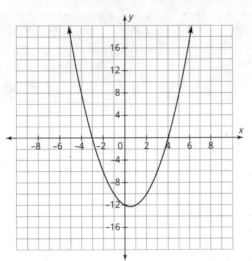

The graph shown represents the function $f(x) = x^2 - x - 12$. The axis of symmetry is $x = -\frac{(-1)}{2(1)} = \frac{1}{2}$. The vertex is $\left(\frac{1}{2}, -12\frac{1}{4}\right)$. The x-intercepts, or zeros, of the function are $x = -3$ and $x = 4$, so the function can be written in factored form as $f(x) = (x + 3)(x - 4)$. The y-intercept is $(0, -12)$. The domain of the function is all real numbers and the range is all real numbers greater than or equal to $-12\frac{1}{4}$. The graph has an interval of decrease from $-\infty$ to $\frac{1}{2}$ and an interval of increase from $\frac{1}{2}$ to ∞.

You can use the fact that the graph of a quadratic function is symmetric about the axis of symmetry to determine a second point on the parabola given a point on the parabola, and to determine the axis of symmetry given two symmetric points on the parabola.

For example, the vertex of a parabola is (3, 5). A point on the parabola is (0, 3). Another point on the parabola is (6, 3).

$$\frac{0 + a}{2} = 3$$
$$0 + a = 6$$
$$a = 6$$

Suppose two symmetric points on a parabola are $(-7, 20)$ and $(4, 20)$. The axis of symmetry is $x = -\frac{3}{2}$ because $\frac{-7 + 4}{2} = -\frac{3}{2}$.

LESSON

3

More Than Meets the Eye

You can use function transformation form, $g(x) = A \cdot f(B(x - C)) + D$, to transform quadratic functions.

Vertical translations are performed on a basic quadratic function $g(x) = x^2$ by adding a constant to or subtracting a constant from the function. Adding to the function translates it up, and subtracting translates it down. Horizontal translations are performed on the basic quadratic function $g(x) = x^2$ by adding a constant to or subtracting a constant from the argument, x, of the function. Adding to the argument translates the function to the left, and subtracting from the argument translates the function to the right.

Vertical translations

$g(x) = x^2$ basic function

$c(x) = g(x) + 4$ $g(x)$ translated 4 units up, so
$(x, y) \longrightarrow (x, y + 4)$.

$d(x) = g(x) - 4$ $g(x)$ translated 4 units down, so
$(x, y) \longrightarrow (x, y - 4)$.

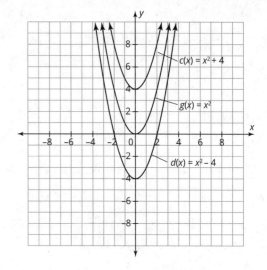

Horizontal translations

$g(x) = x^2$ basic function

$j(x) = g(x + 4)$ $g(x)$ translated 4 units left,
so $(x, y) \longrightarrow (x - 4, y)$.

$k(x) = g(x - 4)$ $g(x)$ translated 4 units right,
so $(x, y) \longrightarrow (x + 4, y)$.

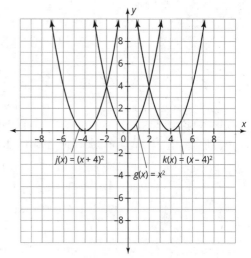

Multiplying the basic quadratic function by −1 results in a reflection across the line $y = 0$. Multiplying the argument of the basic quadratic function by −1 results in a reflection across the line $x = 0$, which ends up being the same as the original function because quadratic functions have a vertical axis of symmetry.

Reflections

$g(x) = x^2$ basic function

$m(x) = -g(x)$ $g(x)$ is reflected across $y = 0$, so $(x, y) \longrightarrow (x, -y)$.

$n(x) = g(-x)$ $g(x)$ is reflected across $x = 0$, so $(x, y) \longrightarrow (-x, y)$.

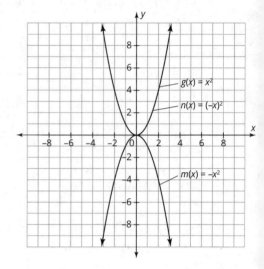

A vertical dilation of a function is a transformation in which the y-coordinate of every point on the graph of the function is multiplied by a common factor called the dilation factor. A vertical dilation stretches or shrinks the graph of a function vertically. For the transformed basic quadratic function, $g(x) = A \cdot f(x)$, when $|A| > 1$, the graph of $f(x)$ is stretched vertically. When $0 < |A| < 1$, $f(x)$ shrinks vertically. You can use the coordinate notation shown to indicate a vertical dilation.

$(x, y) \longrightarrow (x, Ay)$, where A is the dilation factor.

A horizontal dilation of a function is a transformation in which the x-coordinate of every point on the graph of the function is multiplied by a dilation factor. For the transformed basic quadratic function, $g(x) = f(Bx)$, when $|B| > 1$, the graph of the function is compressed horizontally. When $0 < |B| < 1$, the function is stretched horizontally. You can use the coordinate notation shown to indicate a horizontal dilation.

$(x, y) \longrightarrow \left(\dfrac{1}{|B|} x, y \right)$, where $\dfrac{1}{|B|}$ is the dilation factor.

Vertical dilations

$g(x) = x^2$ basic function

$v(x) = 2g(x)$ $g(x)$ stretched by a dilation factor of 2, so $(x, y) \longrightarrow (x, 2y)$.

$w(x) = \frac{1}{2}g(x)$ $g(x)$ shrunk by a dilation factor of $\frac{1}{2}$, so $(x, y) \longrightarrow (x, \frac{1}{2}y)$.

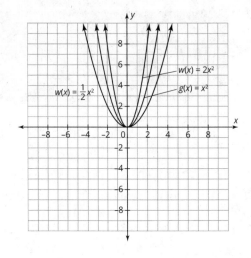

Horizontal dilations

$g(x) = x^2$ basic function

$v(x) = g(2x)$ $g(x)$ compressed by a dilation factor of $\frac{1}{2}$, so $(x, y) \longrightarrow \left(\frac{1}{2}x, y\right)$.

$w(x) = g\left(\frac{1}{2}x\right)$ $g(x)$ stretched by a dilation factor of 2, so $(x, y) \longrightarrow (2x, y)$.

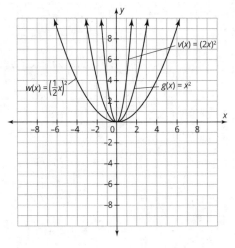

Given $y = f(x)$ is the basic function, you can use reference points to graph $y = A \cdot f(B(x - C)) + D$ without the use of technology. Any point (x, y) on $f(x)$ maps to the point $(\frac{1}{B}x + C, Ay + D)$.

Given $f(x) = x^2$, the function $g(x) = 2f(x - 3) + 4$ has been graphed.

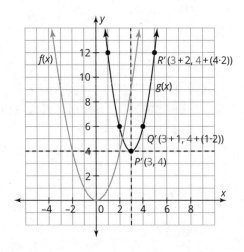

A quadratic function written in **vertex form** is in the form $f(x) = a(x - h)^2 + k$, where $a \neq 0$. The variable h represents the x-coordinate of the vertex. The variable k represents the y-coordinate of the vertex.

You can use different representations of quadratic functions to analyze their key characteristics.

For example, the functions $f(x)$ shown with a table and $g(x)$ shown with a graph can be compared to determine which quadratic function has the greater maximum.

x	$f(x)$
0	0
0.5	1
0.75	1.125
1	1
1.5	0

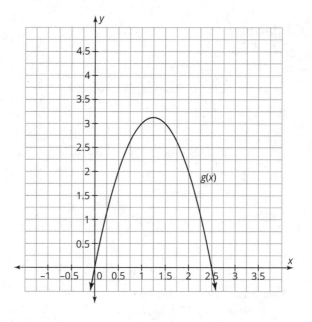

From the table, you can determine the maximum of $f(x)$ is (0.75, 1.125). From the graph, you can determine that the maximum of $g(x)$ is greater than $y = 3$. Therefore, $g(x)$ has a greater maximum than $f(x)$.

TOPIC 2
Solving Quadratic Equations

You can translate a parabola horizontally by subtracting a constant before squaring—for example, $(x - 2)^2$.

Module 5: Maximizing and Minimizing

TOPIC 2: SOLVING QUADRATIC EQUATIONS

Students review polynomials. They use different methods to add, subtract, and multiply polynomials. Students use what they know about square roots and graphs of quadratic equations to solve equations of the form $x^2 = n$ and $ax^2 - c = n$. Students see in the graphs that the solutions are both equidistant from the axis of symmetry. Students then learn to factor or complete the square to solve quadratic equations and real-world problems. Finally, students derive the Quadratic Formula. Students see the structure of solutions to quadratic equations in the Quadratic Formula: the axis of symmetry plus or minus the distance to the parabola. The complex number system is introduced, and students learn that a quadratic equation that does not cross the x-axis has two imaginary roots.

Where have we been?

Students know the characteristics that define a quadratic function. They have explored zeros of functions and have interpreted their meaning in contextual situations. Students know that the factored form of a quadratic equation gives the zeros of the function. They can sketch quadratic equations using key characteristics from an equation written in general form, factored form, or vertex form. Importantly, students have extensive experience with locating solutions to equations using a graphical representation.

Where are we going?

The techniques for solving quadratics will be applicable as students solve higher-order polynomials in Algebra 2 and beyond. Understanding the structure and symmetry of a quadratic equation allows students to solve quadratics with complex roots as well as higher-order polynomials.

Completing the Square

The quadratic expression $x^2 + 10x$ can be represented in a square shape as $x^2 + 5x + 5x$. To complete the square, add $5 \cdot 5$, or 25. The expression $x^2 + 10x + 25$ can then be written in factored form as $(x + 5)(x + 5)$, or $(x + 5)^2$.

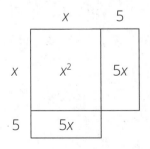
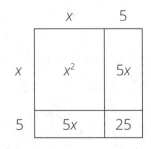

Math Legends

One of the most brilliant of ancient Greek mathematicians was a man named Pythagoras. He believed that every number could be expressed as a ratio of two integers.

Yet, legend tells us that one day at sea, one of Pythagoras's students pointed out to him that the diagonal of a square which measures 1 unit by 1 unit would be $\sqrt{2}$, a number that could not possibly be represented as a ratio of two integers.

This student was allegedly thrown overboard and the rest of the group was sworn to secrecy!

Talking Points

Equivalent forms of quadratic equations is an important topic to know about for college admissions tests.

Here is a sample question:

The graph of $y = (x - 8)(x + 2)$ is a parabola in the xy-plane. Rewrite the equation in an equivalent form so that the x- and y-coordinates of the vertex of the parabola appear as constants.

To solve this, students might use the process of completing the square.

$y = (x - 8)(x + 2)$
$y = x^2 - 6x - 16$
$y + 16 = x^2 - 6x$
$y + 16 + 9 = x^2 - 6x + 9$
$y + 25 = (x - 3)^2$
$y = (x - 3)^2 - 25$ is the vertex form of the equation of the parabola with vertex at (3, −25).

Key Terms

polynomial
A polynomial is a mathematical expression involving the sum of powers in one or more variables multiplied by coefficients.

degree of a polynomial
The greatest exponent in a polynomial determines the degree of the polynomial.

difference of two squares
The difference of two squares is an expression in the form $a^2 - b^2$ that has factors $(a + b)$ and $(a - b)$.

double root
The quadratic function $q(x) = x^2$ has two solutions at $y = 0$, so the function $q(x) = x^2$ is said to have a double root.

This Time, With Polynomials

Adding, Subtracting, and Multiplying Polynomials

Warm Up

Rewrite each expression by combining like terms.

1. $-3x + 4y - 9x - 5y$

2. $2xy^2 + 5x^2y - 7xy + xy^2$

3. $6 - m^2 + 5m^2$

4. $-8 - (-4k) + 7 + 1 - 4k$

Learning Goals

- Name polynomials by number of terms or degree.
- Understand that operations can be performed on functions as well as numbers.
- Add, subtract, and multiply polynomials.
- Explain why polynomials are closed under addition, subtraction and multiplication.
- Recognize and use special products when multiplying binomials.

Key Terms

- polynomial
- monomial
- binomial
- trinomial
- degree of a polynomial
- closed, closure
- difference of two squares
- perfect square trinomial

You know that a linear expression is one type of polynomial expression. What are other polynomial expressions, and how do you add, subtract, and multiply them?

Sorting It Out

You are familiar with many types of mathematical expressions. Cut out the 12 expressions located at the end of this lesson. Analyze and sort them into groups based upon common characteristics.

1. **Summarize the groups you formed by listing the expressions that you grouped together and your description for each group. Use mathematical terms in your descriptions.**

2. **Compare your groups of expressions to your classmates' groups. Describe any similarities and differences.**

3. **Jimmy and Andrew agree that $4x - 6x^2$ and $25 - 18m^2$ belong in the same group. They each are adding the expressions shown to the group. Who is correct? Explain your reasoning.**

Jimmy	Andrew
$5 - 7h$	$y^2 - 4y + 10$
$78j^3 - 3j$	$-3 + 7n + n^2$
$-13s + 6$	

4. **What characteristics do all twelve expressions share?**

Categorizing Polynomials

Previously, you worked with linear expressions in the form $ax + b$ and quadratic expressions in the form $ax^2 + bx + c$. Each is also part of a larger group of expressions known as *polynomials*.

A **polynomial** is a mathematical expression involving the sum of powers in one or more variables multiplied by coefficients. A polynomial in one variable is the sum of terms of the form ax^k, where a is any real number and k is a non-negative integer. In general, a polynomial is of the form $a_1x^k + a_2x^{k-1} + \ldots + a_nx^0$. Within a polynomial, each product is a term, and the number being multiplied by a power is a coefficient.

Worked Example

The polynomial $m^3 + 8m^2 - 10m + 5$ has four terms. Each term is written in the form ax^k.

- The first term is m^3.
- The power is m^3, and its coefficient is 1.
- In this term, the variable is m and the exponent is 3.

---

1. **Write each term from the worked example and identify the coefficient, power, and exponent. The first term has already been completed for you.**

	1st	2nd	3rd	4th
Term	m^3			
Coefficient	1			
Variable	m			
Power	m^3			
Exponent	3			

2. Identify the terms and coefficients in each polynomial.

    a. $-2x^2 + 100x$

    b. $4m^3 - 2m^2 - 5$

    c. $y^5 - y + 3$

Polynomials are named according to the number of terms they have. Polynomials with only one term are **monomials**. Polynomials with exactly two terms are **binomials**. Polynomials with exactly three terms are **trinomials**.

The degree of a term in a polynomial is the exponent of the term. The greatest exponent in a polynomial determines the **degree of the polynomial**. In the polynomial $4x + 3$, the greatest exponent is 1, so the degree of the polynomial is 1.

3. Khalil says that $3x^{-2} + 4x - 1$ is a trinomial with a degree of 1 because 1 is the greatest exponent. Jazmin disagrees and says that this is not a polynomial at all because the power on the first term is not a whole number. Who is correct? Explain your reasoning.

4. Determine whether each expression is a polynomial. Explain your reasoning.

   $5^x + 4^{x-1} + 3^{x-2}$ $x^2 + \sqrt{x}$ $x^4y + x^3y^2 + x^2y$

A polynomial is written in general form when the terms are in descending order, starting with the term with the largest degree and ending with the term with the smallest degree.

5. Revisit the cards you sorted in the Getting Started.

a. Identify any polynomial not written in general form and rewrite it in general form on the card.

b. Identify the degree of each polynomial and write the degree on the card.

c. Glue each card in the appropriate column based on the number of terms in each polynomial. Write your own polynomial to complete any empty boxes.

Monomial	Binomial	Trinomial

ACTIVITY 1.2

Interpreting the Graphs of Polynomial Functions

The graphs of functions $V(x)$ and $A(x)$ are shown. The function $V(x)$ models people's reaction times to visual stimuli in milliseconds, based upon the age of a person in years. The function $A(x)$ models people's reaction times to audio stimuli in milliseconds based on the age of a person in years.

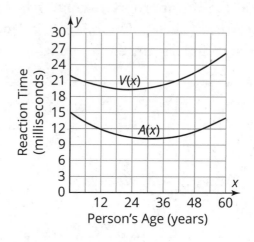

1. **Interpret the graphs of the functions.**

   a. **Describe the functions $V(x)$ and $A(x)$.**

   b. **Write a summary to describe people's reaction times to visual stimuli and audio stimuli.**

   c. **Do you think a person would react faster to a car horn or a flashing light? Explain your reasoning.**

2. Estimate the age that a person has the quickest reaction time to each stimuli. Explain how you determined each answer.

   a. visual stimuli

   b. audio stimuli

Many times, auto insurance companies use test results similar to the ones shown to create insurance policies for different drivers.

3. How do you think the information provided in the graphic representation may be used by an auto insurance company?

4. Consider a new function $h(x)$, where $h(x) = V(x) - A(x)$. What does $h(x)$ mean in terms of the problem situation?

5. Write a report about drivers' reaction times to visual and audio stimuli. Discuss actions that may improve drivers' reaction times and distractions that may worsen drivers' reaction times. Discuss the importance of flashing lights and sirens on emergency vehicles.

Ask yourself:

How can you incorporate information about auto insurance rates and a driver's age in your report?

Adding and Subtracting Polynomial Functions

You are playing a new virtual reality game called "Species." You are an environmental scientist who is responsible for tracking two species of endangered parrots, the orange-bellied parrot and the yellow-headed parrot. Suppose the orange-bellied parrots' population can be modeled by the function $B(x)$, where x represents the number of years since the current year. Suppose that the population of the yellow-headed parrot can be modeled by the function $H(x)$.

$$B(x) = -18x + 120$$

$$H(x) = 4x^2 - 5x + 25$$

The two polynomial functions are shown on the coordinate plane.

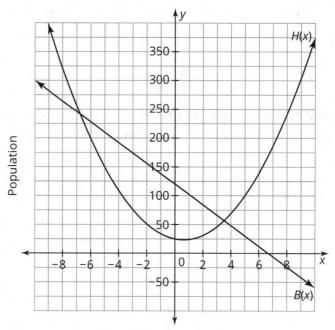

Time Since Present (years)

Ask yourself:

One place to start the sketch of $T(x)$ would be to consider the y-intercept for each function. What would the new y-intercept be for $T(x)$?

Your new task in this game is to determine the total number of these endangered parrots each year over a six-year span. You can calculate the total population of parrots using the two graphed functions.

1. **Use the graphs of $B(x)$ and $H(x)$ to determine the function, $T(x)$, to represent the total population of parrots.**

   a. **Write $T(x)$ in terms of $B(x)$ and $H(x)$.**

b. Predict the shape of the graph of T(x).

x	B(x)	H(x)	T(x)

c. Sketch a graph of T(x) on the coordinate plane shown. First choose any 5 x-values and add their corresponding y-values to create a new point on the graph of T(x). Then connect the points with a smooth curve. Record the values in the table.

d. Did the graph of T(x) match your prediction in part (b)? Identify the function family to which T(x) belongs.

You can write a function, T(x), in terms of x to calculate the total number of parrots at any time.

Worked Example

$T(x) = B(x) + H(x)$ Write T(x) in terms of two known functions.

$T(x) = (-18x + 120) + (4x^2 - 5x + 25)$ Substitute the functions in terms of x.

$T(x) = 4x^2 + (-18x + (-5x)) + (120 + 25)$ Use the Commutative Property to reorder and the Associative Property to group like terms.

$T(x) = 4x^2 - 23x + 145$ Combine like terms.

2. **Choose any two x-values in your table. Use the new polynomial function, T(x), to confirm that your solution in the table for those times is correct. Show your work.**

Remember:

3. **Use technology to confirm that your graph and the remaining solutions in the table are correct. Explain any discrepancies and how you corrected them.**

The table feature on a graphing calculator is an efficient tool to determine y-values.

4. Zoe says that using $T(x)$ will not work for any time after 6 years from now because by that point the orange-bellied parrot will be extinct. Is Zoe's statement correct? Why or why not?

Throughout the game "Species," you must always keep track of the difference between the population of each type of species. If the difference gets to be too great, you lose the game. The graphs of $B(x) = -18x + 120$ and $H(x) = 4x^2 - 5x + 25$ are shown.

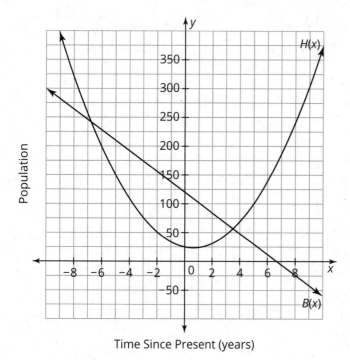

Time Since Present (years)

5. Use the graphs of $B(x)$ and $H(x)$ to determine the function, $D(x)$, to represent the difference between the populations of each type of species.

a. Write $D(x)$ in terms of $B(x)$ and $H(x)$.

b. Predict the shape of the graph of $D(x)$.

c. Sketch a graph of $D(x)$ on the coordinate plane shown. First choose any 5 x-values and subtract their corresponding y-values to create a new point on the graph of $D(x)$. Then connect the points with a smooth curve. Record the values in the table.

d. Did the graph of $D(x)$ match your prediction in part (b)? Identify the function family to which $D(x)$ belongs.

x	B(x)	H(x)	D(x)

6. Write a function, $D(x)$, in terms of x to calculate the difference between the population of the orange-bellied parrots and the yellow-headed parrots. Write $D(x)$ as a polynomial in general form.

Think
about:

Refer to the Worked Example for adding polynomials as a guide.

7. Choose any two x-values in your table. Use your new polynomial function to confirm that your solution in the table for those times is correct. Show your work.

8. Use technology to confirm that your graph and the remaining solutions in the table are correct. Explain any discrepancies and how you corrected them.

9. Eric uses his function $D(x) = -4x^2 - 13x + 95$ to determine that the difference between the number of orange-bellied parrots and the number of yellow-headed parrots 7 years from now will be −192. Is Eric correct or incorrect? If he is correct, explain to him what his answer means in terms of the problem situation. If he is incorrect, explain where he made his error and how to correct it.

10. The next round of the Species game included the red-winged parrot, whose population can be modeled by the function $W(x) = -9x + 80$ and the rainbow lorikeet parrot, whose population can be modeled by the function $L(x) = 2x^2 - 4x + 10$. In both cases, x represents the number of years since the current year.

    a. Write a function, $S(x)$, in terms of x to calculate the total number of red-winged parrots and rainbow lorikeet parrots at any time.

    b. Write a function, $M(x)$, in terms of x to calculate the difference in the number of red-winged parrots and rainbow lorikeet parrots at any time.

    c. Calculate $S(4)$ and $M(4)$. Interpret the meaning of your results.

    d. In four years, how many red-winged parrots will there be? How many rainbow lorikeet parrots will there be?

In this activity, you will practice adding and subtracting polynomials.

1. **Analyze each student's work. Determine the error and make the necessary corrections.**

Marco

$3x^2 + 5x^2 = 8x^4$

Kamiah

$2x - (4x + 5)$

$2x - 4x + 5$

$-2x + 5$

Alexis

$(4x^2 - 2x - 5) + (3x^2 + 7)$

$(4x^2 + 3x^2) - (2x) - (5 + 7)$

$7x^2 - 2x - 12$

Consider each polynomial function.

$A(x) = x^3 + 5x^2 - 9$ $B(x) = -3x^2 - x + 1$ $C(x) = 2x^2 + 7x$ $D(x) = -2x^2 - 8x$

2. **Determine each function. Write your answers in general form.**

a. $J(x) = A(x) + C(x)$

b. $K(x) = D(x) - B(x)$

c. $L(x) = C(x) + D(x)$

d. $M(x) = B(x) - A(x)$

e. $N(x) = A(x) - C(x) - D(x)$

3. Are the functions $J(x)$, $K(x)$, $L(x)$, $M(x)$ and $N(x)$ polynomial functions? Explain why or why not.

When an operation is performed on any of the numbers in a set and the result is a number that is also in the same set, the set is said to be **closed**, or have **closure**, under that operation.

For example, the set of integers is closed under addition and subtraction. That means whenever two integers are added or subtracted, the result is also an integer.

The definition of closure can also be applied to polynomials.

4. **Based on the definition of closure, determine whether polynomials are closed under addition and subtraction. Justify your answer.**

Multiplying Polynomial Functions

Consider the dog enclosure scenario from the previous topic.

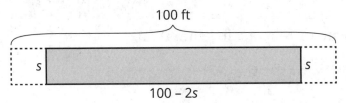

100 ft

s

s

100 − 2s

The area of the enclosure is expressed as $A(s) = s(100 - 2s)$, or the product of a monomial and a binomial.

1. **Consider how Jason and Julie wrote an equivalent polynomial function in general form by calculating the product.**

Remember:

Jason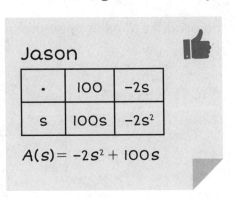

·	100	−2s
s	100s	−2s²

$A(s) = -2s^2 + 100s$

Julie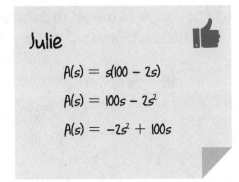

$A(s) = s(100 - 2s)$

$A(s) = 100s - 2s^2$

$A(s) = -2s^2 + 100s$

Develop a habit of writing answers in general form. It makes them easier to compare with others' answers.

a. **Describe the strategy Jason used to calculate the product.**

b. **How is Jason's strategy similar to Julie's strategy?**

Consider the ghost tour scenario from the previous topic. The revenue for the business is expressed as the product of a binomial times a binomial.

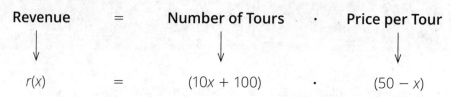

Revenue	=	Number of Tours	·	Price per Tour
$r(x)$	=	$(10x + 100)$	·	$(50 - x)$

2. **Finish Jason's process to write an equivalent polynomial function for revenue in general form.**

The process of using a multiplication table to multiply polynomials is referred to as an area model.

·	50	−x
10x	$500x$	$-10x^2$
100		

Ask yourself:

Does it matter where you place the polynomials in the multiplication table?

3. **Use an area model to calculate the product of each polynomial. Write each product in general form.**

a. $(3x + 2)(x - 4)$

b. $(x - 5)(x + 5)$

c. $(2x + 3)^2$

d. $(4x^2 + x - 1)(3x - 7)$

In Question 1, Julie uses the Distributive Property to multiply a monomial and a binomial. She wants to use the Distributive Property to multiply any polynomials.

Worked Example

Consider the polynomials $x + 5$ and $x - 2$. You can use the Distributive Property to multiply these polynomials.

Distribute x to each term of $(x - 2)$, and then distribute 5 to each term of $(x - 2)$.

$$(x + 5)(x - 2) = (x)(x - 2) + (5)(x - 2)$$

$$= x^2 - 2x + 5x - 10$$

$$= x^2 + 3x - 10$$

Think

about:

How can you use technology to check your answers?

4. **Use the Distributive Property to determine each product. Write the polynomial in general form.**

   a. $(5x - 1)(2x + 1)$

   b. $(x - 7)(x + 7)$

   c. $(x + 2)(x - 9)$

   d. $(2x^2 + 1)(3x^2 + x - 1)$

5. **Explain the mistake in Cheyanne's thinking. Then determine the correct product.**

   Cheyanne

   $$(x + 4)^2 = x^2 + 16.$$

   I can just square each term to determine the product.

6. **Based on the definition of closure, are polynomials closed under the operation of multiplication? Justify your answer.**

ACTIVITY 1.6 — Special Products When Multiplying Binomials

In this activity you will investigate the product of two linear factors when one is the sum of two terms and the other is the difference of the same two terms, and when the two linear factors are the same.

1. **Determine each product.**

    a. $(x - 4)(x + 4) = $ _____

     $(x + 4)(x + 4) = $ _____

     $(x - 4)(x - 4) = $ _____

    b. $(x - 3)(x + 3) = $ _____

     $(x + 3)(x + 3) = $ _____

     $(x - 3)(x - 3) = $ _____

    c. $(3x - 1)(3x + 1) = $ _____

     $(3x + 1)(3x + 1) = $ _____

     $(3x - 1)(3x - 1) = $ _____

    d. $(2x - 1)(2x + 1) = $ _____

     $(2x + 1)(2x + 1) = $ _____

     $(2x - 1)(2x - 1) = $ _____

2. **What patterns do you notice between the factors and the products?**

3. **Multiply each pair of binomials.**

    $(ax - b)(ax + b) = $ _____

    $(ax + b)(ax + b) = $ _____

    $(ax - b)(ax - b) = $ _____

In Questions 1 and 3, you should have observed a few special products. The first type of special product is called the *difference of two squares*. The **difference of two squares** is an expression in the form $a^2 - b^2$ that has factors $(a - b)(a + b)$.

4. **Label the expressions in Questions 1 and 3 that are examples of the difference of two squares.**

The second type of special product is called a *perfect square trinomial*. A **perfect square trinomial** is an expression in the form $a^2 + 2ab + b^2$ or the form $a^2 - 2ab + b^2$. A perfect square trinomial can be written as the square of a binomial.

$$a^2 + 2ab + b^2 = (a + b)^2$$
$$a^2 - 2ab + b^2 = (a - b)^2$$

5. **Label the expressions in Questions 1 and 3 that are examples of perfect square trinomials.**

6. **Use special products to determine each product.**

a. $(x - 8)(x - 8)$ b. $(x + 8)(x - 8)$

c. $(x + 8)^2$ d. $(3x + 2)^2$

e. $(3x - 2)(3x - 2)$ f. $(3x - 2)(3x + 2)$

TALK the TALK

Putting It Into Practice

Match each expression with the equivalent polynomial.

Expressions	Polynomials
1. $(x^2 - 3) + (x^2 + 2)$	A. -1
2. $(x^2 - 3) - (x^2 + 2)$	B. $-2x^2 - 1$
3. $(x^2 - 3) - (x^2 - 2)$	C. $-2x^2 - 5$
4. $(x^2 - 3) + (x^2 - 2)$	D. $2x^2 - 1$
5. $-(x^2 + 3) - (x^2 - 2)$	E. $2x^2 - 5$
6. $-(x^2 + 3) - (x^2 + 2)$	F. -5
7. $(x - 3)(x + 2)$	G. $x^2 + 5x + 6$
8. $(x + 3)(x - 2)$	H. $x^2 - 5x + 6$
9. $(x + 3)(x + 2)$	I. $x^2 - x - 6$
10. $(x - 3)(x - 2)$	J. $x^2 + x - 6$

Expression Cards

$4x - 6x^2$	$125p$	$\frac{4}{5}r^3 + \frac{2}{5}r - 1$
$-\frac{2}{3}$	$y^2 - 4y + 10$	$5 - 7h$
$-3 + 7n + n^2$	-6	$-13s + 6$
$12.5t^3$	$78j^3 - 3j$	$25 - 18m^2$

Assignment

Write

Match each definition with its corresponding term.

1. polynomial
2. term
3. coefficient
4. monomial
5. binomial
6. trinomial
7. degree of a term
8. degree of a polynomial

a. a polynomial with only 1 term
b. the degree of the term with the greatest exponent
c. a mathematical expression involving the sum of powers in one or more variables multiplied by coefficients
d. a polynomial with exactly 3 terms
e. any number being multiplied by a power within a polynomial expression
f. each product in a polynomial expression
g. a polynomial with exactly 2 terms
h. the exponent of a term in a polynomial

Remember

- The difference of two squares is an expression in the form $a^2 - b^2$ that has factors $(a + b)(a - b)$.
- A perfect square trinomial is an expression in the form $a^2 + 2ab + b^2$ or in the form $a^2 - 2ab + b^2$ that has the factors $(a + b)^2$ and $(a - b)^2$, respectively.

Practice

1. Ramona and James each build a rocket launcher. They launch a model rocket using Ramona's launcher and on its way back down it lands on the roof of a building that is 320 feet tall. The height of the rocket can be represented by the equation $H_1(x) = -16x^2 + 200x$, where x represents the time in seconds and $H_1(x)$ represents the height. Ramona and James take the stairs to the roof of the building and re-launch the rocket using James's rocket launcher. The rocket lands back on the ground. The height of the rocket after this launch can be represented by the equation $H_2(x) = -16x^2 + 192x + 320$.
   a. Compare and contrast the polynomial functions.
   b. Use technology to sketch a graph of the functions.
   c. Does it make sense in terms of the problem situation to graph the functions outside of Quadrant I? Explain your reasoning.
   d. Explain why the graphs of these functions do not intersect.
   e. Ramona believes that she can add the two functions to determine the total height of the rocket at any given time. Write a function $S(x)$ that represents the sum of $H_1(x)$ and $H_2(x)$. Show your work.

f. Is Ramona correct? Explain your reasoning.

g. Subtract $H_1(x)$ from $H_2(x)$ and write a new function, $D(x)$, that represents the difference. Then, explain what this function means in terms of the problem situation.

2. Determine whether each expression is a polynomial. If so, identify the terms, coefficients, and degree of the polynomial. If not, explain your reasoning.

a. $-2b^4 + 4b - 1$

b. $6 - g^{-2}$

c. $8h^4$

d. $9w - w^3 + 5w^2$

e. $x^{\frac{1}{2}} + 2$

f. $\frac{4}{5}y + \frac{2}{3}y^2$

3. Given $A(x) = x^3 - 5x + 4$, $B(x) = 2x^2 + 5x - 6$, and $C(x) = -x^2 + 3$, determine each function. Write your answer in general form.

a. $D(x) = B(x) + C(x)$

b. $E(x) = A(x) + B(x)$

c. $F(x) = A(x) - C(x)$

d. $G(x) = C(x) - B(x)$

e. $H(x) = A(x) + B(x) - C(x)$

f. $J(x) = B(x) - A(x) + C(x)$

4. Determine each product.

a. $(x - 7)(x - 7)$

b. $(x + 10)(x - 10)$

c. $(x + 6)^2$

d. $(2x + 5)^2$

e. $(2x - 5)(2x - 5)$

f. $(2x - 5)(2x + 5)$

Stretch

Consider the binomials $(x + 3)$, $(2x + 1)$, and $(x - 4)$.

1. Without multiplying, make a conjecture about the degree of the product of these binomials. Explain how you determined your answer.

2. Without multiplying, make a conjecture about the number of terms in the product of these binomials. Explain your reasoning.

3. Two students determine the product of the 3 binomials using two different methods. Student 1 uses a multiplication table, and Student 2 uses the distributive Property. Their work is shown below. Determine which student multiplied correctly and identify the mistake the other student made. Explain how you determined your answer.

Student 1

·	x	3	$2x$	1
x	x^2	$3x$	$2x^2$	x
-4	$-4x$	-12	$-8x$	-4

The product is $3x^2 - 8x - 16$.

Student 2

$(x + 3)(2x + 1)(x - 4) = (2x^2 + 7x + 3)(x - 4)$
$= 2x^3 - x^2 - 25x - 12$

The product is $2x^3 - x^2 - 25x - 12$.

Review

1. Alfonzo is building a deck on his house. He was originally going to make it a square with a side length of x feet. Alfonzo decides to make it a rectangular deck, with 1 foot added to one pair of opposite sides and 2 feet added to the other pair of opposite sides.

   a. Determine the expressions for the length and width of the new deck in terms of x, the length of the sides of the original deck.

   b. Write the function for the area of the new deck, $A(x)$, in terms of x, the length of the sides of the original deck. Does this function have a minimum or maximum? Explain your answer.

2. Analyze each pair of representations. Then, answer each question and justify your reasoning.

   a. Which function's axis of symmetry has a greater x-value?

   b. Which function has a greater absolute minimum?

   Function A

   $$f(x) = x^2 - 4x + 9$$

   Function A

   $$f(x) = 3(x - 2)^2 - 6$$

   Function B

   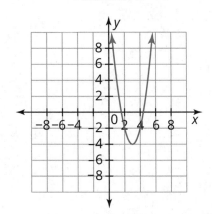

   Function B

x	y
1	2
3	5
5	18

3. Write the equation of the function, $g(x)$, whose graph transforms the graph $f(x) = x^2$ by reflecting it across the x-axis, vertically stretching it by a factor of 2, and translating it up 5 units.

4. Graph the function, $g(x)$, whose graph transforms the graph $f(x) = x^2$ by vertically compressing it by a factor of $\frac{1}{3}$ and translating it down 7 units.

Solutions, More or Less

Representing Solutions to Quadratic Equations

Warm Up

1. Complete the grid by continuing to make squares with side lengths of 4 through 8. Connect the side lengths together, and then write an equation using exponents to represent each perfect square.

Learning Goals

- Identify the zeros of a quadratic function, the roots of a quadratic equation, and the x-intercepts of a parabola using the equation of a quadratic function.
- Identify the double root of a quadratic equation as the two solutions of a quadratic equation at the minimum or maximum of the function.
- Write solutions of quadratic equations at specific output values using the axis of symmetry and the positive and negative square roots of the output value.
- Identify quadratic equations written as the difference of two perfect squares and rewrite these equations in factored form with a leading coefficient of 1.

Key Terms
- principal square root
- roots
- double root
- Zero Product Property

You have studied the graphs and equations for quadratic functions. How can you determine solutions of quadratic equations given different output values?

Plus or Minus

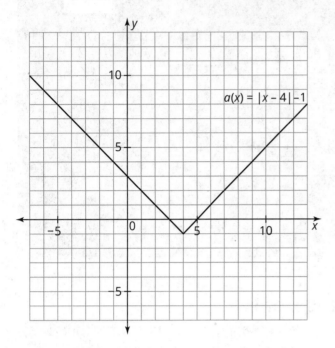

$$a(x) = |x - 4| - 1$$

Consider the absolute value function graphed.

1. **Describe how the function is transformed from the basic function $f(x) = |x|$.**

2. **For each $y > -1$, how many solutions does the equation $y = |x - 4| - 1$ have? Use the graph to explain your answer.**

3. **Determine the solutions to $|x - 4| - 1 = 0$ and identify the solutions on the graph.**

Remember:

Solutions for a function at $y = 0$ are called the zeros of the function. The symbol $\pm$ means "plus or minus."

4. **Use the graph and the function equation to explain why Escher's equation is correct.**

Escher

This absolute value function is symmetric about the line $x = 4$. So, for every y-value greater than -1, the solutions to the absolute value function are $x = 4 \pm (y + 1)$.

Solutions of a Quadratic Function

Recall that a quadratic function is a function of degree 2, because the greatest power for any of its terms is 2. This means that it has 2 zeros, or 2 solutions at $y = 0$.

The two solutions of a basic quadratic function can be represented as square roots of numbers. Every positive number has two square roots, a positive square root (which is also called the **principal square root**) and a negative square root. To solve the equation $x^2 = 9$, you can take the square root of both sides of the equation.

$$\sqrt{x^2} = \pm\sqrt{9}$$
$$x = \pm 3$$

Solving $x^2 = 9$ on a graph means that you are looking for the points of intersection between $y = x^2$ and $y = 9$.

> **Remember:**
>
> The square root property is $\sqrt{a^2} = \pm a$.

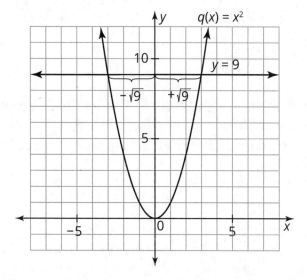

1. **Consider the graph of the function $q(x) = x^2$ shown.**

   a. **What is the equation for the axis of symmetry? Explain how you can use the function equation to determine your answer.**

   b. **Explain how the graph shows the two solutions for the function at $y = 9$ and their relationship to the axis of symmetry. Use the graph and the function equation to explain your answer.**

c. Describe how you can determine the two solutions for the function at $y = 2$. Indicate the solutions on the graph.

d. Describe how you can determine the two solutions for the function at each y-value for $y \geq 0$.

The x-coordinates of the x-intercepts of a graph of a quadratic function are called the zeros of the quadratic function. The zeros are called the **roots** of the quadratic equation.

The quadratic function $q(x) = x^2$ has two solutions at $y = 0$. Therefore, it has 2 zeros: $x = +\sqrt{0}$ and $x = -\sqrt{0}$. These two zeros of the function, or roots of the equation, are the same number, 0, so $y = x^2$ is said to have a **double root**, or **1 unique root**.

The root of an equation indicates where the graph of the equation crosses the x-axis. A double root occurs when the graph just touches the x-axis but does not cross it.

2. **Look back at Escher's equation in the Getting Started. How can you write the solutions for the function $q(x) = x^2$ in the same way, using the axis of symmetry? Explain your reasoning.**

The graphs of three quadratic functions, $f(x)$, $h(x)$, and $g(x)$, are shown.

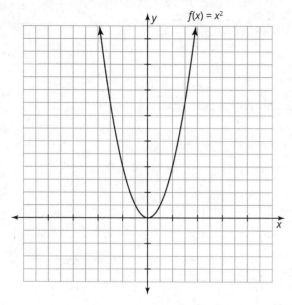

$f(x) = x^2$

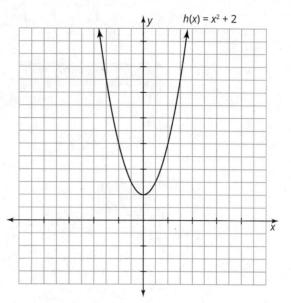

$h(x) = x^2 + 2$

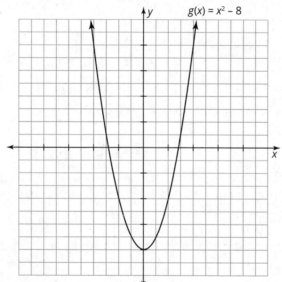

$g(x) = x^2 - 8$

3. Use the graphs to identify the solutions to each equation. Then determine the solutions algebraically and write the solutions in terms of their respective distances from the axis of symmetry.

a. $14 = x^2 + 2$

b. $x^2 = 10$

c. $-5 = x^2 - 8$

d. $19 = x^2 + 4$

e. $x^2 - 8 = 1$

f. $6 = x^2$

4. Consider the graphs of $f(x)$, $h(x)$, and $g(x)$, which function has a double root? Explain your answer.

When you are solving quadratic equations you may encounter solutions that are not perfect squares. You can either determine the approximate value of the radical or rewrite it in an equivalent radical form.

Worked Example

You can determine the approximate value of $\sqrt{75}$.

Determine the perfect square that is closest to but less than 75. Then determine the perfect square that is closest to but greater than 75.

$$64 \leq 75 \leq 81$$

Determine the square roots of the perfect squares.

$$\sqrt{64} = 8 \qquad \sqrt{75} = ? \qquad \sqrt{81} = 9$$

Now that you know that $\sqrt{75}$ is between 8 and 9, you can test the squares of numbers between 8 and 9.

$$8.6^2 = 73.96 \qquad 8.7^2 = 75.69$$

Since 75 is closer to 75.69 than 73.96, 8.7 is the approximate square root of $\sqrt{75}$.

Ask yourself:

Can you name all the perfect squares from 1^2 through 15^2?

Think about:

How could listing the prime factors of a radical expression help to extract square roots of perfect squares?

Worked Example

You can use prime factors to rewrite $\sqrt{75}$ in an equivalent radical form.
First, rewrite the product of 75 to include any perfect square factors, and then extract the square roots of those perfect squares.

$$\begin{aligned}
\sqrt{75} &= \sqrt{3 \cdot 5 \cdot 5} \\
&= \sqrt{3 \cdot 5^2} \\
&= \sqrt{3} \cdot \sqrt{5^2} \\
&= 5\sqrt{3}
\end{aligned}$$

5. **Estimate the value of each radical expression. Then, rewrite each radical by extracting all perfect squares, if possible.**

   a. $\sqrt{20}$

   b. $\sqrt{26}$

   c. $\sqrt{18}$

   d. $\sqrt{116}$

6. **Rewrite your answers from Question 3 by extracting perfect squares, if possible. Verify your rewritten answers using the graphs in Question 3.**

ACTIVITY

2.2

Solutions from Standard Form to Factored Form

Think about:

Do you recognize the form of this quadratic?

Recall that a quadratic function written in factored form is in the form $f(x) = a(x - r_1)(x - r_2)$, where $a \neq 0$. In factored form, r_1 and r_2 represent the x-intercepts of the graph of the function.

1. **Determine the zeros of the function $z(x) = x^2 - 16$. Then, write the function in factored form.**

The function $z(x)$ in factored form is a quadratic function made up of two linear factors. Let's analyze the linear factors as separate linear functions, $g(x)$ and $h(x)$. Therefore $z(x) = g(x) \cdot h(x)$.

2. **Complete the table by writing the algebraic expressions to represent $g(x)$ and $h(x)$, and then determine the output values for the two linear factors and the quadratic product. Finally, sketch a graph of $z(x)$.**

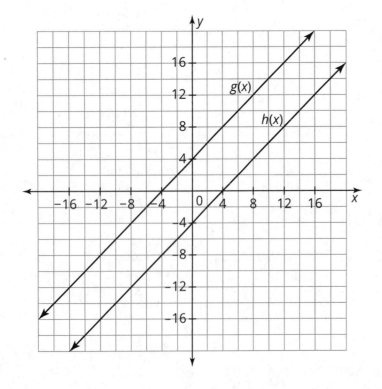

x	$g(x)$	$h(x)$	$z(x)$
			$x^2 - 16$
-4			
-2			
0			
2			
4			

The **Zero Product Property** states that if the product of two or more factors is equal to zero, then at least one factor must be equal to zero.

Worked Example

You can use the Zero Product Property to identify the zeros of a function when the function is written in factored form.

$0 = x^2 - 16$

$0 = (x + 4)(x - 4)$ Rewrite the quadratic as linear factors.

$x - 4 = 0$ and $x + 4 = 0$ Apply the Zero Product Property.

     $x = 4$ $x = -4$ Solve each equation for x.

---

3. **Explain how the zeros of the linear function factors are related to the zeros of the quadratic function product.**

The function $z(x) = x^2 - 16$ has an a-value of 1 and a b-value of 0. You can use a similar strategy to determine the zeros of a function when the leading coefficient is not 1, but the b-value is still 0.

Worked Example

You can determine the zeros of the function $f(x) = 9x^2 - 1$ by setting $f(x) = 0$ and using the Properties of Equality to solve for x.

$$9x^2 - 1 = 0$$

$$9x^2 = 1$$

$$x^2 = \frac{1}{9}$$

$$x = \pm\frac{1}{3}$$

You can then use the leading coefficient of 9 and the zeros at $\frac{1}{3}$ and $-\frac{1}{3}$ to rewrite the quadratic function in factored form.

$$f(x) = 9\left(x - \frac{1}{3}\right)\left(x + \frac{1}{3}\right)$$

---

4. **Consider the worked example.**

   a. **Explain why $\sqrt{\frac{1}{9}} = \pm\frac{1}{3}$.**

b. Use graphing technology to verify that
$9x^2 - 1 = 9\left(x - \frac{1}{3}\right)\left(x + \frac{1}{3}\right)$. How can you tell from
the graph that the two equations are equivalent?

Three students tried to rewrite the quadratic function
$f(x) = 9\left(x - \frac{1}{3}\right)\left(x + \frac{1}{3}\right)$ as two linear factors using what they
know about the difference of two squares.

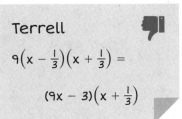

Terrell 👎

$9\left(x - \frac{1}{3}\right)\left(x + \frac{1}{3}\right) =$

$(9x - 3)\left(x + \frac{1}{3}\right)$

Jackson 👎

$9\left(x - \frac{1}{3}\right)\left(x + \frac{1}{3}\right) =$

$(4.5x - 1.5)(4.5x + 1.5)$

Raychelle 👍

$9\left(x - \frac{1}{3}\right)\left(x + \frac{1}{3}\right) =$

$(3x - 1)(3x + 1)$

Ask yourself:

Are these expressions still in factored form?

5. Explain why Terrell and Jackson are incorrect and why Raychelle is correct.

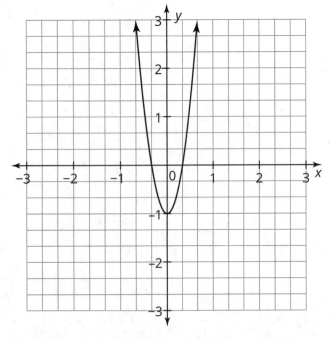

6. The graph of $f(x) = 9x^2 - 1$ is shown.

a. Use Raychelle's function, $f(x) = (3x - 1)(3x + 1)$, to sketch a graph of the linear factors. Then use graphing technology to verify that $9x^2 - 1 = (3x - 1)(3x + 1)$.

b. How do the zeros of the function relate to its two linear factors?

7. For each function:

- Sketch a graph. Label the axis of symmetry and the vertex.
- Use the Properties of Equality to identify the zeros, and then write the zeros in terms of their respective distances from the line of symmetry.
- Use what you know about the difference of two squares to rewrite each quadratic as the product of two linear factors. Then use the Zero Product Property to verify the values of x, when $f(x) = 0$.
- Use graphing technology to verify that the product of the two linear factors is equivalent to the given function.

a. $f(x) = 4x^2 - 9$

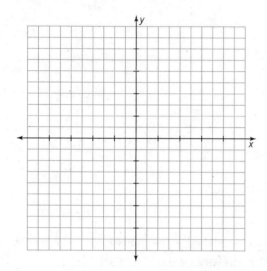

b. $f(x) = x^2 - 2$

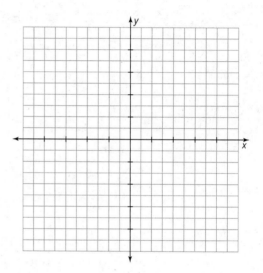

c. $f(x) = 25x^2 - 1$

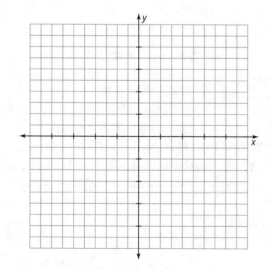

TALK the TALK

The Difference of Squares

In this lesson you determined the zeros of quadratics written in the form $f(x) = ax^2 - c$.

1. Solve each equation.

  a. $x^2 - 25 = 0$ b. $4x^2 - 1 = 0$

  c. $9x^2 - 2 = 0$ d. $x^2 - 80 = 0$

2. Rewrite each quadratic function as two linear factors using what you know about the difference of two squares.

  a. $f(x) = x^2 - 49$ b. $f(x) = \frac{4}{9}x^2 - 1$

  c. $f(x) = 16x^2 - 10$ d. $f(x) = x^2 + 9$

3. Explain how to write any function of the form $f(x) = ax^2 - c$, where a and c are any real numbers, as two linear factors using what you know about the difference of two squares.

Assignment

Write

Complete each definition.

1. The Zero Product Property states that if the product of two or more factors is equal to _____, then at least one factor must be equal to _____.

2. Every positive number has both a _____ square root and a _____ square root.

3. The function $f(x) = x^2$ has a _____ at (0, 0).

Remember

Any quadratic function of the form $f(x) = ax^2 - d$ can be rewritten as two linear factors in the form $(\sqrt{ax} - \sqrt{d})(\sqrt{ax} + \sqrt{d})$.

Practice

1. Determine the solutions for each equation. Identify the solutions on one of the graphs. Then, write the solutions in terms of their respective differences from the axis of symmetry.

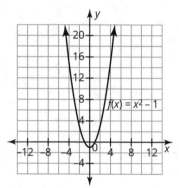 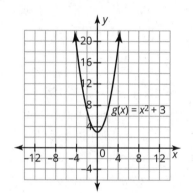 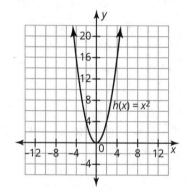

a. $8 = x^2 + 3$

b. $7 = x^2$

c. $2 = x^2 - 1$

d. $x^2 = 11$

e. $x^2 + 9 = 13$

f. $14 = x^2 - 1$

2. Estimate the value of each radical expression. Then, rewrite each radical by extracting all perfect squares, if possible.

a. $\sqrt{21}$

b. $\sqrt{80}$

c. $\sqrt{63}$

d. $\sqrt{32}$

e. $\sqrt{98}$

f. $\sqrt{192}$

3. Rewrite each quadratic function as two linear factors using what you know about the difference of two squares.

a. $f(x) = 9x^2 - 16$

b. $f(x) = x^2 - 8$

c. $f(x) = 36x^2 - 1$

d. $f(x) = 25x^2 - 12$

Stretch

1. Consider the graph of the function $f(x) = x^2 + 3x - 5$.

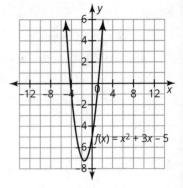

   a. Determine the solutions for the equation $x^2 + 3x - 5 = 5$.
      Identify the solutions on the graph.

   b. Rewrite the equation from part (a) so that the right side of the
      equation is 0. What do the solutions from part (a) represent in this
      new equation?

   c. Use your solutions from part (a) to write a product of two binomials,
      $(x - a)(x - b)$, where a and b are the solutions from part (a). How does
      this relate to the left side of the equation in part (b)?

Review

1. Identify the axis of symmetry of the graph of $f(x) = -5(x - 3)(x + 12)$.

2. Write a quadratic function in factored form to represent a parabola that opens downward
   and has zeros at $(-6, 0)$ and $(-2, 0)$.

3. Determine each product. Show your work.

   a. $(2x - 3)(4x + 7)$ b. $(3x + 5)\left(-\frac{1}{2}x + 16\right)$.

4. Write the equation of the function, $g(x)$, whose graph transforms the graph $f(x) = x^2 + 1$ by reflecting
   it across the x-axis, shifting it up 6 units, and shifting it to the left 4 units.

5. Graph the function, $g(x)$, whose graph transforms the graph $f(x) = (x - 4)^2$ by vertically stretching it
   by a factor of 2, reflecting it across the x-axis, and moving it to the left 3 units.

3

Transforming Solutions

Solutions to Quadratic Equations in Vertex Form

Warm Up

Describe the transformations to the graph of the basic function $f(x) = x^2$ given each equation.

1. $y = (x - 4)^2$

2. $y = \frac{1}{2}(x + 1)^2$

3. $y = -(10 + x)^2 - 3$

4. $y = (8 + x)^2 + 1$

Learning Goals

- Identify solutions to and roots of quadratic equations given in the form $f(x) = (x - c)^2$.
- Identify solutions to and roots of quadratic equations given in the form $f(x) = a(x - c)^2$.
- Identify solutions to and roots of quadratic equations given in the form $f(x) = a(x - c)^2 + d$.
- Identify zeros of quadratic functions written in vertex form.

You have explored transformations of quadratic functions and vertex form. How can you use vertex form and transformations to determine solutions to quadratic equations?

Slide, Slide, Slippity Slide

The coordinate plane shows the graph of the function $f(x) = (x - 1)^2$.

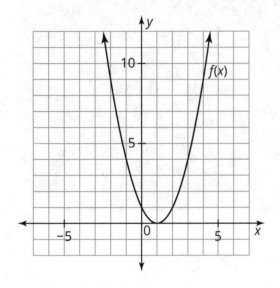

1. **Describe the transformation applied to the basic function $f(x) = x^2$ that produces the graph of this function.**

Lindsay and Casey determined the zeros of the function $f(x) = (x - 1)^2$ algebraically in different ways.

Lindsay 👍

$$0 = (x - 1)^2$$

$$0 = (x - 1)(x - 1)$$

The Zero Product Property says that one or both of the factors is equal to 0.

So, $x = 1$.

The equation has a double root at $x = 1$.

Casey 👍

$$(x - 1)^2 = 0$$

$$\sqrt{(x - 1)^2} = \sqrt{0}$$

$$\pm(x - 1) = 0$$

$+(x - 1) = 0$	$-(x - 1) = 0$
$x = 1$	$-x + 1 = 0$
	$-x = -1$
	$x = 1$

The only unique solution for $y = 0$ is $x = 1$.

2. **How can you use Lindsay's or Casey's work to write solutions to the function in terms of their respective distances from the axis of symmetry?**

You have used graphs to solve equations. In this activity, you will use the graph of a quadratic equation to determine its solutions.

Remember:

Solving $(x - 1)^2 = 9$ on a graph means locating where $y = (x - 1)^2$ intersects with $y = 9$.

Worked Example

Consider the equation $(x - 1)^2 = 9$.
You can use the Properties of Equality to determine the solutions to an equation in this form.
First take the square root of both sides of the equation and then isolate x.

$$(x - 1)^2 = 9$$
$$\sqrt{(x - 1)^2} = \sqrt{9}$$
$$x - 1 = \pm 3$$
$$x = 1 \pm 3$$

---

1. **Consider the graph of $y = (x - 1)^2$ in the Getting Started.**

   a. **Graph the equation $y = 9$ on the same graph.**

   b. **Show the solutions on the graph. Interpret the solutions 1 ± 3 in terms of the axis of symmetry and the points on the parabola $y = (x - 1)^2$.**

   c. **What are the solutions to the equation $(x - 1)^2 = 9$?**

2. For each equation, show the solutions on the graph and interpret the solutions in terms of the axis of symmetry and the points on the parabola. Then write the solutions.

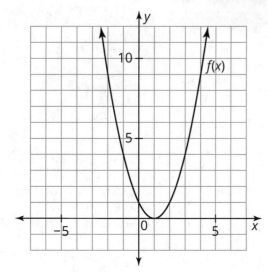

a. $(x - 1)^2 = 4$

b. $(x - 1)^2 = 5$

3. Determine the exact and approximate solutions for each of the given equations.

a. $(r + 8)^2 = 83$

b. $(17 - d)^2 = 55$

You have seen how to solve an equation for a quadratic function in the form $f(x) = (x - c)^2$, which represents a horizontal translation of the function. In this activity, you will consider quadratic equations with an additional vertical dilation. First, let's start with just a horizontal translation.

1. **Consider the function $f(x) = (x - 5)^2$.**

   a. **Determine the solutions to $0 = (x - 5)^2$. Solve algebraically and label the solution on the graph.**

   b. **Interpret your solutions in terms of the axis of symmetry and the parabola $y = (x - 5)^2$.**

   c. **Describe the zeros of this function.**

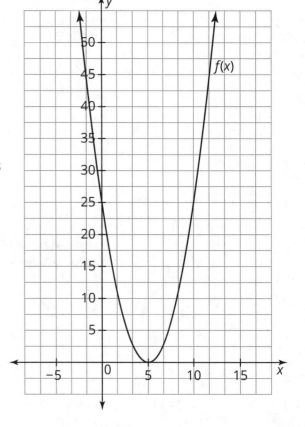

Now let's add a dilation factor.

2. **Consider the function $g(x) = 2(x - 5)^2$.**

   a. **Write $g(x)$ in terms of $f(x)$ and describe the transformation.**

   b. **Sketch a graph on the same coordinate plane as $f(x)$.**

   c. **How have the zeros changed from $f(x)$ to $g(x)$?**

3. **Parker formulated a conjecture about how the solutions of the transformed quadratic equation change from the original equation.**

The solutions of the original function are $x = 5 \pm \sqrt{y}$, so the solutions to the transformed equation will be $x = 5 \pm 2\sqrt{y}$.

Is Parker correct? If so, explain why. If not, describe the correct solutions for the transformed quadratic equation.

4. **Make a conjecture. How does changing the sign of the a-value affect the solutions to the quadratic equations in this form?**

5. **Solve each quadratic equation. Give both exact and approximate solutions.**

   a. $(x - 4)^2 = 2$

   b. $2(x - 1)^2 = 18$

   c. $-2(x - 1)^2 = -18$

   d. $4(x + 5)^2 = 21$

   e. $-\frac{1}{2}(x + 8)^2 = -32$

   f. $\frac{2}{3}(12 - x)^2 = 1$

Solutions for Vertical Translations

You have determined solutions to quadratic equations, given an equation in the form $f(x) = a(x - c)^2$. How can you solve a quadratic equation that also includes a vertical translation in the form $f(x) = a(x - c)^2 + d$?

The graph of $g(x) = 2(x - 5)^2$ is shown. You know that the solution to the equation $0 = 2(x - 5)^2$ is $x = 5$.

Remember:

A quadratic function in vertex form is written $f(x) = a(x - k)^2 + h$.

1. Consider the function $h(x) = 2(x - 5)^2 - 1$.

   a. Write $h(x)$ in terms of $g(x)$ and describe the transformation.

   b. Sketch a graph of $h(x)$ on the same coordinate plane as $g(x)$.

2. Consider the equation $0 = 2(x - 5)^2 - 1$.

   a. Determine the solution algebraically and label the solution on the graph.

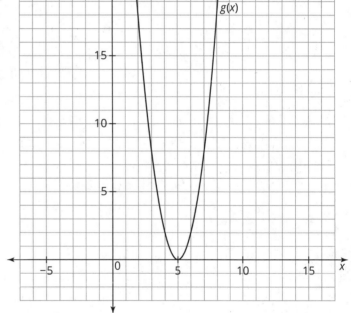

   b. Interpret the solutions in terms of the axis of symmetry and the parabola $y = 2(x - 5)^2 - 1$.

   c. Describe the zeros of this function.

Now, let's investigate the effect of an equation in the form $f(x) = a(x - c)^2 + d$, where $a > 0$ and $d > 0$. Consider the function $j(x) = 2(x - 5)^2 + 1$ graphed as shown.

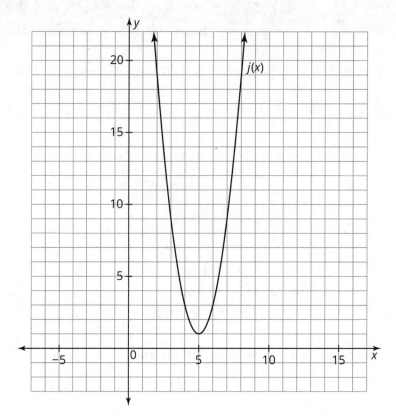

Notice the graph of $j(x)$ does not cross the x-axis, which means there are no real zeros for this function.

3. **Solve $0 = 2(x - 5)^2 + 1$ algebraically to show that x is not a real number.**

While there are no real zeros in this function, there is another type of zero you will learn about later in this topic.

4. **Sketch a graph of each quadratic function. Determine the types of zeros of each function. Solve algebraically and interpret on the graph in terms of the axis of symmetry and the points on the parabola.**

> A quadratic function can have 1 unique real zero, 2 real zeros, or no real zeros.

a. $f(x) = -3(x - 2)^2 + 4$

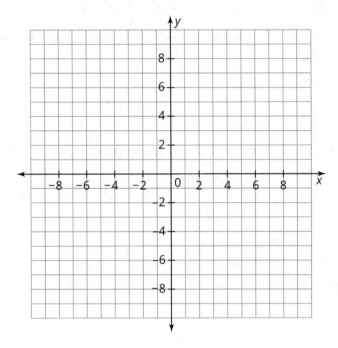

b. $f(x) = \frac{1}{4}(x + 5)^2 + 2$

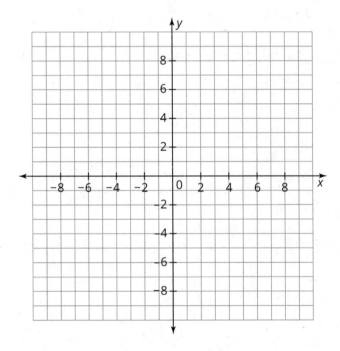

TALK the TALK

Spell It Out

1. Describe the solution of any quadratic equation in the form $(x - c)^2 = 0$.

2. Describe the solution of any quadratic equation in the form $(x - c)^2 + d = 0$.

3. Describe the solution of any quadratic equation in the form $a(x - c)^2 + d = 0$.

4. Write an equation and sketch a graph that shows each number of zeros.

   a. 1 unique real zero

   b. 2 real zeros

   c. no real zeros

Write

Describe the number of possible real zeros for any quadratic function.

Remember

The solutions to a quadratic equation can be represented as the axis of symmetry plus or minus its distance to the parabola.

Practice

1. Sketch a graph of each quadratic function. Determine the zeros of each function and write each in terms of the axis of symmetry and its distance to the parabola.

   a. $f(x) = (x - 3)^2$

   b. $f(x) = (x + 5)^2$

   c. $f(x) = \left(x - \frac{1}{2}\right)^2$

   d. $f(x) = (x - 6)^2$

   e. $f(x) = \left(x + \frac{15}{7}\right)^2$

   f. $f(x) = (x + 7)^2$

2. Sketch a graph of each quadratic function. Determine the zeros of each function and write in terms of the axis of symmetry and its distance to the parabola.

   a. $f(x) = 2(x - 1)^2 - 1$

   b. $f(x) = \frac{1}{2}(x + 2)^2 - 5$

   c. $f(x) = 4\left(x + \frac{1}{3}\right)^2 - 1$

   d. $f(x) = -3(x - 6)^2$

   e. $f(x) = \frac{3}{4}(x + 5)^2 - \frac{2}{3}$

   f. $f(x) = (x - 4)^2 - 2$

Stretch

A quadratic function has zeros at $x = -2 \pm \sqrt{15}$. Write the function in general form. Show your work.

Review

1. Use the given characteristics to write a function $R(x)$ in vertex form. Then, sketch the graph of $R(x)$ and the basic function $f(x) = x^2$ on a coordinate plane.

   a. The function has an absolute maximum, is vertically dilated by a factor of $\frac{1}{3}$, and is translated 8 units down and 4 units to the left.

   b. The function has an absolute minimum, is vertically dilated by a factor of 4, and is translated 2 units up and 6 units to the right.

2. Estimate the value of the radical expression $\sqrt{54}$. Then, rewrite the radical by extracting all perfect squares, if possible.

3. Rewrite the quadratic function, $f(x) = 16x^2 - 3$, as the product of linear factors.

4. Identify the form of each quadratic equation. Then identify what characteristic of the function can be determined by the structure of the equation.

   a. $y = (x - 7)(x + 5)$

   b. $y = -3(x + 1)^2 - 4$

The Missing Link

Factoring and Completing the Square

Warm Up

Use the Distribute Property to determine each product.

1. $(x + 1)(x + 2)$

2. $(x + 4)(x - 5)$

3. $(2x - 3)(x - 4)$

4. $(x + 2)^2$

Learning Goals

- Factor out the greatest common factor (GCF) of polynomials.
- Rewrite quadratic equations of the form $x^2 + bx$ in vertex form by completing the square.
- Factor quadratic trinomials to determine the roots of quadratic equations and to rewrite quadratic functions in forms that reveal different key characteristics.
- Demonstrate the reasoning behind the method of completing the square and use the method to determine the roots of quadratic equations of the form $ax^2 + bx + c$.

Key Term

- completing the square

You have solved many different quadratic equations written as binomials. How can you solve trinomial quadratic equations?

LOL the GCF Again

In previous lessons, you multiplied two linear expressions to determine a quadratic expression. You have also rewritten quadratics in factored form.

You may remember that one way to factor an expression is to factor out the greatest common factor.

Worked Example

Consider the polynomial $3x + 15$. You can factor out the greatest common factor of the two terms, 3.

$$3x + 15 = 3x + 3(5)$$

$$= 3(x + 5)$$

$$3x + 15 = 3(x + 5)$$

---

1. **Factor out the greatest common factor for each polynomial, if possible.**

   a. $4x + 12$ b. $x^2 - 5x$

   c. $3x^2 - 9x - 3$ d. $-x - 7$

   e. $2x - 11$ f. $5x^2 - 10x + 5$

Factoring Trinomials

You have used special products—the difference of two squares and perfect square trinomials—to rewrite trinomials in factored form. In this activity, you will rewrite trinomials that are not special products in factored form.

1. **Consider the equation $y = x^2 + 10x + 16$.**

   a. **Use the graph to identify the roots of the equation.**

   b. **Rewrite the original equation in factored form.**

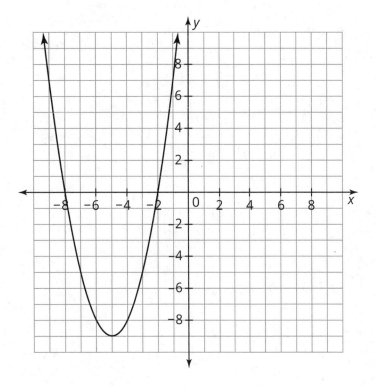

Let's consider a strategy to factor a trinomial without graphing.

You can use a multiplication table to factor trinomials.

> **Worked Example**
>
> Factor the trinomial $x^2 + 10x + 16$.
>
> Start by writing the leading term (x^2) and the constant term (16) in the table.
>
> | $\cdot$ | | |
> |---|---|---|
> | | x^2 | |
> | | | 16 |
>
> Determine the two factors of the leading term and write them in the table.
>
> | $\cdot$ | x | |
> |---|---|---|
> | x | x^2 | |
> | | | 16 |
>
> Determine the factor pairs of the constant term. The factors of 16 are (1)(16), (2)(8), and (4)(4). Experiment with factors of the constant term to determine the pair whose sum is the coefficient of the middle term, 10.
>
> | $\cdot$ | x | 8 |
> |---|---|---|
> | x | x^2 | $8x$ |
> | 2 | $2x$ | 16 |
>
> The sum of $2x$ and $8x$ is $10x$.
> So, $x^2 + 10x + 16 = (x + 2)(x + 8)$.

2. **Explain why the other factor pairs for $c = 16$ do not work.**

3. Use the worked example to factor each trinomial.

a. $x^2 + 17x + 16$

·		
	x^2	
		16

b. $x^2 + 6x - 16$

·		
	x^2	
		−16

c. $x^2 - 6x - 16$

·		
	x^2	
		−16

4. Factor each trinomial.

a. $x^2 + 5x - 24$

b. $x^2 - 3x - 28$

5. Consider the two examples shown.

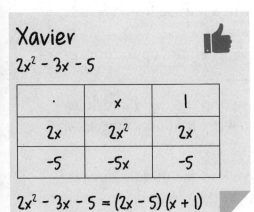

Xavier 👍
$2x^2 - 3x - 5$

·	x	1
2x	$2x^2$	2x
-5	-5x	-5

$2x^2 - 3x - 5 = (2x - 5)(x + 1)$

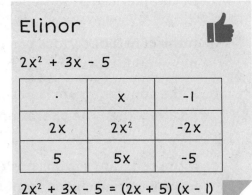

Elinor 👍
$2x^2 + 3x - 5$

·	x	-1
2x	$2x^2$	-2x
5	5x	-5

$2x^2 + 3x - 5 = (2x + 5)(x - 1)$

a. Compare the two given trinomials. What is the same and what is different about the values of a, b, and c?

Remember:

The general form of a quadratic equation is a trinomial in the form $y = ax^2 + bx + c$.

b. Compare the factored form of each trinomial. What do you notice?

6. Choose from the list to write the correct factored form for each trinomial.

a. $x^2 + 5x + 4 = $ _____   • $(x + 1)(x - 4)$
   $x^2 - 5x + 4 = $ _____   • $(x + 1)(x + 4)$
   $x^2 + 3x - 4 = $ _____   • $(x - 1)(x + 4)$
   $x^2 - 3x - 4 = $ _____   • $(x - 1)(x - 4)$

b. $2x^2 + 7x + 3 = $ _____   • $(2x - 1)(x - 3)$
   $2x^2 - 7x + 3 = $ _____   • $(2x - 1)(x + 3)$
   $2x^2 + 5x - 3 = $ _____   • $(2x + 1)(x + 3)$
   $2x^2 - 5x - 3 = $ _____   • $(2x + 1)(x - 3)$

c. $x^2 + 7x + 10 = $ _____   • $(x - 2)(x + 5)$
   $x^2 - 7x + 10 = $ _____   • $(x + 2)(x + 5)$
   $x^2 + 3x - 10 = $ _____   • $(x - 2)(x - 5)$
   $x^2 - 3x - 10 = $ _____   • $(x + 2)(x - 5)$

7. Analyze the signs of each quadratic expression written in general form and the operations in the binomial factors in Question 6. Then complete each sentence with a phrase from the box.

| the same |
| different |
| both positive |
| both negative |
| one positive and one negative |

a. If the constant term is positive, then the operations in the binomial factors are _____.

b. If the constant term is positive and the middle term is positive, then the operations in the binomial factors are

   _____.

c. If the constant term is positive and the middle term is negative, then the operations in the binomial factors are

   _____.

d. If the constant term is negative, then the operations in the binomial factors are _____.

e. If the constant term is negative and the middle term is positive, then the operations in the binomial factors are

   _____.

f. If the constant term is negative and the middle term is negative, then the operations in the binomial factors are

   _____.

8. **Factor each quadratic expression.**

   a. $x^2 + 8x + 15 =$ _____

   $x^2 - 8x + 15 =$ _____

   $x^2 + 2x - 15 =$ _____

   $x^2 - 2x - 15 =$ _____

   b. $x^2 + 10x + 24 =$ _____

   $x^2 - 10x + 24 =$ _____

   $x^2 + 2x - 24 =$ _____

   $x^2 - 2x - 24 =$ _____

9. **Grace, Elaine, and Maggie were asked to factor the trinomial $15 + 2x - x^2$.**

Grace	Elaine	Maggie
$15 + 2x - x^2$	$15 + 2x - x^2$	$15 + 2x - x^2$
$(5 - x)(3 + x)$	$(5 - x)(3 + x)$	$-x^2 + 2x + 15$
	$(x - 5)(x + 3)$	$-(x^2 - 2x - 15)$
		$-(x - 5)(x + 3)$

   Who's correct? Explain how that student(s) determined the factors. For the student(s) who is not correct, state why and make the correction.

Marilynn and Jake were working together to factor the trinomial $4x^2 + 22x + 24$. They first noticed that there was a greatest common factor and rewrote the trinomial as

$$2(2x^2 + 11x + 12).$$

Next, they considered the factor pairs for $2x^2$ and the factor pairs for 12.

$2x^2$: $(2x)(x)$
12: (1)(12)
   (2)(6)
   (3)(4)

Marilynn listed out all the possible combinations.

$2(2x + 1)(x + 12)$
$2(2x + 12)(x + 1)$

$2(2x + 2)(x + 6)$
$2(2x + 6)(x + 2)$

$2(2x + 3)(x + 4)$
$2(2x + 4)(x + 3)$

Jake immediately eliminated four out of the six possible combinations because the terms of one of the linear expressions contained common factors.

$2(2x + 1)(x + 12)$
~~$2(2x + 12)(x + 1)$~~

~~$2(2x + 2)(x + 6)$~~
~~$2(2x + 6)(x + 2)$~~

$2(2x + 3)(x + 4)$
~~$2(2x + 4)(x + 3)$~~

10. **Explain Jake's reasoning. Then circle the correct factored form of $4x^2 + 22x + 24$.**

ACTIVITY 4.2

Solving Quadratic Equations by Factoring

You have used Properties of Equality to solve equations in the forms shown.

$$y = x^2 + d$$
$$y = (x - c)^2$$
$$y = a(x - c)^2$$
$$y = a(x - c)^2 + d$$

Let's consider strategies to solve quadratics in the form $y = ax^2 + bx + c$ using the factoring strategies you just learned.

Worked Example

You can calculate the roots for the quadratic equation $x^2 - 4x = -3$.

$$x^2 - 4x = -3$$
$$x^2 - 4x + 3 = -3 + 3$$
$$x^2 - 4x + 3 = 0$$
$$(x - 3)(x - 1) = 0$$

$(x - 3) = 0$	and	$(x - 1) = 0$
$x - 3 + 3 = 0 + 3$	and	$x - 1 + 1 = 0 + 1$
$x = 3$	and	$x = 1$

Remember:

The Zero Product Property states that if the product of two or more factors is equal to zero, then at least one factor must be equal to zero.

1. **Consider the worked example. Why is 3 added to both sides in the first step?**

Think about:

What is the connection between the Worked Example and determining the roots from factored form, $y = a(x - r_1)(x - r_2)$?

2. **Determine each student's error and then solve each equation correctly.**

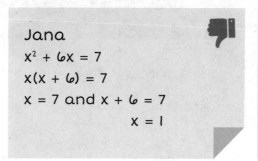

Jana

$x^2 + 6x = 7$

$x(x + 6) = 7$

$x = 7$ and $x + 6 = 7$

$x = 1$

Reese

$x^2 + 5x + 6 = 6$

$(x + 2)(x + 3) = 6$

$x + 2 = 6$ and $x + 3 = 6$

$x = 4$ and $x = 3$

3. **Use factoring to solve each quadratic equation, if possible.**

a. $x^2 - 8x + 12 = 0$

b. $x^2 - 5x - 24 = 0$

c. $x^2 + 10x - 75 = 0$

d. $x^2 - 11x = 0$

e. $x^2 + 8x = -7$

f. $x^2 - 5x = 13x - 81$

g. $\frac{2}{3}x^2 - \frac{5}{6}x = 0$

h. $f(x) = x^2 + 10x + 12$

Think about:

What efficiency strategies did you use to solve linear equations with fractional coefficients?

4. Describe the different strategies and reasoning that Deon and Kayla used to solve $4x^2 - 25 = 0$.

Deon 👍

$4x^2 - 25 = 0$

$4x^2 = 25$

$x^2 = \frac{25}{4}$

$x = \pm\sqrt{\frac{25}{4}}$

$x = \pm\frac{5}{2}$

Kayla 👍

$4x^2 - 25 = 0$

$(2x - 5)(2x + 5) = 0$

$2x - 5 = 0$ and $2x + 5 = 0$

$2x = 5 \qquad\qquad 2x = -5$

$x = \frac{5}{2}$ and $\qquad x = -\frac{5}{2}$

If you cannot factor a quadratic function, does that mean it does not have zeros?

1. **Consider the quadratic equation $y = x^2 + 10x + 12$.**
    Use technology to graph the equation and then sketch it on the coordinate plane. Does this function have zeros? Explain your reasoning.

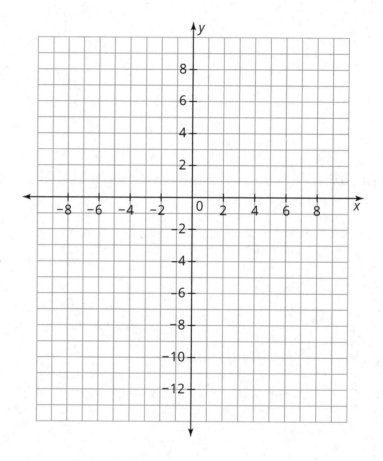

The quadratic function you graphed has zeros but cannot be factored, so you must consider another method for calculating its zeros. You can use your understanding of the relationship among the coefficients of a perfect square trinomial to construct a procedure to solve any quadratic equation.

Previously, you factored trinomials of the form $a^2 + 2ab + b^2$ as the perfect square $(a + b)^2$. This knowledge can help you develop a procedure to solve any quadratic equation.

2. The expression $x^2 + 10x$ can be represented geometrically as shown. Write the area of each rectangle within the diagram.

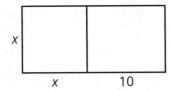

3. This figure can now be modified into the shape of a square by splitting the second rectangle in half and rearranging the pieces.

   a. Complete the side length labels for the split rectangle and write the area of each piece within the diagram.

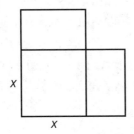

Ask yourself:

Why do you divide the second rectangle in half?

   b. Do the two figures represent the same expression? Explain your reasoning.

c. Complete the figure to form a square. Label the area of the piece you added.

d. Add the term representing the additional area to the original expression. What is the new expression?

e. Factor the new expression.

The process you just worked through is a method known as *completing the square*. **Completing the square** is a process for writing a quadratic expression in vertex form which then allows you to solve for the zeros.

4. Draw a model to complete the square for each expression. Then factor the resulting trinomial.

a. $x^2 + 8x$

b. $x^2 + 5x$

5. Analyze your work in Question 4.

a. Explain how to complete the square on an expression of the
form $x^2 + bx$ where b is an integer.

b. Describe how the coefficient of the middle term, b, is related
to the constant term, c, in each trinomial you wrote in
Question 4.

6. Use the descriptions you provided in Question 5 to determine
the unknown second or third term to make each expression
a perfect square trinomial. Then write the expression as a
binomial squared.

a. $x^2 - 8x +$ _____ = _____

b. $x^2 + 5x +$ _____ = _____

c. $x^2 -$ _____ $+ 100 =$ _____

d. $x^2 +$ _____ $+ 144 =$ _____

So far, you have considered quadratic equations that can be rewritten by completing the square or factoring a trinomial.

You can use the completing the square method to determine the roots of a quadratic equation that cannot be factored.

Worked Example

Determine the roots of the equation $x^2 + 10x + 12 = 0$.

Isolate $x^2 - 4x$. You can complete the square and rewrite this as a perfect square trinomial.

$$x^2 + 10x + 12 - 12 = 0 - 12$$
$$x^2 + 10x = -12$$

Determine the constant term that would complete the square.
Add this term to both sides of the equation.

$$x^2 + 10x + \underline{} = -12 + \underline{}$$
$$x^2 + 10x + 25 = -12 + 25$$
$$x^2 + 10x + 25 = 13$$

Factor the left side of the equation.

$$(x + 5)^2 = 13$$

Determine the square root of each side of the equation.

$$\sqrt{(x + 5)^2} = \pm\sqrt{13}$$
$$x + 5 = \pm\sqrt{13}$$

Set the factor of the perfect square trinomial equal to each square root of the constant.
Solve for x.

$$x + 5 = \sqrt{13} \quad \text{and } x + 5 = -\sqrt{13}$$
$$x = -5 + \sqrt{13} \text{ and } \quad x = -5 - \sqrt{13}$$
$$x \approx -1.39 \quad \text{and} \quad x \approx -8.61$$

The roots are approximately 3.41 and 0.59.

Ask

yourself:

How was equality of the equation maintained through the completing the square process?

1. Consider the equation $y = x^2 + 8x + 10$.

   a. Use this method to determine the roots of the equation. Show your work.

   b. Use your work to label the zeros on the graph of the function $f(x) = x^2 + 8x + 10$.

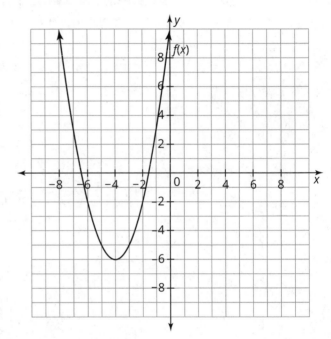

2. Determine the roots of each equation by completing the square.

   a. $x^2 - 6x + 4 = 0$

   b. $x^2 - 12x + 6 = 0$

Rewriting a Quadratic in Vertex Form

You can identify the axis of symmetry and the vertex of any quadratic function written in general form by completing the square.

Worked Example

Consider the equation $y = ax^2 + bx + c$.

Step 1: $\qquad y - c = ax^2 + bx$

Step 2: $\qquad y - c = a\left(x^2 + \frac{b}{a}x\right)$

Step 3: $\quad y - c + a\left(\frac{b}{2a}\right)^2 = a\left(x^2 + \frac{b}{a}x + \left(\frac{b}{2a}\right)^2\right)$

Step 4: $\qquad y - c + \frac{b^2}{4a} = a\left(x + \frac{b}{2a}\right)^2$

Step 5: $\qquad y = a\left(x + \frac{b}{2a}\right)^2 + \left(c - \frac{b^2}{4a}\right)$

> Notice that the *a*-value was factored out before completing the square!

1. **Explain why $a\left(\frac{b}{2a}\right)^2$ was added to the left side of the equation in Step 3.**

2. **Given a quadratic function in the form $y = ax^2 + bx + c$:**

   a. **Identify the axis of symmetry.**

   b. **Identify the location of the vertex.**

3. Rewrite each quadratic equation in vertex form. Then identify the zeros and sketch a graph of each function. Write the zeros in terms of the axis of symmetry and the parabola.

a. $y = x^2 + 8x - 9$

b. $y = 3x^2 + 2x - 1$

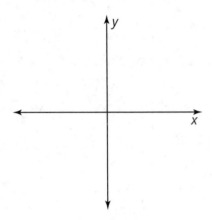

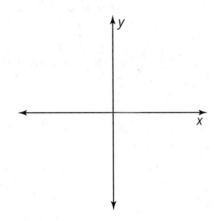

4. A ball is thrown straight up from 4 feet above the ground with a velocity of 32 feet per second. The height of the ball over time can be modeled with the function $h(t) = -16t^2 + 32t + 4$. What is the maximum height of the ball?

5. Jessie is fencing in a rectangular plot outside of her back door so that she can let her dogs out to play. She has 60 feet of fencing and only needs to place it on three sides of the rectangular plot because the fourth side will be bound by her house. What dimensions should Jesse use for the plot so that the maximum area is enclosed? What is the maximum area? Draw a diagram to support your work.

NOTES

TALK the TALK

Play It Again

1. Consider the quadratic equation $y = x^2 - 4x - 5$.

   a. Rewrite the equation in factored form and vertex form.

   b. Graph the function. Identify the vertex, x- and y-intercepts, and the axis of symmetry. Then explain how these are evident in each form of the equation.

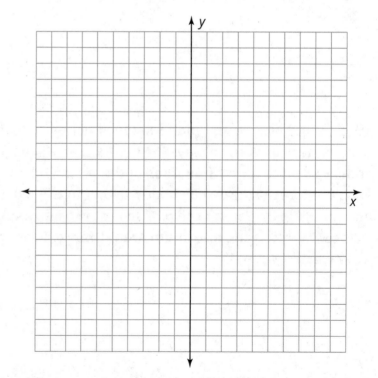

Assignment

Write

Describe the process to solve a quadratic equation by factoring.

Remember

- Completing the square is a process for writing a quadratic expression in vertex form which then allows you to solve for the zeros.
- Given a quadratic equation in the form $y = ax^2 + bx + c$, the vertex of the function is located at $x = \frac{-b}{2a}$ and $y = c - \frac{b^2}{4a}$.

Practice

1. Solve each equation.

   a. $0 = x^2 - 7x - 18$ b. $x^2 + 10x = 39$

   c. $0 = x^2 - 10x + 12$ d. $2x^2 + 4x = 0$

   e. $3x^2 - 22x + 7 = 0$

2. Determine the roots of the equation $y = x^2 + 9x + 3$. Check your solutions.

3. Consider the equation $y = 2x^2 + 10x - 8$.

   a. Graph the equation.

   b. Use the graph to estimate the solutions to the equation. Explain how you determined your answer.

   c. Two students completed the square to determine the solutions to this equation. Their work is shown. Who is correct? Explain your reasoning.

Student 1

$$y = 2x^2 + 10x - 8$$
$$2x^2 + 10x - 8 = 0$$
$$2x^2 + 10x = 8$$
$$2x^2 + 10x + 25 = 8 + 25$$
$$(2x + 5)^2 = 33$$
$$\sqrt{(2x + 5)^2} = \pm\sqrt{33}$$
$$2x + 5 = \pm\sqrt{33}$$
$$x = \frac{-5 \pm \sqrt{33}}{2}$$
$$X \approx -5.372 \text{ and } x \approx 0.372$$

Student 2

$$y = 2x^2 + 10x - 8$$
$$2x^2 + 10x - 8 = 0$$
$$\frac{2x^2 + 10x - 8}{2} = 0$$
$$x^2 + 5x = 4$$
$$x^2 + 5x + \frac{25}{4} = 4 + \frac{25}{4}$$
$$\left(x + \frac{5}{2}\right)^2 = \frac{41}{4}$$
$$\sqrt{\left(x + \frac{5}{2}\right)^2} = \pm\sqrt{\frac{41}{4}}$$
$$x + \frac{5}{2} = \pm\frac{\sqrt{41}}{2}$$
$$x = \frac{-5 \pm \sqrt{41}}{2}$$
$$x \approx -5.702 \text{ and } x \approx 0.702$$

   d. Compare the different solutions. Identify what the student who got the correct answer did that allowed him or her to correctly complete the square.

   e. Write a statement about the value of the coefficient of the x^2-term before you can complete the square.

4. Determine the roots of the equation $y = 3x^2 + 24x - 6$. Check your solutions.

5. Determine the roots and the location of the vertex of $y = x^2 + 20x + 36$. Write the zeros in terms of the axis of symmetry and the parabola.

Stretch

The function g is defined by $g(x) = x^2 - 3x - 10$. If $g(x + 3) = x^2 + bx - c$, what are the values of b and c? Show your work and justify your answer.

Review

1. For each quadratic function, determine if it has an absolute minimum or absolute maximum, if the graph opens upward or downward, and identify the y-intercept.

   a. $f(x) = 3x^2 + 6x - 72$.

   b. $f(x) = -\frac{1}{2}(x - 2)(x + 5)$.

2. Sketch a graph of each quadratic function. Determine the zeros of each function.

   a. $f(x) = (x + 6)^2$

   b. $f(x) = 3(x - \frac{9}{2})^2 - 5$

3. Write the equation of the function, $g(x)$, whose graph transforms the graph $f(x) = x^2$ by reflecting it across the x-axis, vertically compressing it by a factor of $\frac{1}{2}$, and moving it down 3 units.

4. Graph the function, $g(x)$, whose graph transforms the graph $f(x) = x^2$ by vertically stretching it by a factor of 3 and moving it up 4 units.

Ladies and Gentlemen, Please Welcome the Quadratic Formula!

The Quadratic Formula

Warm Up

A bucket of paint falls from the top of a skyscraper that is 564 feet tall.

1. Write a quadratic function to represent the height of the can over time.

2. Use technology to graph the function.

3. How many seconds will it take for the can of paint to hit the ground?

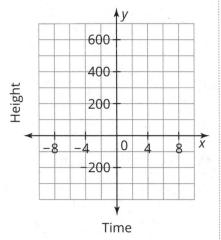

Learning Goals

- Derive the Quadratic Formula from a quadratic equation written in general form.
- Connect the Quadratic Formula to a graphical representation.
- Use the discriminant of the Quadratic Formula to determine the number of roots or zeros.
- Use the Quadratic Formula to determine roots and zeros.
- Determine whether a solution is rational or irrational when performing operations with rational and irrational numbers.
- Determine whether a function has complex solutions from a graph and from an equation in radical form.
- Understand that equations with no solutions in one number system may have solutions in a larger number system.

Key Terms

- Quadratic Formula
- discriminant
- the number i
- imaginary roots
- imaginary zeros
- complex numbers
- real part of a complex number
- imaginary part of a complex number
- imaginary numbers
- pure imaginary numbers

You know several strategies to solve quadratic equations, depending on the structure of the equation. Is there a single strategy that will work to solve any quadratic equation?

Really, They Aren't the Same

Consider each graph.

Graph A

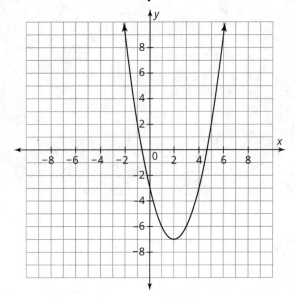

Graph B

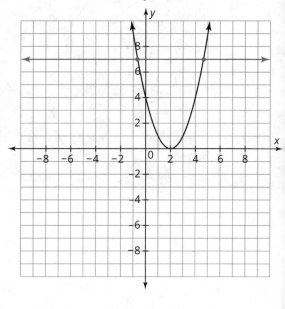

Graph C

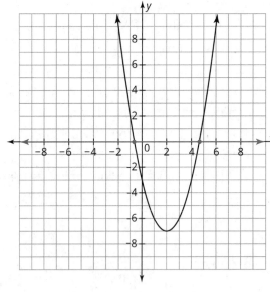

1. **Match each equation to its corresponding graph.**

   a. $(x - 2)^2 - 7 = 0$

   b. $y = (x - 2)^2 - 7$

   c. $(x - 2)^2 = 7$

2. **How do each of the graphs show solutions? How are the solutions related to the axis of symmetry?**

Introducing the Quadratic Formula

In the previous lesson, you took the general form of a quadratic equation, $y = ax^2 + bx + c$, and rewrote it in vertex form, $y = a\left(x + \frac{b}{2a}\right)^2 + \left(c - \frac{b^2}{4a}\right)$, by completing the square in order to determine the vertex and axis of symmetry for graphing purposes.

Now, let's take the general form of a quadratic equation, $y = ax^2 + bx + c$, and set $y = 0$ to determine the roots. You can complete the square in order to solve for the x-values when $y = 0$.

Worked Example

Write the equation in general form with $y = 0$.	$ax^2 + bx + c = 0$
Complete the square.	$ax^2 + bx = -c$ $x^2 + \frac{b}{a}x = -\frac{c}{a}$ $x^2 + \frac{b}{a}x + \left(\frac{b}{2a}\right)^2 = -\frac{c}{a} + \left(\frac{b}{2a}\right)^2$ $\left(x + \frac{b}{2a}\right)^2 = \left(\frac{b}{2a}\right)^2 - \frac{c}{a}$
Rewrite the right side of the equation.	$\left(x + \frac{b}{2a}\right)^2 = \frac{b^2}{4a^2} - \frac{c}{a}$ $\left(x + \frac{b}{2a}\right)^2 = \frac{b^2}{4a^2} - \frac{4ac}{4a^2}$ $\left(x + \frac{b}{2a}\right)^2 = \frac{b^2 - 4ac}{4a^2}$
Now that equation is written in the form $(x - c)^2 = q$, the square root can be taken on each side. Extract the square roots. Solve for x. These are the roots for the quadratic equation in the general form, $ax^2 + bx + c = 0$.	$x + \frac{b}{2a} = \pm\sqrt{\frac{b^2 - 4ac}{4a^2}}$ $x = -\frac{b}{2a} \pm \frac{\sqrt{b^2 - 4ac}}{2a}$ $x = \frac{-b}{2a} + \frac{\sqrt{b^2 - 4ac}}{2a} \qquad x = \frac{-b}{2a} - \frac{\sqrt{b^2 - 4ac}}{2a}$

This approach can be taken one step further and rewritten as a single fraction.

$$x = \frac{-b \pm \sqrt{b^2 - 4ac}}{2a}$$

Think about:

So really, the Quadratic Formula is just taking the general form of a quadratic equation and isolating or solving for x.

This equation is known as the *Quadratic Formula*. The **Quadratic Formula**, $x = \dfrac{-b \pm \sqrt{b^2 - 4ac}}{2a}$, can be used to calculate the solutions to any quadratic equation of the form $ax^2 + bx + c = 0$, where a, b, and c represent real numbers and $a \neq 0$.

You can use the Quadratic Formula to determine the zeros of the function $f(x) = -4x^2 - 40x - 99$.

Worked Example

Rewrite the function as an equation to be solved for x when $y = 0$.	$-4x^2 - 40x - 99 = 0$
Determine the values of a, b, and c.	$a = -4, b = -40, c = -99$
Substitute the values into the Quadratic Formula.	$x = \dfrac{-(-40) \pm \sqrt{(-40)^2 - 4(-4)(-99)}}{2(-4)}$
Perform operations to rewrite the expression.	$x = \dfrac{40 \pm \sqrt{1600 - 1584}}{-8}$ $x = \dfrac{40 \pm \sqrt{16}}{-8}$ $x = \dfrac{40 \pm 4}{-8}$ $x = \dfrac{40 + 4}{-8}$ and $x = \dfrac{40 - 4}{-8}$ $x = \dfrac{44}{-8}$ and $x = \dfrac{36}{-8}$ $x = -5.5$ and $x = -4.5$
Interpret the solution.	The zeros of the function $f(x) = -4x^2 - 40x - 99$ are $x = -5.5$ and $x = -4.5$.

The Perris Pandas baseball team has a new promotional activity to encourage fans to attend games: launching free T-shirts! They can launch a T-shirt in the air with an initial velocity of 91 feet per second from $5\frac{1}{2}$ feet off the ground (the height of the team mascot).

A T-shirt's height can be modeled with the quadratic function $h(t) = -16t^2 + 91t + 5.5$, where t is the time in seconds and $h(t)$ is the height of the launched T-shirt in feet. They want to know how long it will take for a T-shirt to land back on the ground after being launched (if no fans grab it before then!)

Ask yourself:

What would a sketch showing the height of the T-shirt over time look like?

1. **Why does it make sense to use the Quadratic Formula to solve this problem?**

2. **Use the Quadratic Formula to determine how long it will take for a T-shirt to land back on the ground after being launched.**

Ask yourself:

Do you think an exact solution or approximate solution is more appropriate for this context?

3. **Classify your solutions as rational or irrational.**

ACTIVITY 5.2 Interpreting the Quadratic Formula Graphically

You used the Quadratic Formula to solve a quadratic equation. Let's connect the Quadratic Formula to the graph. Remember, the Quadratic Formula can be written to show two roots.

$$x = \frac{-b}{2a} \pm \frac{\sqrt{b^2 - 4ac}}{2a}$$

$$x = \frac{-b}{2a} + \frac{\sqrt{b^2 - 4ac}}{2a} \qquad x = \frac{-b}{2a} - \frac{\sqrt{b^2 - 4ac}}{2a}$$

Think about:

How do the two roots relate to the graph?

How do these roots, $x = \frac{-b}{2a} + \frac{\sqrt{b^2 - 4ac}}{2a}$ and $x = \frac{-b}{2a} - \frac{\sqrt{b^2 - 4ac}}{2a}$ relate to the graph?

1. **What does the first term of each root represent on the graph?**

2. **The second term of each root represents the distance the root lies from the axis of symmetry. Why is the second term in each root the same except for the sign?**

Let's analyze how the structure of the Quadratic Formula is evident in the graphical representation of the zeros of a quadratic function.

Worked Example

Consider this graphical representation to determine the real roots of the quadratic equation $y = 2x^2 - x - 15$.

Steps	Graph
Set y equal to zero and identify the values of a, b, and c. $0 = 2x^2 - x - 15$ $a = 2 \quad b = -1 \quad c = -15 \quad a > 0$	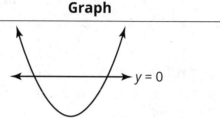
Identify the axis of symmetry and label the point where it intersects $y = 0$. $x = \dfrac{-(-1)}{2(2)} = \dfrac{1}{4}$	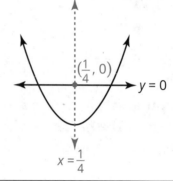
Identify the distance from the axis of symmetry to the parabola along $y = 0$. $+ \dfrac{\sqrt{b^2 - 4ac}}{2a} =$ $\dfrac{\sqrt{(-1)^2 - 4(2)(-15)}}{2(2)} = \dfrac{\sqrt{121}}{4} = \dfrac{11}{4}$ $- \dfrac{\sqrt{b^2 - 4ac}}{2a} = -\dfrac{11}{4}$	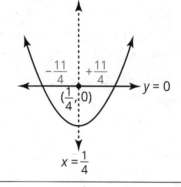
Identify the roots and label them on the graph. $\dfrac{1}{4} + \dfrac{11}{4} = \dfrac{12}{4} = 3$ $\dfrac{1}{4} - \dfrac{11}{4} = -\dfrac{10}{4} = -\dfrac{5}{2}$	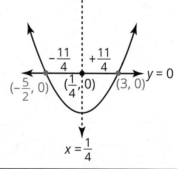
The real roots of $y = 2x^2 - x - 15$ are $x = 3$ and $x = -\dfrac{5}{2}$.	

3. Repeat the process to determine the real roots of the equation $y = 2x^2 - 9x + 4$.

Steps	Graph
a. Let $y = 0$ and identify the values of a, b, and c.	(parabola with line labeled $y = 0$)
b. Identify the axis of symmetry and label the point where it intersects the x-axis.	(parabola with axis of symmetry and line labeled $y = 0$)
c. Identify the distance from the axis of symmetry to the parabola along $y = 0$.	(parabola with axis of symmetry and line labeled $y = 0$)
d. Identify the roots and label them on the graph.	(parabola with axis of symmetry and line labeled $y = 0$)
e. Summarize.	

The graphs of quadratic equations are parabolas that have either an absolute maximum or an absolute minimum. A quadratic equation with two real roots crosses the x-axis in two places. A quadratic equation with a double real root, or one unique real root, touches the x-axis but does not cross it.

Quadratic Equations

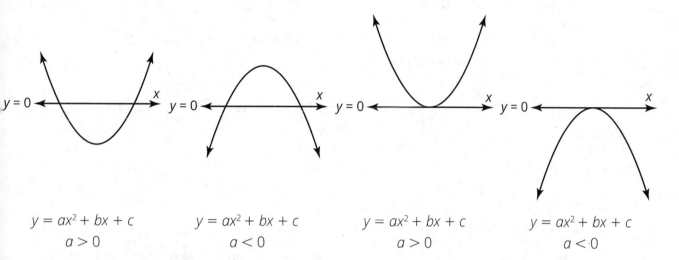

With Two Real Roots

With Double Real Roots

$y = ax^2 + bx + c$
$a > 0$

$y = ax^2 + bx + c$
$a < 0$

$y = ax^2 + bx + c$
$a > 0$

$y = ax^2 + bx + c$
$a < 0$

4. **Draw and label the following components on each graph in terms of the equation $y = ax^2 + bx + c$.**

a. **vertex**

b. **axis of symmetry**

c. **intersection of the x-axis and line of symmetry**

d. **the distance represented by the expression $+\dfrac{\sqrt{b^2 - 4ac}}{2a}$**

e. **the distance represented by the expression $-\dfrac{\sqrt{b^2 - 4ac}}{2a}$**

f. **each root**

Let's analyze the structure of the Quadratic Formula and examine common student mistakes. Consider Javier's work.

1. **Javier is determining the exact zeros for $f(x) = x^2 - 14x + 19$. His work is shown.**

   Javier

   $f(x) = x^2 - 14x + 19$

   $a = 1, b = -14, c = 19$

   $x = \dfrac{-(-14) \pm \sqrt{(-14)^2 - 4(1)(19)}}{2(1)}$

   $x = \dfrac{14 \pm \sqrt{196 - 76}}{2}$

   $x = \dfrac{14 \pm \sqrt{120}}{2}$

   $x = \dfrac{14 \pm \sqrt{30 \cdot 4}}{2}$

   $x = \dfrac{14 \pm 2\sqrt{30}}{2}$

   $x = 7 \pm 2\sqrt{30}$

   a. **Identify the error Javier made when determining the zeros.**

   b. **Determine the correct zeros of the function.**

2. **Use the Quadratic Formula to determine the zeros for each function given. Leave the solutions in exact form and classify them as rational or irrational.**

   > "Leave the solutions in exact form" means not to estimate any radical values with rounded decimals.

   a. $f(x) = -2x^2 - 3x + 7$

   b. $r(x) = -3x^2 + 19x - 7$

3. Lauren is solving the quadratic equation $x^2 - 7x - 8 = 3$.
   Her work is shown.

   a. Identify Lauren's error.

   b. Use the Quadratic Formula correctly
      to determine the solution to Lauren's
      quadratic equation. Classify the solutions
      as rational or irrational.

   Lauren

   $x^2 - 7x - 8 = 3$

   $a = 1, b = -7, c = -8$

   $x = \dfrac{-(-7) \pm \sqrt{(-7)^2 - 4(1)(-8)}}{2(1)}$

   $x = \dfrac{7 \pm \sqrt{49 + 32}}{2}$

   $x = \dfrac{7 \pm \sqrt{81}}{2}$

   $x = \dfrac{7 \pm 9}{2}$

   $x = \dfrac{7 + 9}{2}$ or $x = \dfrac{7 - 9}{2}$

   $x = \dfrac{16}{2} = 8$ or $x = \dfrac{-2}{2} = -1$

   The roots are 8 and -1.

   c. Use technology to graph each side of the original quadratic
      equation $x^2 - 7x - 8 = 3$. Sketch your graph. Then interpret
      the meaning of the intersection points.

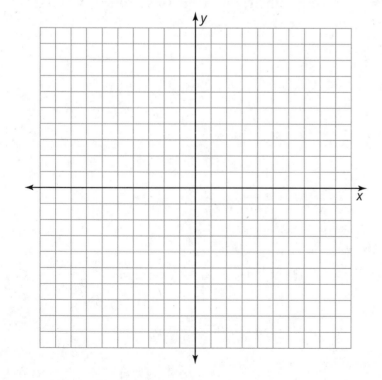

d. Next, rewrite the given quadratic equation so that one side of the equation is equal to zero. Use technology to graph each side of the quadratic equation. Sketch your graph. Interpret the meaning of the intersection points.

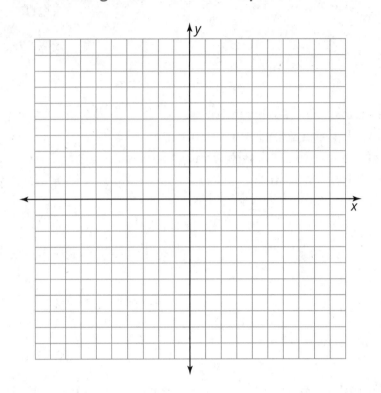

Think

about:

What does it mean to determine the solutions to a quadratic equation? What does it mean to determine the roots of a quadratic equation?

e. Compare the *x*-values of the intersection points from part (c), the *x*-values of the intersection points in part (d), and the solutions using the Quadratic Formula. What do you notice?

4. **Use the Quadratic Formula to determine the zeros for each function. Round the solutions to the nearest hundredth and classify them as either rational or irrational.**

   a. $f(x) = 2x^2 + 10x - 1.02$

   b. $h(x) = 3x^2 - 11x - 2$

5. **Reflect on the different quadratic functions you have solved so far in this lesson.**

   a. **How many zeros does each quadratic function in this lesson have?**

   b. **Do all quadratic functions have two zeros? Explain why or why not.**

Ask yourself:

How can you use graphs to support your reasoning?

   c. **Do you think that a quadratic function could have no zeros? Explain why or why not.**

   d. **Could a quadratic function have more than two zeros? Explain why or why not.**

A quadratic function can have one unique real zero, two real zeros, or at times, no real zeros. Let's investigate how the Quadratic Formula can inform you about different types of zeros.

Consider three quadratic equations and their graphs.

$y = x^2$

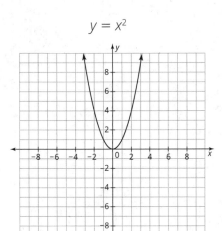

$y = x^2 - 1$

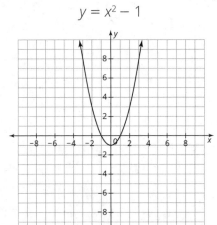

$y = x^2 + 1$

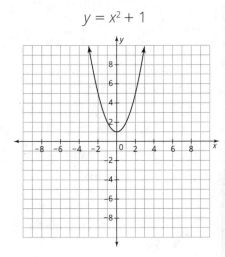

1. **Use the Quadratic Formula to solve each quadratic equation. Show your work.**

Think about:

You have analyzed many graphs of quadratic equations. What do you know about the roots of a quadratic equation that touches but does not intersect the x-axis or intersects the x-axis at two points?

2. **What do you notice about the relationship between the number of real roots, the graph, and the results of substituting the values a, b, and c into the Quadratic Formula?**

Because the $b^2 - 4ac$ portion of the Quadratic Formula "discriminates" the number of real zeros, or roots, it is called the **discriminant.**

3. **Using the discriminant, write an inequality to describe when a quadratic function has each solution.**

    a. **no real roots/zeros**

    b. **one unique real root/zero**

    c. **two unique real roots/zeros**

Ask yourself:

How can you tell how many zeros a function will have by thinking about its graph before you use the Quadratic Formula?

The table shown summarizes the types of solutions for any quadratic equation or function.

Equation/ Function	Solutions	Interpretation of the Solutions		Sketch
		Number of Unique Real Zeros	Number of x-Intercepts	
$f(x) = x^2$	$x = \dfrac{-0 \pm \sqrt{0^2 - 4(1)(0)}}{2(1)}$ $= \dfrac{0 \pm \sqrt{0}}{2}$ $= 0 \pm \sqrt{0}$	1	1	
$g(x) = x^2 - 1$	$x = \dfrac{-0 \pm \sqrt{0^2 - 4(1)(-1)}}{2(1)}$ $= \dfrac{0 \pm \sqrt{4}}{2}$ $= 0 \pm 1$	2	2	
$h(x) = x^2 + 1$	$x = \dfrac{-0 \pm \sqrt{0^2 - (4)(1)(1)}}{2(1)}$ $= \dfrac{0 \pm \sqrt{-4}}{2}$	0	0	

Every quadratic equation with real coefficients has either 2 real roots or 0 real roots. However, if a graph of a quadratic equation has 1 x-intercept, the equation *still* has 2 real roots. In this case, the 2 real roots are considered a double root.

4. **Use the discriminant to determine the number of real roots for each equation. Then solve for the roots/zeros.**

   a. $y = 2x^2 + 12x - 2$

   b. $0 = 2x^2 + 12x + 20$

   c. $y = x^2 + 12x + 36$

   d. $y = 3x^2 + 7x - 20$

   e. $y = 4x^2 - 9$

   f. $0 = 9x^2 + 12x + 4$

Operations with Rational and Irrational Numbers

In the previous activity, you used the discriminant of the Quadratic Formula to determine whether there were 2, 1, or 0 real roots to a quadratic equation. Remember that the set of real numbers is made up of the set of rational and the set of irrational numbers. Let's take a closer look at these two specific types of real numbers.

1. **What characteristic of the discriminant determines whether the roots are rational or irrational?**

2. **Based on the number and nature of each of the roots, decide if the discriminant is positive, negative, or zero and if the discriminant is or is not a perfect square.**

   a. **no real roots/zeros**   b. **one rational root/zero**

   c. **two rational roots/zeros**   d. **two irrational roots/zeros**

Throughout this lesson, you have solved quadratic equations with rational and irrational roots.

You have interpreted solutions as the sum or difference of a quantity from the axis of symmetry. In each case, the c-value that defines the axis of symmetry, $x = c$, is a rational number. In some cases, you added and subtracted a rational number. In other cases, you added and subtracted an irrational number.

Consider each equation and its corresponding roots.

$$y = (x - 2)^2 - 9$$
$$x = 2 \pm 3$$

$$y = (x - 2)^2 - 7$$
$$x = 2 \pm \sqrt{7}$$

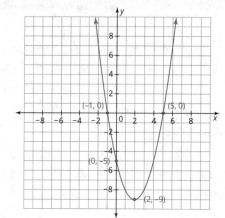
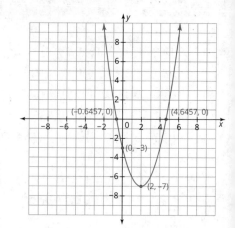

3. **Describe the roots of each equation as rational or irrational.**

4. **Let *m* represent a nonzero rational number and let *n* represent an irrational number. Which expression could represent a rational number? Explain your reasoning and provide an example.**

   a. $m + n$

   b. mn

   c. $-n$

   d. n^2

5. Consider a quadratic function with integer coefficients and two distinct zeros. If one zero is irrational, which statement is true about the other zero? Explain your reasoning and provide an example.

   a. The other zero must be rational.

   b. The other zero must be irrational.

   c. The other zero can be either rational or irrational.

   d. The other zero must be non-real.

6. Use the given values for W, X, Y, and Z to determine which expression results in a rational number. Explain your reasoning.

   $W = \sqrt{4}$ $X = 2\sqrt{2}$ $Y = \sqrt{3}$ $Z = \sqrt{25}$

   a. $W + X$ b. $X + Y$

   c. $Y + Z$ d. $Z + W$

Consider the function $p(x) = x^2 + 1$ and its graph from the previous activity.

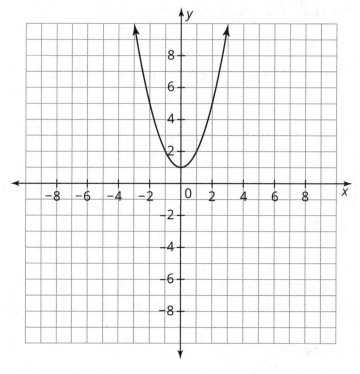

Elena and Mark determined the zeros of the function.

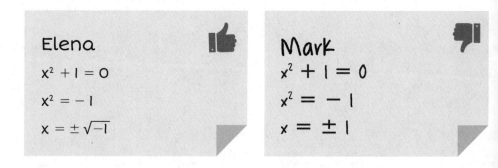

Elena 👍

$x^2 + 1 = 0$

$x^2 = -1$

$x = \pm\sqrt{-1}$

Mark 👎

$x^2 + 1 = 0$

$x^2 = -1$

$x = \pm 1$

1. **What did Mark do wrong? Use the graph to justify your answer.**

2. **Consider Elena's solution. Does the solution fall within the real number system? Explain your reasoning.**

In order to calculate the square of any real number, there must be some way to calculate the square root of a negative number. That is, there must be a number such that when it is squared, it is equal to a negative number. For this reason, mathematicians defined what is called *the number i*. **The number *i*** is a number such that $i^2 = -1$. The number *i* is also called the imaginary identity.

3. If $i^2 = -1$, then what is the value of *i*?

> The number *i* is similar to the number π: even though they are both numbers, each is special enough that it gets its very own symbol.

4. **Recall the function $x^2 + 1$. Write the roots of the function in terms of *i*.**

Functions and equations that have solutions requiring *i* have **imaginary roots** or **imaginary zeros**.

> Equations with no solutions in one number system may have solutions in a larger number system.

5. **How can you tell from the graph of a quadratic equation whether or not it has real solutions or imaginary solutions?**

6. **Do you think you can determine the imaginary solutions by examining the graph? Explain your reasoning.**

The set of **complex numbers** is the set of all numbers written in the form $a + bi$, where a and b are real numbers. The term a is called the **real part of a complex number**, and the term bi is called the **imaginary part of a complex number**. The set of complex numbers is represented by the notation $\mathbb{C}$.

The set of **imaginary numbers** is the set of all numbers written in the form $a + bi$, where a and b are real numbers and b is not equal to 0. The set of imaginary numbers is represented by the notation $\mathbb{I}$. A **pure imaginary number** is a number of the form $a + bi$, where a is equal to 0 and b is not equal to 0.

This is the entire universe of numbers. Seriously, like all of them!

The ∈ symbol means "an element of." Therefore, "$a, b \in \mathbb{R}$" means that the values for a and b are elements of the set of real numbers.

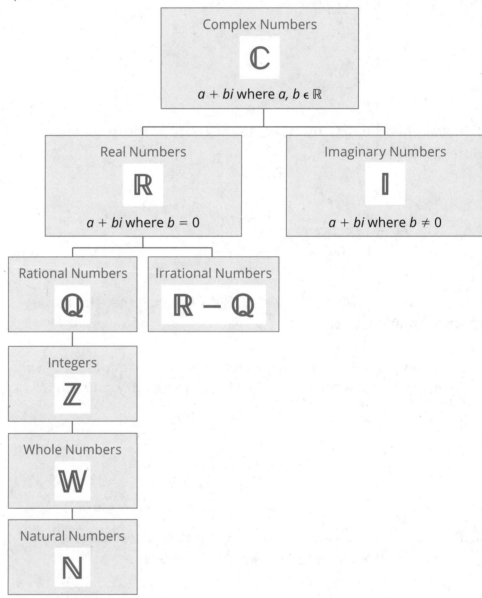

7. Complete each statement with *always, sometimes,* or *never.*

   a. If a number is an imaginary number, then it is _____ a complex number.

   b. If a number is a complex number, then it is _____ an imaginary number.

   c. If a number is a real number, then it is _____ a complex number.

   d. If a number is a real number, then it is _____ an imaginary number.

   e. If a number is a complex number, then it is _____ a real number.

8. List all number sets that describe each given number.

   a. 3

   b. $\sqrt{7}$

   c. $3i$

   d. $5.\overline{45}$

   e. $\frac{7}{8}$

   f. $6 - i$

You can simplify expressions involving negative roots by using i.

Worked Example

You can use the number i to rewrite $\sqrt{-25}$.

Factor out -1. $\qquad\qquad\qquad\qquad\qquad\qquad\qquad \sqrt{-25} = \sqrt{(-1)(25)}$

Rewrite the radical expression. $\qquad\qquad\qquad\qquad\qquad = \sqrt{-1} \cdot \sqrt{25}$

Apply the square root on $\sqrt{25}$. $\qquad\qquad\qquad\qquad\; = 5\sqrt{-1}$

Rewrite $\sqrt{-1}$ as i. $\qquad\qquad\qquad\qquad\qquad\qquad\; = 5i$

So, $\sqrt{-25}$ can be rewritten as $5i$.

---

9. **Rewrite each expression using i.**

    a. $\sqrt{-4}$ b. $\sqrt{-12}$

    c. $5 + \sqrt{-50}$ d. $\dfrac{6 - \sqrt{-8}}{2}$

TALK the TALK

Show Me the Ways

1. Determine the real roots of the quadratic equation
   $y = 2x^2 + 4x - 6$ using the four methods you learned in
   this topic.

Factoring	Completing the Square
Using the Quadratic Formula	**Graphing**

2. Casey says that any quadratic equation has only one of these 3 types of solutions:

   - 2 unique real number solutions
   - 2 equal real number solutions (a double root)
   - 1 real and 1 imaginary solution

   Brandon says that any quadratic equation has only one of these 3 types of solutions:

   - 2 unique real number solutions
   - 2 equal real number solutions (a double root)
   - 2 imaginary solutions

   Karl says that any quadratic equation has only one of these 4 types of solutions:

   - 2 unique real number solutions
   - 2 equal real number solutions (a double root)
   - 2 imaginary solutions
   - 1 real and 1 imaginary solution

   Who's correct? Explain your reasoning.

Write

How can you determine the types of solutions when using the Quadratic Formula?

Remember

The Quadratic Formula, $x = \dfrac{-b \pm \sqrt{b^2 - 4ac}}{2a}$, can be used to calculate the solutions to any quadratic equation of the form $ax^2 + bx + c = 0$, where a, b, and c represent real numbers and $a \neq 0$.

On the graph of a quadratic function, $\pm \sqrt{b^2 - \dfrac{4ac}{2a}}$ is the distance from $\left(-\dfrac{b}{2a}, 0\right)$ to each root.

Practice

The formula shown can be used to calculate the distance, s, an object travels in t seconds. In this formula, u represents the initial velocity, and a represents a constant acceleration. Use this formula to answer each question.

$$S = ut + \tfrac{1}{2}at^2$$

1. Kian is driving 48 miles per hour and is starting to merge onto the highway; therefore, he must increase his speed. He gradually accelerates at a rate of 7 miles per hour for several seconds.
   a. Substitute the initial velocity and constant acceleration into the formula to write an equation to represent the distance Kian travels.
   b. Use the Quadratic Formula to determine the roots of the equation. What do the roots represent in the context of the problem situation? Explain your reasoning.
2. Sonja is driving her car 32 miles per hour when she passes Dominique's house. She then accelerates at a rate of 3 miles per hour for several minutes until she passes the movie theater. Sonja knows that the movie theater is 2.9 miles from Dominique's house.
   a. Substitute the initial velocity, constant acceleration, and distance into the formula to write an equation represent the distance Sonja travels.
   b. Use the Quadratic Formula to determine the roots of the equation you wrote in part (a). What do the roots represent in the context of the problem situation? Explain your reasoning.
3. Use the discriminant to determine the number of real roots for each equation. Then solve the quadratic equations with real roots.
   a. $4x^2 + 8x - 12 = 0$
   b. $x^2 + 2x - 10 = 0$
   c. $9x^2 - 12x + 4 = 0$
   d. $3x^2 - 4 = 0$
   e. $3x^2 + 2x - 2 = 0$
   f. $x^2 - 3x + 5 = 0$
4. Classify each number according to its most specific number set.
   a. $\dfrac{-4}{\sqrt{9}}$
   b. $\dfrac{\sqrt{-4}}{9}$
   c. $9 - \sqrt{-4}$
   d. $-4 - \sqrt{9}$
5. Rewrite each radical using i.
   a. $\sqrt{-16}$
   b. $\sqrt{-27}$
   c. $\sqrt{-200}$
   d. $5 + \sqrt{-20}$

Stretch

Consider the function $f(x) = -2x^2 + bx - 5$. Determine the b-value(s) that would ensure the function has two real roots. Explain your reasoning.

Review

1. Analyze each pair of representations. Then, answer each question and justify your reasoning.

   a. Which function has a greater y-intercept?

A	B
$f(x) = \frac{3}{4}(x - 2)^2$ 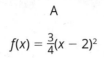	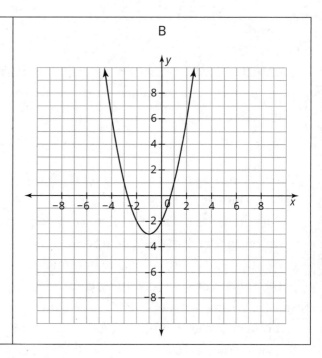

   b. Which function has a greater absolute maximum?

A		B

x	y	
0	24	$f(x) = -2x^2 + 15x - 4$
3	25	
6	24	

2. Complete the square to determine the roots of each equation. Show your work.

   a. $y = 2x^2 + 5x - 14$

   b. $y = -3x^2 - 6x + 10$

3. Consider the function $f(x) = (x + \frac{1}{2})(x - \frac{3}{4})$.

   a. Identify the form of the function as factored, general, or vertex.

   b. Identify the zeros and axis of symmetry of the function.

Solving Quadratic Equations Summary

KEY TERMS

- polynomial
- monomial
- binomial
- trinomial
- degree of a polynomial
- closed, closure
- difference of two squares
- perfect square trinomial

- principal square root
- double root
- Zero Product Property
- completing the square
- Quadratic Formula
- discriminant
- the number i
- imaginary roots

- imaginary zeros
- complex numbers
- real part of a complex number
- imaginary part of a complex number
- imaginary numbers
- pure imaginary number

LESSON 1

This Time, With Polynomials

Linear and quadratic expressions are part of a larger group of expressions known as polynomials. A **polynomial** is an expression involving the sum of powers in one or more variables multiplied by coefficients. A polynomial in one variable is the sum of terms of the form ax^k where a, called the coefficient, is a real number and k is a non-negative integer. A polynomial is written in general form when the terms are in descending order, starting with the term with the greatest degree and ending with the term with the least degree.

$$a_1x^k + a_2x^{k-1} + \ldots a_nx^0$$

Each product in a polynomial is called a term. Polynomials are named according to the number of terms: **monomials** have exactly 1 term, **binomials** have exactly 2 terms, and **trinomials** have exactly 3 terms.

The exponent of a term is the degree of the term, and the greatest exponent in a polynomial is the **degree of the polynomial**.

The characteristics of the polynomial $13x^3 + 5x + 9$ are shown in the chart.

	1st term	2nd term	3rd term
Term	$13x^3$	$5x$	9
Coefficient	13	5	9
Power	x^3	x^1	x^0
Exponent	3	1	0

This trinomial has a degree of 3 because 3 is the greatest degree of the terms in the trinomial.

When an operation is performed on any of the numbers in a set and the result is a number that is also in the same set, the set is said to be **closed** (or to have **closure**) under that operation. The definition of closure can also be applied to polynomials.

Polynomials can be added or subtracted by identifying the like terms of the polynomial functions, using the Associative Property to group the like terms together, and combining the like terms to simplify the expression.

For example, to add the polynomial expressions $(7x^2 - 2x + 12)$ and $(8x^3 + 2x - 3x)$, use the Associative Property to combine the like terms.

$$(7x^2 - 2x + 12) + (8x^3 + 2x - 3x)$$
$$8x^3 + (7x^2 + 2x^2) + (-2x - 3x) + 12$$
$$8x^3 + 9x^2 - 5x + 12$$

The product of 2 binomials can be determined by using a multiplication table, or area model, which organizes the two terms of the binomials as factors of multiplication expressions.

$$(9x - 1)(5x + 7)$$

$\cdot$	**9x**	**−1**
5x	$45x^2$	$-5x$
7	$63x$	-7

$$(9x - 1)(5x + 7) = 45x^2 - 5x + 63x - 7$$
$$= 45x^2 + 58x - 7$$

The Distributive Property can also be used to multiply polynomials. Depending on the number of terms in the polynomials, the Distributive Property may need to be used multiple times.

For example, to multiply the polynomials $x + 5$ and $x - 2$, first, use the Distributive Property to multiply each term of $x + 5$ by the entire binomial $x - 2$.

$$(x + 5)(x - 2) = (x)(x - 2) + (5)(x - 2)$$

Next, distribute x to each term of $x - 2$ and distribute 5 to each term of $x - 2$.

$$x^2 - 2x + 5x - 10$$

Finally, collect the like terms and write the solution in general form.

$$x^2 + 3x - 10$$

There are special products of degree 2 that have certain characteristics. The **difference of two squares** is an expression in the form $a^2 - b^2$ that has factors $(a + b)(a - b)$. A **perfect square trinomial** is formed by multiplying a binomial by itself. It is an expression in the form $a^2 + 2ab + b^2$ or in the form $a^2 - 2ab + b^2$. A perfect square trinomial can be written as the square of a binomial. In these cases, the factors are $(a + b)^2$ and $(a - b)^2$, respectively.

<table>
<tr><td>**LESSON**
2</td><td>Solutions, More or Less</td></tr>
</table>

A quadratic function is a function of degree 2 because the greatest power for any of its terms is 2. This means that it has at most 2 zeros, or at most 2 solutions, at $y = 0$.

The two solutions of a quadratic function can be represented as square roots of numbers. Every positive number has two square roots, a positive square root, which is also called the **principal square root**, and a negative square root. To solve the equation $x^2 = 9$, take the square root of both sides of the equation.

$$\sqrt{x^2} = \sqrt{9}$$
$$x = \pm 3$$

You can solve $x^2 = 9$ on a graph by looking for the points of intersection between $y = x^2$ and $y = 9$. The solutions are both 3 units from the axis of symmetry, $x = 0$.

The x-intercepts of a graph of a quadratic function are called the zeros of the quadratic function. The zeros are called the roots of the quadratic equation.

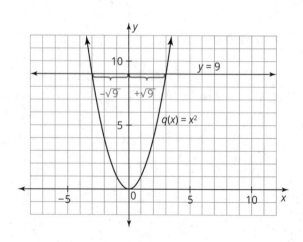

The quadratic function $q(x) = x^2$ has two solutions at $y = 0$. Therefore, it has 2 zeros: $x = +\sqrt{0}$ and $x = -\sqrt{0}$. These two zeros of the function, or roots of the equation, are the same number, 0, so the function $q(x) = x^2$ is said to have a **double root**.

When you encounter solutions that are not perfect squares, you can either determine the approximate value of the radical or rewrite it in an equivalent radical form.

To approximate a square root, determine the perfect square that is closest to, but less than, the given value and the perfect square that is closest to, but greater than, the given value. You can use these square roots to approximate the square root of the given number.

For example, the approximate value of $\sqrt{40}$ falls between $\sqrt{36}$, or 6, and $\sqrt{49}$, or 7. Since $6.3^2 = 39.69$ and $6.4^2 = 40.96$, the approximate value of $\sqrt{40}$ is 6.3.

To rewrite a square root in equivalent radical form, first rewrite the product of the radicand to include any perfect square factors. Then extract the square roots of those perfect squares.

$$\sqrt{27} = \sqrt{9 \cdot 3}$$
$$= \sqrt{9} \cdot \sqrt{3}$$
$$= 3\sqrt{3}$$

A quadratic function written in factored form is in the form $f(x) = a(x - r_1)(x - r_2)$, where $a \neq 0$. In factored form, r_1 and r_2 represent the x-intercepts of the graph of the function. The x-intercepts of the graph of the quadratic function $f(x) = ax^2 + bx + c$ and the zeros of the function are the same as the roots of the equation $ax^2 + bx + c = 0$.

To write a quadratic function in factored form, first determine the zeros of the function $f(x) = x^2 - 9$, set the trinomial expression equal to 0, and solve for x.

$$0 = x^2 - 9$$
$$9 = x^2$$
$$\sqrt{9} = \sqrt{x^2}$$
$$\pm 3 = x$$

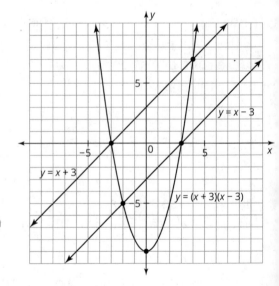

You can then use the zeros to write the function in factored form, $f(x) = (x + 3)(x - 3)$.

The Zero Product Property states that if the product of two or more factors is equal to zero, then at least one factor must be equal to zero. You can see from the graph that the zeros of the function $f(x) = x^2 - 9$ occur where either $y = x + 3$ or $y = x - 3$ are zero.

LESSON 3 · Transforming Solutions

The solutions to any quadratic equation are located on the parabola, equidistant from the axis of symmetry.

A quadratic function in vertex form $f(x) = a(x - h)^2 + k$ is translated horizontally h units, dilated vertically by the factor a, and translated vertically k units.

For the equation $y = (x - c)^2$, the solutions can be represented by $c \pm \sqrt{y}$. For the equation $y = a(x - c)^2$, the solutions can be represented by $c \pm \sqrt{\frac{y}{a}}$. For the equation $y = a(x - c)^2 + d$, the solutions can be represented by $c \pm \sqrt{\frac{y - d}{a}}$.

For example, consider the equation $2(x - 1)^2 + 2 = 20$.

$$x = 1 \pm \sqrt{\frac{20 - 2}{2}}$$
$$= 1 \pm \sqrt{9}$$
$$= 1 \pm 3$$

The solutions to the equation are 3 units away from the axis of symmetry, $x = 1$. The solutions are $x = -2$ and $x = 4$.

LESSON 4 · The Missing Link

You can factor trinomials by rewriting them as the product of two linear expressions.

For example, to factor the trinomial $x^2 + 10x + 16$, determine the factor pairs of the constant term. The factors of 16 are (1)(16), (2)(8), and (4)(4). Then, determine the pair whose sum is the coefficient of the middle term, 10.

·	x	8
x	x^2	$8x$
2	$2x$	16

The sum of $2x$ and $8x$ is $10x$. So, $x^2 + 10x + 16 = (x + 2)(x + 8)$.

You can use factoring and the Zero Product Property to solve quadratics in the form $y = ax^2 + bx + c$.

For example, you can solve the quadratic equation $x^2 - 4x = -3$.

$$x^2 - 4x = -3$$
$$x^2 - 4x + 3 = -3 + 3$$
$$x^2 - 4x + 3 = 0$$
$$(x - 3)(x - 1) = 0$$

$$(x - 3) = 0 \quad \text{or} \quad (x - 1) = 0$$
$$x - 3 + 3 = 0 + 3 \quad \text{or} \quad x - 1 + 1 = 0 + 1$$
$$x = 3 \quad \text{or} \quad x = 1$$

For a quadratic function that has zeros but cannot be factored, there is another method for solving the quadratic equation. **Completing the square** is a process for writing a quadratic expression in vertex form, which then allows you to solve for the zeros.

For example, you can calculate the roots of the equation $x^2 - 4x + 2 = 0$.

Isolate $x^2 - 4x$.

$$x^2 - 4x + 2 - 2 = 0 - 2$$
$$x^2 - 4x = -2$$

Complete the square and rewrite this as a perfect square trinomial.

Determine the constant term that would complete the square.

$$x^2 - 4x + \, ? = -2 + \, ?$$

Add this term to both sides of the equation.

$$x^2 - 4x + 4 = -2 + 4$$
$$x^2 - 4x + 4 = 2$$

Factor the left side of the equation.

Determine the square root of each side of the equation.

$$(x - 2)^2 = 2$$
$$\sqrt{(x - 2)^2} = \sqrt{2}$$
$$(x - 2) = \pm\sqrt{2}$$

Set the factor of the perfect square trinomial equal to each square root of the constant and solve for x.

$$x - 2 = \sqrt{2} \quad \text{or} \quad x - 2 = -\sqrt{2}$$
$$x = 2 + \sqrt{2} \quad \text{or} \quad x = 2 - \sqrt{2}$$

$$x \approx 3.41 \quad \text{or} \quad x \approx 0.59$$

The roots are approximately 3.41 and 0.59.

Completing the square can also be used to identify the axis of symmetry and the vertex of any quadratic function written in standard form.

When a function is written in standard form, $ax^2 + bx + c$, the axis of symmetry is $x = -\frac{b}{2a}$.

Given a quadratic equation in the form $y = ax^2 + bx + c$, the vertex of the function is located at $x = -\frac{b}{2a}$ and $y = c - \frac{b^2}{4a}$.

LESSON

5

Ladies and Gentlemen, Please Welcome the Quadratic Formula!

The **Quadratic Formula**, $x = \frac{-b \pm \sqrt{b^2 - 4ac}}{2a}$, can be used to calculate the solutions to any quadratic equation of the form $ax^2 + bx + c = 0$, where a, b and c represent real numbers and $a \neq 0$.

For example, given the function $f(x) = 2x^2 - 4x - 3$ we can identify the values of a, b and c.

$$a = 2; \ b = -4; \ c = -3$$

Then we use the quadratic formula to solve.

$$x = \frac{-(-4) \pm \sqrt{(-4)^2 - 4(2)(-3)}}{2(2)}$$

$$x = \frac{4 \pm \sqrt{16 - 24}}{4}$$

$$x = \frac{4 \pm \sqrt{40}}{4}$$

$$x \approx \frac{4 + 6.325}{4} \approx 2.581 \quad \text{or} \quad x \approx \frac{4 - 6.325}{4} \approx -0.581$$

The roots are approximately 2.581 and −0.581.

A quadratic function can have one real zero, two real zeros, or at times, no real zeros.

You can use the part of the Quadratic Formula underneath the square root symbol to identify the number of real zeros or roots. Because this portion of the formula "discriminates" the number of real zeros or roots, it is called the **discriminant**.

If the discriminant is positive, the quadratic has two real roots.
If the discriminant is negative, the quadratic has no real roots.
If the discriminant is 0, the quadratic has a double real root.

You can also use the discriminant to describe the nature of the roots. If the discriminant is a perfect square, then the roots are rational. If the discriminant is not a perfect square, then the roots are irrational.

Rational numbers are closed under addition and multiplication. A rational number plus an irrational number is an irrational number. A rational number times an irrational number is an irrational number. An irrational number times an irrational number can have an irrational or rational product.

In order to calculate the square root of any real number, there must be some way to calculate the square root of a negative number. That is, there must be a number such that when it is squared, it is equal to a negative number. For this reason, mathematicians defined what is called **the number i**. The number i is a number such that $i^2 = -1$.

For example, you can simplify the expression $\sqrt{-25}$ by using i.

Factor out -1.	$\sqrt{-25} = \sqrt{(-1)(25)}$
Rewrite the radical expression.	$= \sqrt{-1} \cdot \sqrt{25}$
Apply the square root on $\sqrt{25}$.	$= 5\sqrt{-1}$
Rewrite $\sqrt{-1}$ as i.	$= 5i$

So, $\sqrt{-25}$ simplifies to $5i$.

Functions and equations that have imaginary solutions have **imaginary roots** or **imaginary zeros**, which are the solutions.

The set of **complex numbers** is the set of all numbers written in the form $a + bi$, where a and b are real numbers. The term a is called the **real part of a complex number**, and the term bi is called the **imaginary part of a complex number**.

The set of **imaginary numbers** is a subset of the set of complex numbers. A **pure imaginary number** is a number of the form $a + bi$, where b is not equal to 0.

Applications of Quadratics

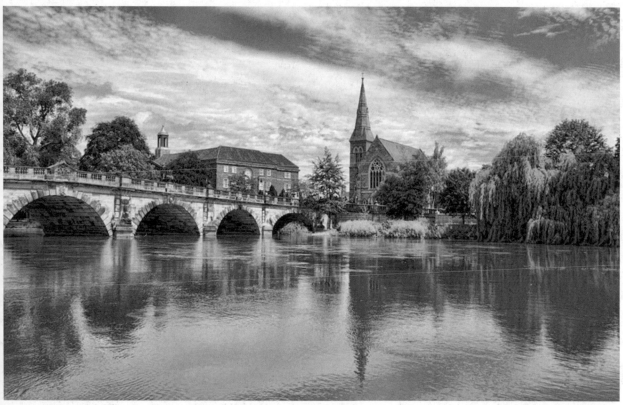

A keystone is the wedge-shaped stone at the top of an arch that locks the other stones in place. If an arch is shaped like a parabola, the vertex (maximum) would be somewhere on the keystone.

Module 5: Maximizing and Minimizing

TOPIC 3: APPLICATIONS OF QUADRATICS

This topic provides students with an opportunity to use what they have learned throughout the module to model and solve problems for situations involving quadratics. Students start with a real-world problem that can be modeled by a quadratic inequality. From there, students are given a scenario that can be modeled by a system of a quadratic function and a linear function. They use technology to graph the system and determine the solutions. Students are presented with a real-world situation and use familiar strategies to complete a quadratic regression to determine the curve of best fit. Finally, students use what they know about inverses to determine the inverses to a quadratic equation.

Where have we been?

Students have graphed and solved linear inequalities in one variable and in two variables, as well as systems of linear inequalities. They use these skills to graph and solve quadratic inequalities, interpreting the solution set in the same way. Students know that a graph represents the solutions to the function it models and that the intersection point(s) of two graphs represent the solution(s) shared by both functions.

Where are we going?

This topic provides students with an opportunity to bring together the advanced techniques that they have learned throughout the course. When students move into the next course, their knowledge of first- and second-degree polynomials will be used and expanded upon as they encounter cubics, quartics, rational functions, and logarithmic functions. Modeling advanced scenarios will be heavily used by students who continue on to calculus and post-secondary mathematics.

Quadratic Inequalities

To solve a quadratic inequality, such as $x^2 - 4x + 3 < 0$, you can first solve the corresponding quadratic equation: $x^2 - 4x + 3 = 0$, which will give you the roots $x = 1$ or $x = 3$. Plot the roots to create intervals on the x-axis.

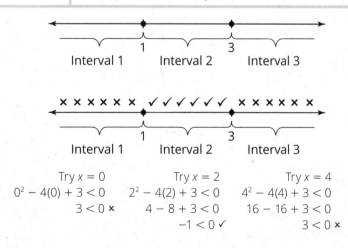

Try $x = 0$

$0^2 - 4(0) + 3 < 0$

$3 < 0$ ✗

Try $x = 2$

$2^2 - 4(2) + 3 < 0$

$4 - 8 + 3 < 0$

$-1 < 0$ ✓

Try $x = 4$

$4^2 - 4(4) + 3 < 0$

$16 - 16 + 3 < 0$

$3 < 0$ ✗

Interval 2 satisfies the original inequality, so the solution includes all numbers between 1 and 3.

Systems

Your body is an amazing collection of different systems. Your cardiovascular system pumps blood throughout your body, your skeletal system provides shape and support, and your nervous system controls communication between your senses and your brain. Your skin, including your hair and fingernails, is a system all by itself—the integumentary system—and it protects all of your body's other systems. You also have a digestive system, endocrine system, excretory system, immune system, muscular system, reproductive system, and respiratory system.

Why do we call these systems "systems"? What do you think makes up a system?

Talking Points

Quadratic functions is an important topic to know about for college admissions tests.

Here is a sample question:

If $p = 0$ and $q < 0$, then which shows the graph of $f(x) = (x - p)(x - q)$?

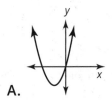
A.

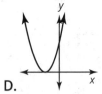
B.

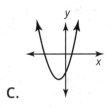
C.

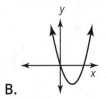
D.

The function is given in factored form, so it has zeros at p and q, which means that the function crosses the x-axis at p and q. Since $p = 0$ and q is negative, the function crosses the x-axis at $x = 0$ and at some negative x-value. Choice A, then, is the correct graph.

Key Terms

restrict the domain
To restrict the domain of a function means to define a new domain for the function that is a subset of the original domain.

one-to-one function
A relation is a one-to-one function if both the relation and its inverse are functions.

Ahead of the Curve

Solving Quadratic Inequalities

Warm Up

Determine the solution of each quadratic equation.

1. $x^2 - 100 = -64$

2. $x^2 + 3x + 5 = 15$

3. $4x^2 + 12x = 7$

4. $x^2 + 4x - 3 = 5$

Learning Goals

- Solve a quadratic inequality by calculating the roots of the quadratic equation which corresponds to the inequality and testing values within intervals determined by the roots.
- Connect the graphical representation of a quadratic function and the solution to a corresponding quadratic inequality represented on a number line.
- Use interval notation to record the solutions to quadratic inequalities.

You have interpreted the solution sets to linear inequalities on a coordinate plane. You have also solved quadratic equations using a variety of methods. How can you interpret the solutions sets to quadratic inequalities on a coordinate plane using what you know about solving quadratic equations?

It Has Its Ups and Downs

A firework is shot straight up into the air with an initial velocity of 500 feet per second from 5 feet off the ground. The graph of the function that represents this situation is shown.

Remember:

A vertical motion model is a quadratic equation of the form $y = -16t^2 + v_0t + h_0$.

1. **Use the graph to approximate when the firework will be at each given height off the ground.**

   a. **0 feet**

   b. **1000 feet**

   c. **2500 feet**

   d. **3900 feet**

2. **Describe any patterns you notice for the number of times the firework reaches a given height.**

3. **Draw a horizontal line on the graph to represent when the firework is 2000 feet off the ground.**

   a. **When is the firework higher than 2000 feet? Circle this portion of the graph.**

   b. **When is the firework below 2000 feet? Draw a box around this portion of the graph.**

   c. **Write a quadratic inequality that represents the times when the firework is below 2000 feet.**

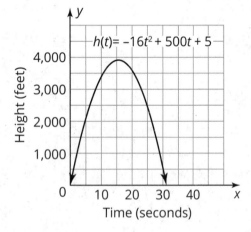

Solving Quadratic Inequalities

Just like with the other inequalities you have studied, the solution to a quadratic inequality is the set of values that satisfy the inequality.

Worked Example

Let's determine the solution of the quadratic inequality $x^2 - 4x + 3 < 0$.

Write the corresponding quadratic equation.

$$x^2 - 4x + 3 = 0$$

Calculate the roots of the quadratic equation using an appropriate method.

$$(x - 3)(x - 1) = 0$$
$$(x - 3) = 0 \quad \text{or} \quad (x - 1) = 0$$
$$x = 3 \quad \text{or} \quad x = 1$$

Plot the roots to divide the number line into three regions.

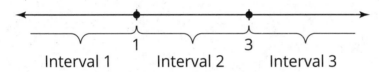

Choose a value from each interval to test in the original inequality.

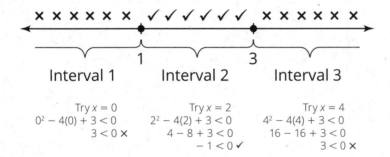

Try $x = 0$
$0^2 - 4(0) + 3 < 0$
$3 < 0$ ✗

Try $x = 2$
$2^2 - 4(2) + 3 < 0$
$4 - 8 + 3 < 0$
$-1 < 0$ ✓

Try $x = 4$
$4^2 - 4(4) + 3 < 0$
$16 - 16 + 3 < 0$
$3 < 0$ ✗

Identify the solution set as the interval(s) in which your test value satisfies the inequality.

Interval 2 satisfies the original inequality, so the solution includes all numbers between 1 and 3.

Solution: $x \in (1, 3)$

The symbol $\in$ is read "is an element of," "is in," or "belongs to." The notation $x \in (1, 3)$ means the same as $1 < x < 3$.

1. **Analyze the worked example.**

The notation $x \in [1, 3]$ means the same as $1 \le x \le 3$.

a. **How would the solution set change if the inequality was less than or equal to? Explain your reasoning.**

b. **How would the solution set change if the inequality was greater than or equal to? Explain your reasoning.**

2. **Graph $y = x^2 - 4x + 3$ on the coordinate plane shown and label the roots of the equation and the vertex. Then describe how the graph supports that the solution set for the associated quadratic inequality $x^2 - 4x + 3 < 0$ is $1 < x < 3$.**

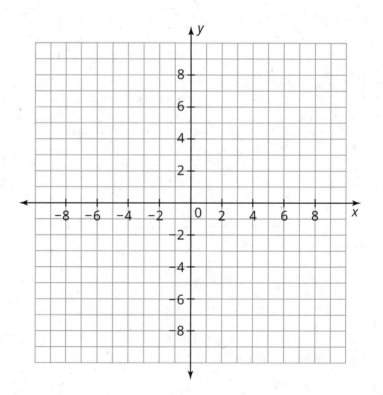

Jeff correctly determined the roots of the quadratic inequality $2x^2 - 14x + 27 \geq 7$ to be $x = 5$ and $x = 2$. However, he incorrectly determined the solution set. His work is shown.

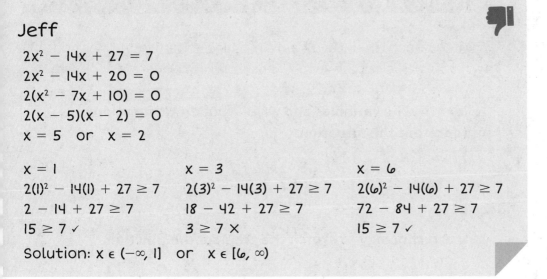

Jeff

$2x^2 - 14x + 27 = 7$

$2x^2 - 14x + 20 = 0$

$2(x^2 - 7x + 10) = 0$

$2(x - 5)(x - 2) = 0$

$x = 5 \quad \text{or} \quad x = 2$

$x = 1$	$x = 3$	$x = 6$
$2(1)^2 - 14(1) + 27 \geq 7$	$2(3)^2 - 14(3) + 27 \geq 7$	$2(6)^2 - 14(6) + 27 \geq 7$
$2 - 14 + 27 \geq 7$	$18 - 42 + 27 \geq 7$	$72 - 84 + 27 \geq 7$
$15 \geq 7$ ✓	$3 \geq 7$ ✗	$15 \geq 7$ ✓

Solution: $x \in (-\infty, 1]$ or $x \in [6, \infty)$

3. **Describe Jeff's error. Then, determine the correct solution set for the inequality.**

Ask yourself:

When testing values from each interval, could you use the factored form of the inequality rather than the original inequality?

Modeling Quadratic Inequalities

A water balloon is launched from a machine upward from a height of 10 feet with an initial velocity of 46 feet per second.

1. **Identify the variables and write a quadratic function to represent this situation.**

2. **Use technology to sketch the graph of the function.**

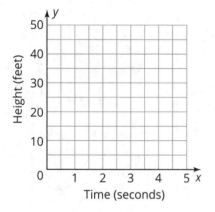

3. **Draw a horizontal line on the graph to represent when the balloon is 30 feet off the ground.**

   a. **Circle the portion of the graph that represents when the balloon is above 30 feet.**

   b. **Write and solve an inequality to determine when the balloon is above 30 feet. Use the graph to explain your solution.**

4. **Determine when the balloon is at or below 43 feet. Interpret your solution in terms of the model you graphed.**

TALK the TALK

Boom! Boom!

In the Getting Started activity, a firework was shot straight up into the air with an initial velocity of 500 feet per second from 5 feet off the ground. The function representing the situation was identified as $h(t) = -16t^2 + 500t + 5$. You determined the firework would be above 2000 feet between about 5 seconds and 27 seconds.

Suppose a second firework was shot straight up into the air with an initial velocity of 500 feet per second from the ground.

1. **Predict whether the second firework will be above 2000 feet for more time, less time, or the same amount of time as the first firework.**

2. **Write a quadratic inequality to represent when the second firework will be above 2000 feet.**

3. **Determine when the second firework will be above 2000 feet.**

4. **Was your prediction made in Question 1 correct?**

5. **Use technology to compare the graph of the first firework to the graph of the second firework. What do you notice?**

Assignment

Practice

1. A nutrition company has determined that the fixed cost associated with producing cases of its special health bars is $1000. The variable cost is $\frac{3}{4}x + 25$ dollars per case that they produce. The selling price of the cases of health bars is $135 - \frac{1}{4}x$ per case that they sell.

   a. Determine the cost function $C(x)$ for this product based on the number of cases, x, that they produce and sell. Simplify if necessary.

   b. Determine the revenue function $R(x)$ for this product based on the number of cases, x, that they produce and sell. Simplify if necessary.

   c. The profit that a company makes is the difference between the revenue and the cost. Determine the profit function $P(x)$ for this product.

   d. Determine when the company will break even.

   e. If they make and sell fewer than 10 cases of health bars, will they have a positive or negative profit? Explain your reasoning.

   f. If they make and sell more than 100 cases of health bars, will they have a positive or negative profit? Explain your reasoning.

   g. Determine how many units the company must produce and sell to make a profit of at least $1800.

2. Solve each inequality.

   a. $2y^2 + 2y - 12 > 0$

   b. $x^2 + 6x \leq 0$

   c. $4b^2 + 14b + 16 < 10$

   d. $a^2 \geq 4(2a - 3)$

   e. $2t^2 > 9t + 18$

   f. $k^2 + 3k + 2 < -3(k + 2)$

Stretch

1. Marelby and Merily both started their own companies with $3000. Marelby's profits can be represented as $g(x) \geq x^2 - 5x + 3$. Merily's profits can be represented by $h(x) \leq -x^2 + 5x + 3$. Graph the solutions to the quadratic inequalities and state what the shaded region means in regards to Marelby and Merily's profits.

Review

1. Determine each product.

   a. $(3x - 9)^2$ b. $(6x^2 + 5x + 4)(-x - 3)$

2. Solve each equation.

   a. $x^2 = 5x - 4$ b. $x^2 + 9x - 23 = 0$

3. Determine the roots of each function.

   a. $f(x) = (x + 5)^2 + 9$ b. $g(x) = x^2 - 3x + 5$

All Systems Are Go!

Systems of Quadratic Equations

Warm Up

Solve each system of equations.

1. $\begin{cases} y = 2x - 5 \\ y = x - 1 \end{cases}$

2. $\begin{cases} y = -3x + 2 \\ y = 5x - 6 \end{cases}$

3. $\begin{cases} y = -2x + 7 \\ y = -4x + 3 \end{cases}$

4. $\begin{cases} y = 3x + 7 \\ y = x + 1 \end{cases}$

Learning Goals

- Solve systems of a linear equation and a quadratic equation.
- Solve systems of two quadratic equations.

You have solved systems of linear equations graphically by determining the point of intersection and algebraically using substitution. How can you use these same methods to solve systems involving a linear and a quadratic equation or systems of two quadratic equations?

Block That Kick!

A punter kicks a football. The height of the football, in meters, is modeled by the function $h(t) = -4.9t^2 + 20t + 0.75$, where t represents time, in seconds. A blocker can only attempt to knock down the football as it travels upward from the punter's foot. The height in meters of the approaching blocker's hands is modeled by the function $h(t) = -0.6t + 3$, where t represents the same time. Can the blocker knock down the football?

1. **Describe the shape of the functions that model the football's height over time and the height of the blocker's hands over time.**

2. **Sketch a graph of the situation. Do you think it is possible for the blocker to knock down the football? Explain your reasoning.**

A system of equations can involve nonlinear equations, such as quadratic equations. The scenario described in the previous activity models the relationship between a quadratic and a linear equation.

1. **Use technology to sketch the graph of the system described in the previous activity.**

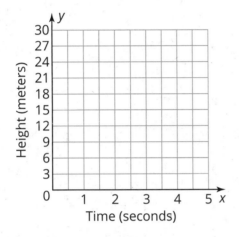

2. **How many solutions does the system have? Explain your reasoning.**

3. **Does every solution make sense in the context of the problem situation? Explain your reasoning.**

4. **Use the graph to approximate at what point the blocker can block the football. Interpret your solution in the context of the problem.**

Methods for solving a system of non-linear equations can be similar to methods for solving a system of linear equations.

1. Consider the system of a linear equation and a quadratic equation shown.

$$\begin{cases} y = 2x + 7 \\ y = x^2 + 4 \end{cases}$$

Ask yourself:

Since y is equal to two different expressions, can you set the expressions equal to each other?

a. Write a new equation you can use to solve this system.

b. Solve the resulting equation for x.

c. Calculate the corresponding values for y.

d. Identify the solution(s) to the system of equations.

e. **Graph each equation of the system and calculate the points of intersection.**

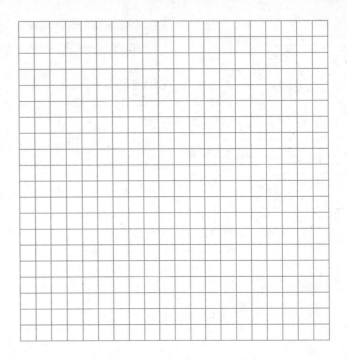

f. **What do you notice about the solutions you calculated algebraically and graphically?**

2. **Think about the graphs of a linear equation and a quadratic equation. Describe the different ways in which the two graphs can intersect and provide a sketch of each case.**

3. Solve each system of equations algebraically over the set of real numbers. Then verify the solution graphically.

a. $\begin{cases} y = -2x + 4 \\ y = 4x^2 + 2x + 5 \end{cases}$

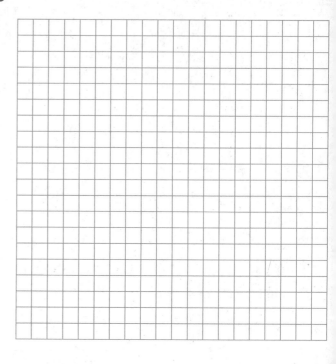

b. $\begin{cases} y = -4x - 7 \\ y = 3x^2 + x - 3 \end{cases}$

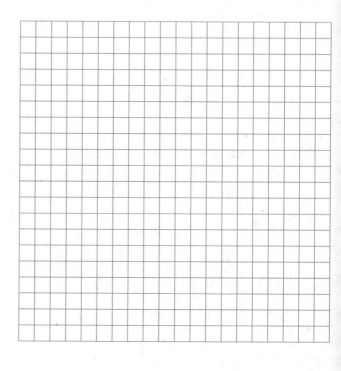

You have solved quadratic equations and systems of linear and quadratic
equations. In this activity, you will apply your knowledge of these concepts
to solve a system of two quadratic equations.

1. **Consider the system of two quadratic equations.**

    $$\begin{cases} y = x^2 + 3x - 5 \\ y = -x^2 + 10x - 1 \end{cases}$$

    a. **Use substitution to solve the system algebraically.**

    b. **Solve the system graphically. Graph
        each equation of the system and
        determine the points of intersection.**

    c. **What do you notice about the
        solutions you calculated algebraically
        and graphically?**

2. **Think about the graphs of two quadratic equations. Describe
    the different ways in which the two graphs can intersect and
    provide a sketch of each case.**

3. **Solve each system of equations algebraically over the set of real numbers. Then verify the solution graphically.**

a. $\begin{cases} y = x^2 + 2x + 1 \\ y = 2x^2 - x - 3 \end{cases}$

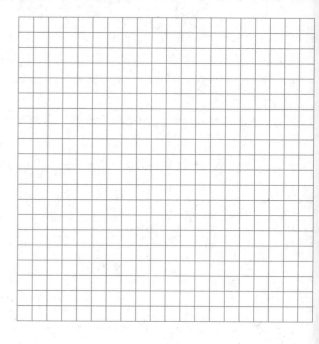

b. $\begin{cases} y = 2x^2 - 7x + 6 \\ y = -2x^2 + 5x - 3 \end{cases}$

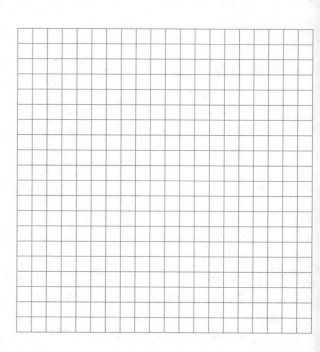

c.
$$\begin{cases} y = x^2 + 5x + 4 \\ y = -x^2 - 5 \end{cases}$$

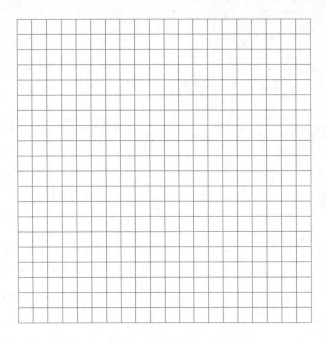

d.
$$\begin{cases} y = x^2 + 4x + 4 \\ y = x^2 + 2x + 6 \end{cases}$$

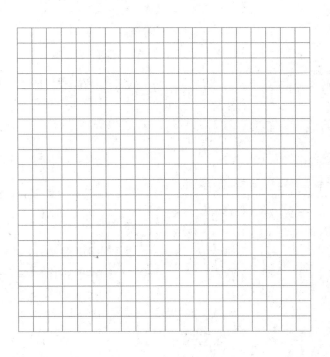

TALK the TALK

System Solutions

1. A system of equations consisting of two linear equations has how many possible solutions?

2. A system of equations consisting of two quadratic equations has how many possible solutions?

3. A system of equations consisting of a linear equation and a quadratic equation has how many possible solutions?

4. Explain why a system of equations consisting of a linear equation and a quadratic equation cannot have an infinite number of solutions.

Assignment

Write

Describe how a graph can be used to determine the solutions to a system of nonlinear equations in your own words.

Remember

A system of equations consisting of a linear and a quadratic equation can have no solution, one solution, or two solutions. A system of equations consisting of two quadratic equations can have no solution, one solution, two solutions, or an infinite number of solutions.

Practice

1. The Fandango Bike Company specializes in children's bikes. Each month, the company must keep track of their costs and revenue. Their costs consist of fixed costs that include rent, utilities, and workers' salaries, as well as the variable cost to make the bikes. The company's costs can be represented by the function $C(x) = 25x + 900$. The company's revenue for every bike sold can be represented by the function $R(x) = 100x - x^2$.

   a. Determine the break-even point(s) for the month.

   b. What is the solution to this system of equations? Explain what the solution means in terms of the problem.

   c. Verify the solution by graphing both the cost and the revenue equations and interpreting the points of intersection.

2. Due to the rising costs of running a business, the Fandango Bike Company anticipates fixed costs in the next year to be \$1800 per month, whereas the cost to make each bike will stay at \$25 per bike.

   a. Determine the number of bikes the company will now need to make for one month to break even if the revenue from selling bikes remains the same.

   b. Verify the solution by graphing both the revenue and the cost equations.

   c. What does the company need to do to be able to break even for the month?

3. The company decides to change its location to a new building that is more energy efficient in order to help decrease fixed costs. It also invests in new machinery to reduce the number of employee hours needed to make a bike. The new monthly cost equation is represented by $C = 0.4x^2 + 15x + 400$. The company then decides to sell the bikes strictly online. The new monthly revenue equation becomes $R = 100x + 0.6x^2$.

   a. Determine the break-even point(s) for the company for each month.

   b. Verify the solution by graphing both the revenue and the cost equations and interpreting the points of intersection.

Stretch

Graph the inequalities given and describe what the double shaded region means in your own words.

$$\begin{cases} y > 2x + 5 \\ y \le -3x^2 + 15x \end{cases}$$

Review

1. Rewrite the radical $\sqrt{72}$ by extracting a perfect square.

2. Solve $x^2 - 12 = 5$.

3. Perform each operation.

    a. $(7x^3 + 5x^2 - 8x) + (3x^3 - 4x^2 + 11)$ b. $(6x - 2y) - (3x - 5y)$.

4. A soccer ball is kicked up off a 5-meter-high platform with an initial velocity of 27 meters per second.

    a. Write an inequality to represent when the soccer ball will be above 40 meters.

    b. Graph the inequality and state when the soccer ball will be above 40 meters.

Model Behavior

Using Quadratic Functions to Model Data

Warm Up

1. Determine a linear regression equation that best models the data.

x	y
1	32
2	35
3	34
4	35
5	39
6	38
7	40
8	42
9	41

Learning Goals

- Use a quadratic function to model data.
- Interpret characteristics of a quadratic function in terms of a problem situation.
- Use graphs of quadratic functions to make predictions.
- Interpret the inverse of a function in terms of a problem situation.
- Determine the inverse of a quadratic function using a graph.
- Determine the equation of the inverse of a quadratic function.
- Determine whether given functions are one-to-one functions.
- Identify function types that are always, sometimes, or never one-to-one functions.

Key Terms

- restrict the domain
- one-to-one function

You know how to model data with regression equations and how to write inverses of linear functions. How can you determine whether a quadratic regression equation may best model the data, and whether the inverse of a quadratic function is also a function?

That Might Be a Bad Idea. . .

A 12-ounce can of soda was put into a freezer. The table shows the volume of the soda in the can, measured at different temperatures.

The first step of the modeling process is to notice and wonder. What do you notice about the data? Is there a question it brings to mind that you wonder about?

Temperature of Can (°F)	Soda Volume cm³
68.0	355.51
50.0	354.98
42.8	354.89
39.2	354.88
35.6	354.89
32.0	354.93
23.0	355.13
14.0	355.54

1. **Describe the data distribution.**

2. **Create a scatter plot of the data. Sketch the plot of points on the coordinate plane shown.**

The second step of the modeling process is to organize and mathematize. The scatter plot is a way to organize the data.

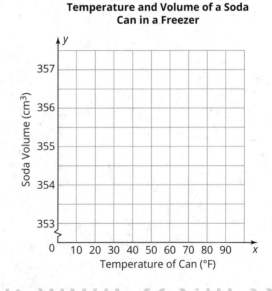

Temperature and Volume of a Soda Can in a Freezer

Using Quadratic Functions to Model Data

Let's continue to analyze the data and make some predictions about the volume of soda at different temperatures.

1. **Use technology to calculate the regression equation that best models the data in the previous activity. Sketch the graph of the regression equation on the coordinate plane on which you created your scatter plot. Explain why the regression equation best models the data.**

   You can mathematize the data by modeling it with an appropriate regression equation.

2. **State the domain and range of your function. How do they compare to the domain and range of this problem situation?**

3. **Use the regression equation to answer each question.**

   a. **Determine the *y*-intercept and interpret its meaning in terms of this problem situation.**

   The third step of the modeling process is to predict and analyze and the fourth step is to test and interpret. These questions focus on these two steps of the process.

   b. **Determine the *x*-intercepts, and interpret the meaning of each in terms of this problem situation.**

4. Predict the volume of the soda can when the temperature is:

   a. 20°F.   b. 60°F.

5. Write a summary of the problem situation, your model as the solution, and any limitations of your model.

Analyzing a Quadratic Model and Its Inverse

Arlen City Police Department is offering special classes for interested high school students this summer. Elsa decides to enroll in an introductory forensic science class. On the first day, Dr. Suarez tells Elsa's class that crime scenes often involve speeding vehicles which leave skid marks on the road as evidence. Taking into account the road surface, weather conditions, the percent grade of the road, and vehicle type, they use this function:

$$f(s) = 0.034s^2 + 0.96s - 26.6$$

to determine the length in feet of skid marks left by a vehicle based on its speed, s, in miles per hour.

1. **Complete the table based on $f(s)$. Label the column titles with the independent and dependent quantities and their units.**

25	
30	
45	
55	
60	
75	
90	
100	
110	

2. **According to the table, what are the domain and range for the problem situation?**

3. **Graph the table values and sketch the graph of $f(s)$ on the grid shown. Label the axes.**

During another class period, Dr. Suarez takes Elsa's class to a mock crime scene to collect evidence.

4. One piece of evidence is a skid mark that is 300 feet long.

   a. Use the graph to estimate the speed of the vehicle that created this skid mark. Explain your process.

   b. Determine the exact speed of the vehicle that created this skid mark. Show your work.

Ask yourself:

How do these data differ from the data in the table?

5. Describe a new function that Elsa can use to determine the speed of a vehicle given the length of a skid mark it created. In your description, include information about the independent and dependent variables, and the domain and range of this problem situation.

6. **Predict what you think the graph of the new function will look like and sketch the graph on the grid shown.**

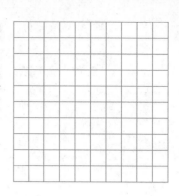

7. **Use your graph to estimate the car's speed before stopping for each given skid mark length.**

   a. **50 feet**

   b. **175 feet**

   c. **350 feet**

8. **Write a report about the length of skid marks left by vehicles and vehicle speeds. Discuss possible factors that would affect the length of the skid marks left by a vehicle, and what effect these factors would have on the graph of $f(s)$ and the graph of its inverse.**

You have determined inverses of linear functions by reflecting a function across the line $y = x$. Consider the basic quadratic function $f(x) = x^2$.

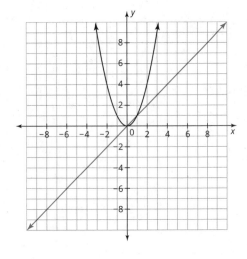

1. **Use patty paper to reflect $f(x)$ across the line $y = x$ to graph its inverse.**

2. **Explain why the inverse is not a function based on its graph.**

3. **What is the domain and range of the function? What is the domain and range of the inverse of the function?**

You can determine the equation of the inverse of the basic quadratic function $f(x) = x^2$ the same way you determined the equation of the inverse of a linear function.

Determining the equations of the inverses of exponential and linear absolute value functions is a bit more complicated, and beyond the scope of this course.

Worked Example

$$f(x) = x^2$$

Step 1: Replace $f(x)$ with y. $\qquad\qquad\qquad y = x^2$
Step 2: Switch the x and y variables. $\qquad\quad x = y^2$
Step 3: Solve for y. $\qquad\qquad\qquad\qquad \pm\sqrt{x} = y$

So, the equation of the inverse is $y = \pm\sqrt{x}$.

4. **Explain why the inverse is not a function based on its equation.**

You know that the inverse of $f(x) = x^2$ is not a function. However, you can *restrict the domain* of this function so that the inverse is also a function. To **restrict the domain** of a function means to define a new domain for the function that is a subset of the original domain.

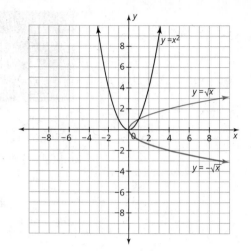

5. Consider the graph of $f(x) = x^2$ and the graphs of the two equations that represent its inverse.

a. Identify the restrictions of $f(x) = x^2$ to produce the inverse equations $y = \sqrt{x}$ and $y = -\sqrt{x}$. Then state the domain and range of each inverse.

Restrictions for $y = x^2$ $y = \sqrt{x}$

Domain: _____   Domain: _____

Range: _____   Range: _____

Restrictions for $y = x^2$ $y = -\sqrt{x}$

Domain: _____   Domain: _____

Range: _____   Range: _____

b. How does the domain and range of the inverse relate to the restricted domain and range of the original function?

c. Do all the graphs represent functions? Explain your reasoning.

More with Inverses of Quadratics

Marissa is competing in the Egg Drop Competition at her school's Science Fair. Competitors in the Egg Drop Competition are required to create a container in which they place a raw egg, and then drop the container from various heights to see if the egg breaks. The winner of the contest is the person whose container is dropped from the greatest height without breaking the egg.

Marissa is testing a container she built for the competition. She placed an egg in her container and dropped it from the roof of a building. The height of the egg can be modeled by the function $f(x) = -16x^2 + 64$, where x represents the time in seconds.

1. **Define the independent and dependent quantities of $f(x)$.**

2. **What is the domain and range of $f(x)$ based on its equation?**

3. **Determine any restrictions on the domain of $f(x)$ based on this problem situation. Explain your reasoning.**

4. Graph $f(x) = -16x^2 + 64$ with the restricted domain based on this problem situation. Be sure to label your graph.

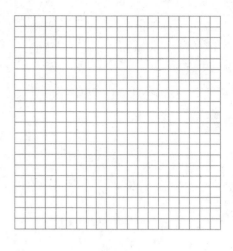

5. Define the independent and dependent quantities of the inverse of $f(x)$.

6. What is the domain and range of the inverse of $f(x)$ with the restricted domain?

7. Graph the inverse of $f(x)$ with the restricted domain. You may use different bounds than you used in Question 4.

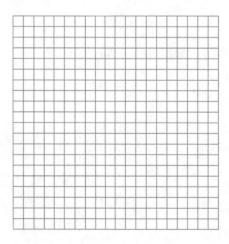

8. Explain why the inverse of $f(x)$ with the restricted domain is a function. Then, write an equation for the inverse.

9. Explain what the inverse models in terms of this problem situation.

10. After 1.5 seconds, what is the egg's height? Explain which function you used and how you determined your answer.

11. After how many seconds is the egg at a height of 55 feet? Explain which function you used and how you determined your answer.

TALK the TALK

1-2-1

In a previous lesson, you determined the inverses of linear functions. You also determined whether the inverses were also functions.

A function is a **one-to-one function** if both the function and its inverse are functions.

1. **Adam and Stacey are working on a homework assignment in which they must identify all functions that are one-to-one functions. Adam says that all linear functions are one-to-one functions, so they don't even need to look at the linear functions. Stacey disagrees, and says that not all linear functions are one-to-one functions. Who is correct? Explain how you determined which student is correct.**

2. **Complete each sentence with *always*, *sometimes*, or *never*.**

   a. **A linear function is _____ a one-to-one function.**

   b. **An exponential function is _____ a one-to-one function.**

   c. **A quadratic function is _____ a one-to-one function.**

   d. **A linear absolute value function is _____ a one-to-one function.**

Assignment

Write

Write a definition for each term in your own words.

1. restricted domain
2. one-to-one function

Remember

Quadratic regression equations can be used to model real-world situations.

Algebraically determining the inverse of a quadratic function is the same process as determining the inverse of a linear function.

Practice

1. The table shows the percent of public schools with internet access from 1994 to 2005. (The largest growth years are shown in the table.)

   a. Predict whether a linear or quadratic regression equation will best fit the data. Explain your reasoning.

   b. Create a scatter plot of the data.

   c. Does your scatter plot change or support your answer to part (a)? Explain your reasoning.

2. Andrew thinks a quadratic regression equation would best fit the data.

   a. Calculate the quadratic regression equation of the data. Do you agree with Andrew? Explain your reasoning.

Year	Percent of Public Schools with Internet Access
1994	35
1995	50
1996	65
1997	78
1998	89
1999	95
2000	98
2001	99
2002	99
2003	100
2005	100

   b. Year 2004 is missing from the data. Calculate the percent of public schools with internet access in 2004. Does your answer make sense in terms of the problem situation? Explain your reasoning.

   c. Calculate the percent of public schools with internet access in 2020. Does your answer make sense in terms of the problem situation? Explain your reasoning.

   d. What are the x-intercepts and what do they mean in terms of the problem situation?

   e. In what year does the percent of public schools with internet access begin to decline? Explain how you determined your answer.

   f. Do you think it is likely that the percent of public schools with internet access will decline? Explain your reasoning.

3. The number of catfish in Lake Paul is growing in a way that can be represented by the quadratic function $c(x) = 2x^2 + 50$, where x represents the number of months since the initial number of catfish was counted.

   a. Determine any restrictions on the domain of $c(x)$ based on the problem situation. Explain your reasoning.

   b. Graph $c(x)$ with the restricted domain based on the problem situation. Be sure to label your graph.

   c. What is the domain and range of the inverse of $c(x)$ with the restricted domain?

   d. Graph the inverse of $c(x)$ with the restricted domain. Be sure to label your graph.

   e. Explain why the inverse of $c(x)$ with the restricted domain is a function. Then, write an equation for its inverse.

   f. If there are 178 catfish in the lake, how many months have gone by since the initial number of catfish was counted? Explain your reasoning.

   g. Five months have gone by since the initial counting of the catfish. How many catfish are in Lake Paul now? Explain your reasoning.

4. Determine the inverse of each function.

   a. $y = x^2 - 9$ b. $y = (x + 4)^2$ c. $y = (x - 3)^2 + 7$ d. $y = x^2 + 5$

Stretch

1. The base of a triangle is represented as $6x$. The height of a triangle is represented as $4x$.

   a. What is the equation for the inverse of the area of the triangle? Explain your reasoning.

   b. If the area of the triangle is 108 meters, what is the value of the inverse of the function? Explain your reasoning.

Review

1. Consider the each function shown.

   $t(x) = (x - 3)^2$

   a. Graph each function on the same coordinate plane.

   $w(x) = 3(x - 3)^2$

   b. Describe how functions w and z have been transformed from function t.

   $z(x) = 3(x - 3)^2 + 1$

2. Consider the function $f(x) = x^2 - 2x - 2$.

   a. Graph the function.

   b. Describe the key characteristics of the graph.

3. The cost of producing chapter books for a company is $C(x) = 6x + 81$. The company's revenue for every chapter book sold is $R(x) = 36x - x^2$.

   a. What is the company's break-even point for the production and sales of chapter books?

   b. What does the solution mean?

   c. Show the solution graphically.

Applications of Quadratics Summary

KEY TERMS

- restrict the domain
- one-to-one function

LESSON
1   Ahead of the Curve

Just like with the other inequalities you have studied, the solution to a quadratic inequality is the set of values that satisfy the inequality.

For example, consider the inequality $x^2 - 4x + 3 < 0$.

Write the corresponding quadratic equation.

$$x^2 - 4x + 3 = 0$$

Calculate the roots of the quadratic equation using an appropriate method.

$$(x - 3)(x - 1) = 0$$
$$(x - 3) = 0 \text{ or } (x - 1) = 0$$
$$x = 3 \text{ or } \quad x = 1$$

Plot the roots to divide the number line into three regions.

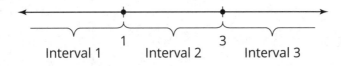

Interval 1   Interval 2   Interval 3

Choose a value from each interval to test in the original inequality. Identify the solution set as the interval(s) in which your test value satisfies the inequality.

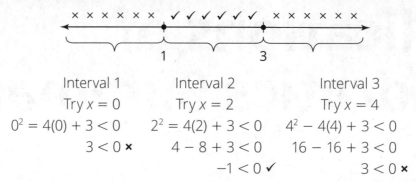

$$0^2 = 4(0) + 3 < 0$$
$$3 < 0 \times$$

Interval 1
Try $x = 0$
$$0^2 = 4(0) + 3 < 0$$
$$3 < 0 \times$$

Interval 2
Try $x = 2$
$$2^2 = 4(2) + 3 < 0$$
$$4 - 8 + 3 < 0$$
$$-1 < 0 \checkmark$$

Interval 3
Try $x = 4$
$$4^2 - 4(4) + 3 < 0$$
$$16 - 16 + 3 < 0$$
$$3 < 0 \times$$

Interval 2 satisfies the original inequality, so the solution includes all numbers between 1 and 3. Solution: $x \in (1, 3)$, or $1 < x < 3$.

LESSON 2

All Systems Are Go!

The graph of a linear equation and the graph of a quadratic equation can intersect at two points, at one point, or not at all. The graphs of two quadratic equations can intersect at two points, at one point, at an infinite number of points, or not at all.

The method to determine the solution or solutions of a system involving quadratic equations is similar to solving a system of linear equations. First, substitute one equation into the other. Then, solve the resulting equation for x and calculate the corresponding values for y. These values represent the point(s) of intersection. Finally, graph each equation of the system to verify the points of intersection.

$$\begin{cases} y = 5x^2 + 8x + 6 \\ y = x^2 - 4x - 3 \end{cases}$$

$$x^2 - 4x - 3 = 5x^2 + 8x + 6$$
$$0 = 4x^2 + 12x + 9$$
$$0 = (2x + 3)(2x + 3)$$

$$2x + 3 = 0$$
$$2x = -3$$
$$x = -\frac{3}{2}$$
$$y = \left(-\frac{3}{2}\right)^2 - 4\left(-\frac{3}{2}\right) - 3$$
$$= 5\frac{1}{4}$$

The system has one solution: $\left(-\frac{3}{2}, 5\frac{1}{4}\right)$.

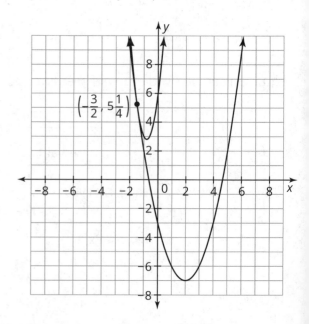

Model Behavior

Quadratic regression equations can be used to model real-world situations and make predictions.

For example, as vans, trucks, and SUVs have increased in popularity, the fuel consumption of these types of vehicles has also increased.

Years Since 1980	Fuel Consumption (billions of gallons)
0	23.8
5	27.4
10	35.6
15	45.6
19	52.8

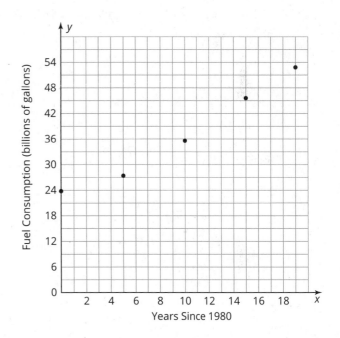

The quadratic regression equation that best fits the data is $y = 0.0407x^2 + 0.809x + 23.3$. The r^2 value for the quadratic regression fit is 0.996. Just as with linear and exponential regressions, the equation can be used to make predictions for the data.

For example, you can predict the fuel consumption in the year 2020 by substituting $x = 40$ into the regression equation.

$y = 0.0407(40)^2 + 0.809(40) + 23.3$
$y \approx 121$

In 2020, fuel consumption will be about 121 billion gallons.

Depending on the information given in a problem situation, a function or its inverse could be used to draw conclusions from the data.

A function is a **one-to-one function** if both the function and its inverse are functions.

A linear and exponential function are always one-to-one functions, but a quadratic function is not. Therefore, you need to restrict the domain of the original quadratic function so that the inverse is also a function. To **restrict the domain** of a function means to define a new domain for the function that is a subset of the original domain.

For example, you can determine the equation of the inverse of the basic quadratic function $f(x) = x^2$ by first restricting the domain to $x > 0$, replacing $f(x)$ with y, switching the x and y variables, and solving for y.

$$f(x) = x^2$$
$$y = x^2$$
$$x = y^2$$
$$y = \sqrt{x}$$

The inverse of $f(x) = x^2$ is $f^{-1}(x) = \sqrt{x}$ for $x > 0$.

Glossary

A

absolute maximum

A function has an absolute maximum if there is a point that has a y-coordinate that is greater than the y-coordinates of every other point on the graph.

Example

The ordered pair (4, 2) is the absolute maximum of the graph of the function $f(x) = -\frac{1}{2}x^2 + 4x - 6$.

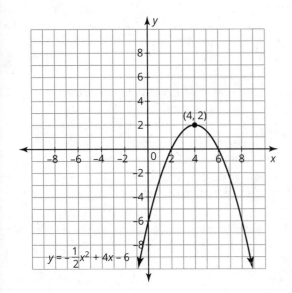

absolute minimum

A function has an absolute minimum if there is a point that has a y-coordinate that is less than the y-coordinates of every other point on the graph.

Example

The ordered pair (1, −4) is the absolute minimum of the graph of the function $y = \frac{2}{3}x^2 - \frac{4}{3}x - \frac{10}{3}$.

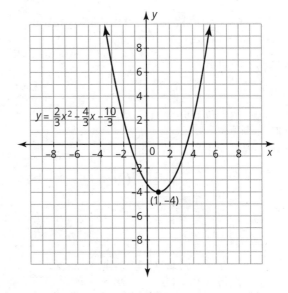

absolute value

The absolute value of a number is its distance from zero on the number line.

Example

$|5| = 5$ because 5 is 5 units from 0 on the number line. $|-3| = 3$ because −3 is 3 units from 0 on the number line.

argument of a function

The argument of a function is the variable on which the function operates.

Example

In the function $f(x + 5) = 32$, the argument is $x + 5$.

arithmetic sequence

An arithmetic sequence is a sequence of numbers in which the difference between any two consecutive terms is a constant.

Example

The sequence 1, 3, 5, 7 is an arithmetic sequence with a common difference of 2.

average rate of change

Another name for the slope of a linear function is average rate of change. The formula for the average rate of change is $\frac{f(t) - f(s)}{t - s}$.

Example

The average rate of change of the function shown is 3.

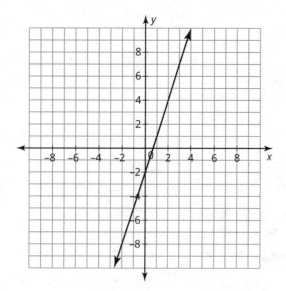

axis of symmetry

The axis of symmetry of a parabola is the vertical line that passes through the vertex and divides the parabola into two mirror images.

Example

Line K is the axis of symmetry of this parabola.

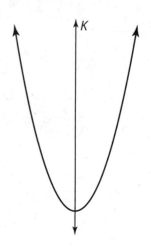

B

---

basic function

A basic function is the simplest function of its type.

Example

The basic linear function is $f(x) = x$.
The basic exponential function is $g(x) = 2^x$.
The basic quadratic function is $h(x) = x^2$.

bin

The width of a bar in a histogram represents an interval of data and is often referred to as a bin.

binomial

Polynomials with exactly two terms are binomials.

Example

The polynomial $3x + 5$ is a binomial.

boundary line

A boundary line, determined by the inequality in a linear inequality, divides the plane into two half-planes and the inequality symbol indicates which half-plane contains all the solutions.

Example

For the linear inequality $y > -x + 8$, the boundary line is a dashed line because no point on that line is a solution.

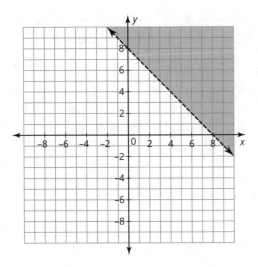

box-and-whisker plot

A box-and-whisker plot displays a data distribution based on a five-number summary.

Example

The box-and-whisker plots compare the test scores from two algebra classes.

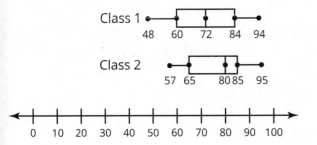

categorical data

Data that can be grouped into categories are called categorical data.

causation

Causation is when one event affects the outcome of a second event.

centroid

The centroid is a point whose x-value is the mean of all the x-values of the points on the scatter plot and its y-value is the mean of all the y-values of the points on the scatter plot.

Example

For the data points (1, 3), (1, 7), (2, 6), (3, 5), and (3, 4), the centroid is (2, 5).

closed (closure)

When an operation is performed on any of the numbers in a set and the result is a number that is also in the same set, the set is said to be closed (or to have closure) under that operation.

Example

The set of whole numbers is closed under addition. The sum of any two whole numbers is always another whole number.

coefficient of determination

The coefficient of determination measures how well the graph of a regression fits the data. It is calculated by squaring the correlation coefficient and represents the percentage of variation of the observed values of the data points from their predicted values.

Example

The correlation coefficient for a data set is -0.9935. The coefficient of determination for the same data set is approximately 0.987, which means 98.7% of the data values should fall on the graph.

common difference

The difference between any two consecutive terms in an arithmetic sequence is called the common difference. It is typically represented by the variable d.

Example

The sequence 1, 3, 5, 7 is an arithmetic sequence with a common difference of 2.

common ratio

The ratio between any two consecutive terms in a geometric sequence is called the common ratio. It is typically represented by the variable r.

Example

The sequence 2, 4, 8, 16 is a geometric sequence with a common ratio of 2.

common response

A common response is when a variable other than the ones measured cause the same result as the one observed in the experiment.

completing the square

Completing the square is a process for writing a quadratic expression in vertex form which then allows you to solve for the zeros.

complex numbers

The set of complex numbers is the set of all numbers written in the form $a + bi$, where a and b are real numbers.

compound inequality

A compound inequality is an inequality that is formed by the union, "or," or the intersection, "and," of two simple inequalities.

Example

The statement $x > 5$ or $x < -5$ is a compound inequality.

compound interest

In a compound interest account, the balance is multiplied by the same amount at each interval.

Example

Sonya opens a savings account with $100. She earns $4 in compound interest the first year. The compound interest y is found by using the equation $y = 100(1 + 0.04)^t$, where t is the time in years.

conditional relative frequency distribution

A conditional relative frequency distribution is the percent or proportion of occurrences of a category given the specific value of another category.

confounding variable

A confounding variable is when there are other variables in an experiment that are unknown or unobserved.

conjecture

A conjecture is a mathematical statement that appears to be true, but has not been formally proven.

conjunction

A compound inequality in the form $a < x < b$, where a and b are any real numbers, is a conjunction.

Example

The compound inequality $x \leq 1$ and $x > -3$ is a conjunction.

consistent systems

Systems that have one or many solutions are called consistent systems.

constant function

If the dependent variable of a function does not change or remains constant over the entire domain, then the function is called a constant function.

Example

The function shown is a constant function.

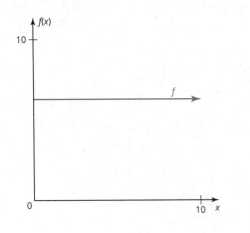

constraints

In a system of linear inequalities, the inequalities are known as constraints because the values of the expressions are "constrained" to lie within a certain region on the graph.

continuous graph

A continuous graph is a graph of points that are connected by a line or smooth curve on the graph. Continuous graphs have no breaks.

Example

The graph shown is a continuous graph.

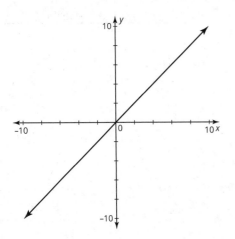

correlation

A measure of how well a regression fits a set of data is called a correlation.

correlation coefficient

The correlation coefficient is a value between −1 and 1, which indicates how close the data are to the graph of the regression equation. The closer the correlation coefficient is to −1 or 1, the stronger the relationship is between the two variables. The variable r is used to represent the correlation coefficient.

Example

The correlation coefficient for these data is −0.9935. The value is negative because the equation has a negative slope. The value is close to −1 because the data are very close to the graph of the equation of the line.

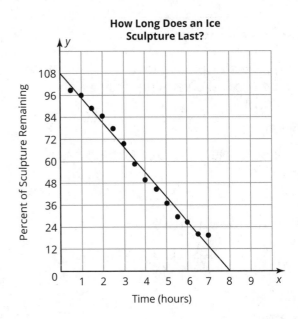

decreasing function

If a function decreases across the entire domain, then the function is called a decreasing function.

Example

The function shown is a decreasing function.

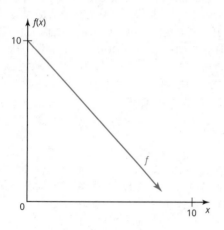

degree of a polynomial

The greatest exponent for any variable term in a polynomial determines the degree of the polynomial.

Example

The polynomial $2x^3 + 5x^2 - 6x + 1$ has a degree of 3.

dependent quantity

When one quantity depends on another in a problem situation, it is said to be the dependent quantity.

Example

In the relationship between driving time and distance traveled, distance is the dependent quantity, because distance depends on the driving time.

difference of two squares

The difference of two squares is an expression in the form $a^2 - b^2$ that can be factored as $(a + b)(a - b)$.

discontinuous graph

A discontinuous graph is a graph that is continuous for some values of the domain with at least one disjoint area between consecutive x-values.

Example

The graph shown is a discontinuous graph.

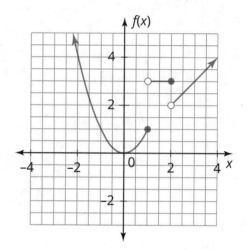

discrete graph

A discrete graph is a graph of isolated points.

Example

The graph shown is a discrete graph.

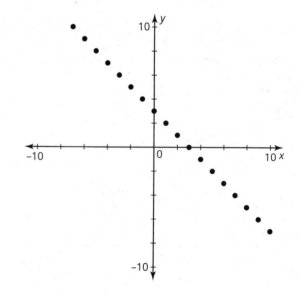

discriminant

The discriminant is the radicand expression in the Quadratic Formula which "discriminates" the number of real roots of a quadratic equation.

Example

The discriminant in the Quadratic Formula is the expression $b^2 - 4ac$.

disjunction

A compound inequality in the form $x < a$ or $x > b$, where a and b are any real numbers, is a disjunction.

Example

The compound inequality $x < -2$ or $x > 1$ is a disjunction.

domain

The domain is the set of input values in a relation.

Example

The domain of the function $y = 2x$ is the set of all real numbers.

dot plot

A dot plot is a graph that shows how discrete data are distributed using a number line.

Example

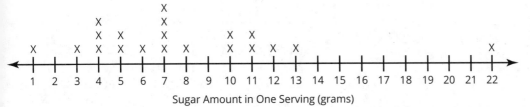

Sugar in Breakfast Cereals

Sugar Amount in One Serving (grams)

double root

The root of an equation indicates where the graph of the equation crosses the x-axis. A double root occurs when the graph just touches the x-axis but does not cross it.

Example

The quadratic equation $y = (x - 2)^2$ has a double root at $x = 2$.

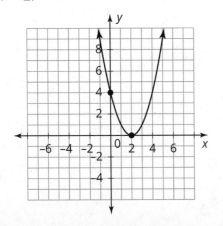

E

equivalent compound inequality

A compound inequality that is the equivalent of an absolute value inequality.

Example

Absolute Value Inequality	Equivalent Compound Inequality
$|ax + b| < c$	$-c < ax + b < c$
$|ax + b| \le c$	$-c \le ax + b \le c$
$|ax + b| > c$	$ax + b < -c$ or $ax + b > c$
$|ax + b| \ge c$	$ax + b \le -c$ or $ax + b \ge c$

explicit formula

An explicit formula of a sequence is a formula for calculating the value of each term of a sequence using the term's position in the sequence. The explicit formula for an arithmetic sequence is $a_n = a_1 + d(n - 1)$. The explicit formula for a geometric sequence is $g_n = g_1 \cdot r^{n-1}$.

Example

The sequence 1, 3, 5, 7, 9, . . . can be described by the rule $a_n = 2n - 1$ where n is the position of the term. The fourth term of the sequence a_4 is $2(4) - 1$, or 7.

exponential decay function

An exponential decay function is an exponential function with a b-value greater than 0 and less than 1 and is of the form $y = a \cdot (1 - r)^x$, where r is the rate of decay.

Example

Greenville has a population of 7000. Its population is decreasing at a rate of 1.75%. The exponential decay function that models this situation is $f(x) = 7000 \cdot 0.9825^x$.

exponential functions

The family of exponential functions includes functions of the form $f(x) = a \cdot b^x$, where a and b are real numbers, and b is greater than 0 but is not equal to 1.

Example

The function $f(x) = 2^x$ is an exponential function.

exponential growth function

An exponential growth function is an exponential function with a b-value greater than 1 and is of the form $y = a \cdot (1 + r)^x$, where r is the rate of growth.

Example

Blueville has a population of 7000. Its population is increasing at a rate of 1.4%. The exponential growth function that models this situation is $f(x) = 7000 \cdot 1.014^x$.

extract the square root

To extract a square root, solve an equation of the form $a^2 = b$ for a.

extrapolation

To make predictions for values of x that are outside of the data set is called extrapolation.

--------------------------------- F ---------------------------------

factored form

A quadratic function written in factored form is in the form $f(x) = a(x - r_1)(x - r_2)$, where $a \neq 0$.

Example

The function $h(x) = x^2 - 8x + 12$ written in factored form is $(x - 6)(x - 2)$.

finite sequence

If a sequence terminates, it is called a finite sequence.

Example

The sequence 22, 26, 30 is a finite sequence.

first differences

First differences are the values determined by subtracting consecutive output values in a table when the input values have an interval of 1.

Example

	Time (minutes)	Height (feet)	First Differences
	0	0	1800 − 0 = 1800
$1 - 0 = 1$	1	1800	3600 − 1800 = 1800
$2 - 1 = 1$	2	3600	5400 − 3600 = 1800
$3 - 2 = 1$	3	5400	

five-number summary

The five-number summary consists of the minimum value, the first quartile (Q1), the median, the third quartile (Q3), and the maximum value.

Example

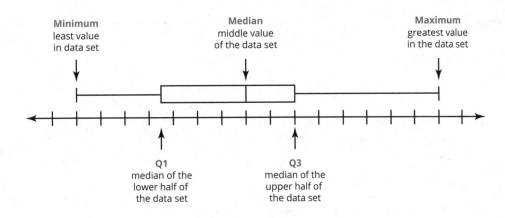

frequency

The height of each bar in a histogram indicates the frequency, which is the number of data values included in any given bin.

frequency distribution

A frequency distribution displays the frequencies for categorical data in a two-way table.

Example

Favorite Meals of Students

Grade Level	Burgers	Chicken Nuggets	Pizza	Salad Bar	Total
9th grade	4	1	3	5	13
10th grade	3	7	3	4	17
Total	7	8	6	9	30

function

A function is a relation that assigns to each element of the domain exactly one element of the range.

Example

The equation $y = 2x$ is a function. Every value of x has exactly one corresponding y-value.

function family

A function family is a group of functions that share certain characteristics.

Example

Linear functions and exponential functions are examples of function families.

function notation

Function notation is a way of representing functions algebraically.

Example

In the function $f(x) = 0.75x$, f is the name of the function, x represents the domain, and $f(x)$ represents the range.

G
---

general form (standard form) of a quadratic function

A quadratic function written in the form $f(x) = ax^2 + bx + c$, where $a \neq 0$, is in general form, or standard form.

Example

The function $f(x) = -5x^2 - 10x + 1$ is written in general form.

geometric sequence

A geometric sequence is a sequence of numbers in which the ratio between any two consecutive terms is a constant.

Example

The sequence 2, 4, 8, 16 is a geometric sequence with a common ratio of 2.

greatest integer function (floor function)

The greatest integer function, also known as a floor function, is defined as the greatest integer less than or equal to x.

Example

For $f(x) = \lfloor x \rfloor$, if $x = 3.16$, $f(x) = 3$.

H
---

half-plane

The graph of a linear inequality is a half-plane, or half of a coordinate plane.

Example

The shaded portion of the graph is a half-plane.

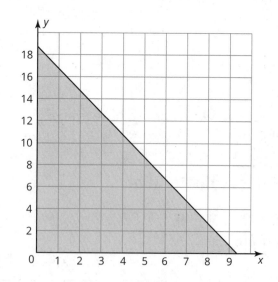

histogram

A histogram is a graphical way to display quantitative data using vertical bars.

Example

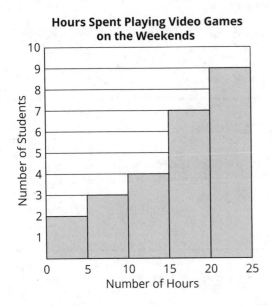

horizontal asymptote

A horizontal asymptote is a horizontal line that a function gets closer and closer to, but never intersects.

Example

The graph shows a horizontal asymptote at $y = -1$.

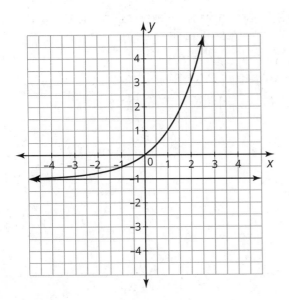

---

imaginary numbers

The set of imaginary numbers is the set of all numbers written in the form $a + bi$, where a and b are real numbers and b is not equal to 0.

imaginary part of a complex number

In a complex number of the form $a + bi$, the term bi is called the imaginary part of a complex number.

imaginary roots/imaginary zeros

Imaginary roots are imaginary solutions to equations. Quadratic functions that do not cross the x-axis have imaginary zeros.

inconsistent systems

Systems with no solution are called inconsistent systems.

increasing function

If a function increases across the entire domain, then the function is called an increasing function.

Example

The function shown is an increasing function.

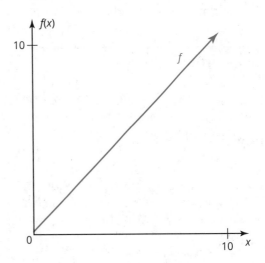

independent quantity

The quantity that the dependent quantity depends upon is called the independent quantity.

Example

In the relationship between driving time and distance traveled, driving time is the independent quantity, because it does not depend on any other quantity.

infinite sequence

If a sequence continues on forever, it is called an infinite sequence.

Example

The sequence 22, 26, 30, 34 . . . is an infinite sequence.

infinite solutions

An equation with infinite solutions means that any value for the variable makes the equation true.

Example

The equation $2x + 1 = 2x + 1$ has infinite solutions.

interpolation

Using a linear regression to make predictions within the data set is called interpolation.

interquartile range (IQR)

The interquartile range, IQR, measures how far the data are spread out from the median.

Example

In the data set 13, 17, 23, 24, 25, 29, 31, 45, 46, 53, 60, the median, 29, divides the data into two halves. The first quartile, 23, is the median of the lower half of the data. The third quartile, 46, is the median of the upper half of the data. The interquartile range is $46 - 23$, or 23.

inverse of a function

An inverse of a function takes the output value, performs some operation(s) on this value, and arrives back at the original function's input value.

Example

The inverse of the function $y = 2x$ is the function $x = 2y$, or $y = \frac{x}{2}$.

—— J ——

joint frequency

Any frequency recorded within the body of a two-way frequency table is known as a joint frequency.

—— L ——

leading coefficient

The leading coefficient of a polynomial is the numeric coefficient of the term with the greatest power.

Example

In the polynomial $-7x^2 + x + 25$, the value -7 is the leading coefficient.

least integer function (ceiling function)

The least integer function, also known as the ceiling function, is defined as the least integer greater than or equal to x.

Example

For $f(x) = \lceil x \rceil$, if $x = 3.16$, $f(x) = 4$.

Least Squares Method

The Least Squares Method is a method that creates a regression line for a scatter plot that has two basic requirements: 1) the line must contain the centroid of the data set, and 2) the sum of the squares of the vertical distances from each given data point is at a minimum with the line.

Example

The regression line shown was created using the Least Squares Method.

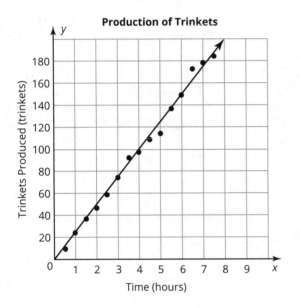

linear absolute value equation

An equation in the form $|x + a| = c$ is a linear absolute value equation.

Example

The equation $|x - 1| = 6$ is a linear absolute value equation.

linear absolute value functions

The family of linear absolute value functions includes functions of the form $f(x) = a|x + b| + c$, where a, b, and c are real numbers, and a is not equal to 0.

Example

The function $f(x) = |x - 3| - 2$ is a linear absolute value function.

linear absolute value inequality

An inequality in the form $|x + a| < c$ is a linear absolute value inequality.

Example

The inequality $|w - 145.045| \leq 3.295$ is a linear absolute value inequality.

linear combinations method

The linear combinations method is a process used to solve a system of equations by adding two equations together, resulting in an equation with one variable.

Example

Solve the following system of equations by using the linear combinations method:

$$\begin{cases} 6x - 5y = 3 \\ 2x + 2y = 12 \end{cases}$$

First, multiply the second equation by -3. Then, add the equations and solve for the remaining variable. Finally, substitute $y = 3$ into the first equation and solve for x. The solution of the system is $(3, 3)$.

linear functions

The family of linear functions includes functions of the form $f(x) = ax + b$, where a and b are real numbers.

Example

The function $f(x) = 3x + 2$ is a linear function.

linear piecewise functions

Linear piecewise functions include linear functions that have equation changes for different parts, or pieces, of the domain.

Example

The function $f(x)$ is a linear piecewise function.

$$f(x) = \begin{cases} x + 5, & x \leq -2 \\ -2x + 1, & -2 < x \leq 2 \\ 2x - 9, & x > 2 \end{cases}$$

linear programming

Linear programming is a branch of mathematics that determines the maximum and minimum value of linear expressions on a region produced by a system of linear inequalities.

line of reflection

A line of reflection is the line that the graph is reflected across.

Example

The graph of $y = |x| + 2$ was reflected across the line of reflection, $y = 0$.

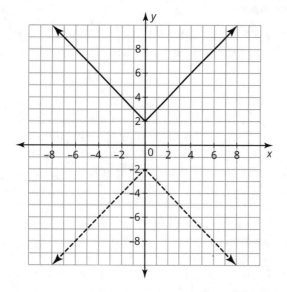

literal equation

Literal equations are equations in which the variables represent specific measures.

Example

The equations $I = Prt$ and $A = lw$ are literal equations.

lower fence

The value of $Q1 - (IQR \cdot 1.5)$ is known as the lower fence.

--- M ---

marginal frequency distribution

A marginal frequency distribution displays the total of the frequencies of the rows or columns of a frequency distribution.

marginal relative frequency distribution

Displaying the relative frequencies for the rows or columns in a two-way table is a marginal relative frequency distribution. The marginal relative frequency distribution provides the ratio of total occurrences for each category to the total number of occurrences.

mathematical modeling

Mathematical modeling is explaining patterns in the real world based on mathematical ideas.

measure of central tendency

A measure of central tendency is a numeric value used to describe the overall clustering of data in a set.

Example

The mean, median, and mode are the most common measures of central tendency.

monomial

Polynomials with only one term are monomials.

Example

The expressions $5x$, 7, $-2xy$, and $13x^3$ are monomials.

necessary condition

A correlation is a necessary condition for causation, meaning that for one variable to cause another, they must be correlated.

no solution

An equation with no solution means that there is no value for the variable that makes the equation true.

Example

The equation $2x + 1 = 2x + 3$ has no solution.

the number i

The number i is a number such that $i^2 = -1$.

one-to-one function

A function is a one-to-one function if both the function and its inverse are functions.

Example

The equation $y = x^3$ is a one-to-one function because its inverse, $\sqrt[3]{x} = y$, is a function. The equation $y = x^2$ is not a one-to-one function because its inverse, $\pm\sqrt{x} = y$, is not a function.

outlier

An outlier is a data value that is significantly greater or lesser than other data values in a data set.

Example

In the data set 1, 1, 3, 3, 4, 4, 5, 1000, the outlier is 1000.

parabola

The shape that a quadratic function forms when graphed is called a parabola. A parabola is a smooth curve with reflectional symmetry.

Example

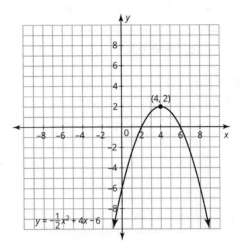

perfect square trinomial

A perfect square trinomial is an expression in the form $a^2 + 2ab + b^2$ or in the form $a^2 - 2ab + b^2$.

piecewise function

A piecewise function is a function that can be represented by more than one function, each which corresponds to a part of the domain.

Example

The graph represents a piecewise function.

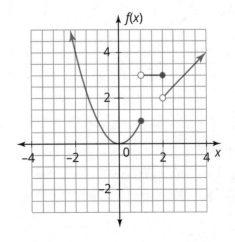

polynomial

A polynomial is a mathematical expression involving the sum of powers in one or more variables multiplied by coefficients.

Example

The expression $3x^3 + 5x - 6x + 1$ is a polynomial.

principal square root

A positive square root of a number.

pure imaginary number

A pure imaginary number is a number of the form bi, where b is not equal to 0.

Q

Quadratic Formula

The Quadratic Formula is $x = \dfrac{-b \pm \sqrt{b^2 - 4ac}}{2a}$, and can be used to calculate the solutions to any quadratic equation of the form $ax^2 + bx + c$, where a, b, and c represent real numbers and $a \neq 0$.

quadratic functions

The family of quadratic functions includes functions of the form $f(x) = ax^2 + bx + c$, where a, b, and c are real numbers, and a is not equal to 0.

Examples

The equations $y = x^2 + 2x + 5$ and $y = -4x^2 - 7x + 1$ are quadratic functions.

R
---

range

The range is the set of output values in a relation.

Example

The range of the function $y = x^2$ is the set of all numbers greater than or equal to zero.

real part of a complex number

In a complex number of the form $a + bi$, the term a is called the real part of a complex number.

recursive formula

A recursive formula expresses each new term of a sequence based on the preceding term in the sequence. The recursive formula for an arithmetic sequence is $a_n = a_{n-1} + d$. The recursive formula for a geometric sequence is $g_n = g_{n-1} \cdot r$.

Example

The formula $a_n = a_{n-1} + 2$ is a recursive formula. Each successive term is calculated by adding 2 to the previous term. If $a_1 = 1$, then $a_2 = 1 + 2 = 3$.

reflection

A reflection of a graph is a mirror image of the graph about a line of reflection.

Example

The triangle on the right is a reflection of the triangle on the left.

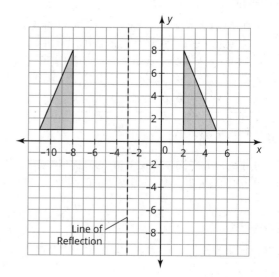

regression line

On a scatter plot, a regression line is a mathematical model that can be used to predict the values of a dependent variable based upon the values of an independent variable.

relation

A relation is the mapping between a set of input values called the domain and a set of output values called the range.

Example

The set of points {(0, 1), (1, 8), (2, 5), (3, 7)} is a relation.

relative frequency distribution

Representing the relative frequencies for joint data displayed in a two-way table is a relative frequency distribution. The relative frequency distribution provides the ratio of occurrences in each category to the total number of occurrences.

residual

A residual is the vertical distance between an observed data value and its predicted value using a regression equation.

residual plot

A residual plot is a scatter plot of the independent variable on the x-axis and the residuals on the y-axis.

Example

The graph on the right shows a residual plot of the braking distance data.

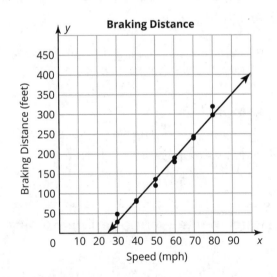

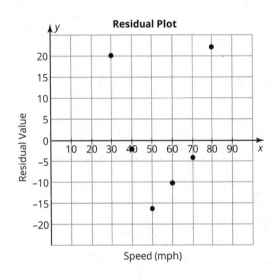

restrict the domain

To restrict the domain of a function means to define a new domain for the function that is a subset of the original domain.

root (roots)

The root or roots of an equation indicate where the graph of the equation crosses the x-axis.

Example

The roots of the quadratic equation $x^2 - 4x + 3 = 0$ are $x = 3$ and $x = 1$.

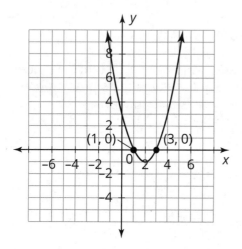

────────── S ──────────

second differences

Second differences are the differences between consecutive values of the first differences.

Example

x	y	First Differences	Second Differences
-3	-5		
		5	
-2	0		-2
		3	
-1	3		-2
		1	
0	4		-2
		-1	
1	3		-2
		-3	
2	0		-2
		-5	
3	-5		

sequence

A sequence is a pattern involving an ordered arrangement of numbers, geometric figures, letters, or other objects.

Example

The numbers 1, 1, 2, 3, 5, 8, 13 form a sequence.

simple interest

In a simple interest account, the interest earned at the end of each interval is a percent of the starting balance (also known as the principal).

Example

Tonya deposits $200 in a 3-year certificate of deposit that earns 4% simple interest. The amount of interest that Tonya earns can be found using the simple interest formula.

$$I = (200)(0.04)(3)$$
$$I = 24$$

Tonya earns $24 in interest.

solution

The solution to an equation is any value for the variable that makes the equation a true statement.

Example

The solution of the equation $3x + 4 = 25$ is 7 because 7 makes the equation true: $3(7) + 4 = 25$, or $25 = 25$.

solution of a compound inequality

The solution of a compound inequality is the part or parts of the solutions that satisfy both of the inequalities.

Example

The number line shows the solution of the compound inequality $x < -2$ or $x > 1$.

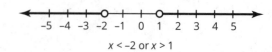

$x < -2$ or $x > 1$

solution of a system of linear inequalities

The solution of a system of linear inequalities is the intersection of the solutions to each inequality. Every point in the intersection region satisfies all inequalities in the system.

Example

The solution of this system of linear inequalities ...

$$\begin{cases} 200a + 100c \leq 800 \\ 75(a - 1) + 50c \geq 150 \end{cases}$$

... is shown by the shaded region, which represents the intersection of the solutions to each inequality.

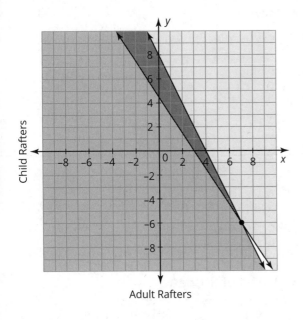

solve an inequality

To solve an inequality means to determine the values of the variable that make the inequality true.

Example

The inequality $x + 5 > 6$ can be solved by subtracting 5 from each side of the inequality. The solution is $x > 1$. Any number greater than 1 will make the inequality $x + 5 > 6$ true.

standard deviation

Standard deviation is a measure of how spread out the data are from the mean.

statistics

Statistics are numerical characteristics of data.

step function

A step function is a piecewise function on a given interval whose pieces are discontinuous constant functions.

Example

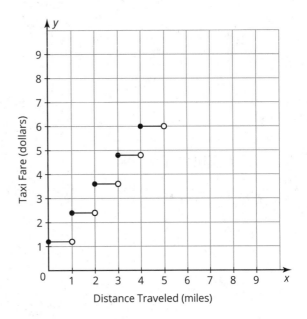

sufficient condition

A correlation is not a sufficient condition for causation, meaning that a correlation between two variables is not enough to establish that one variables causes another.

system of linear equations

When two or more linear equations define a relationship between quantities, they form a system of linear equations.

Example

The equations $y = 3x + 7$ and $y = -4x$ are a system of linear equations.

$$\begin{cases} y = 3x + 7 \\ y = -4x \end{cases}$$

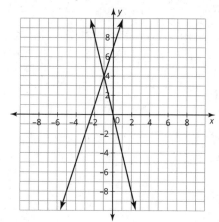

term of a sequence

A term of a sequence is an individual number, figure, or letter in the sequence.

Example

In the sequence 2, 4, 6, 8, 10, the first term is 2, the second term is 4, and the third term is 6.

trinomial

Polynomials with exactly three terms are trinomials.

Example

The polynomial $5x^2 - 6x + 9$ is a trinomial.

two-way frequency table

A two-way frequency table displays categorical data by representing the number of occurrences that fall into each group for two variables.

Example

Favorite Meals of Students

		Burgers	Chicken Nuggets	Pizza	Salad Bar
Grade Level	9th grade	//// 4	/ 1	/// 3	//// 5
	10th grade	/// 3	//// // 7	/// 3	//// 4

upper fence

The value of Q3 + (IQR · 1.5) is known as the upper fence.

vertex form

A quadratic function written in vertex form is in the form $f(x) = a(x - h)^2 + k$, where $a \neq 0$.

Example

The quadratic equation $y = 2(x - 5)^2 + 10$ is written in vertex form. The vertex of the graph is the point (5, 10).

vertex of a parabola

The vertex of a parabola is the lowest or highest point on the graph of the quadratic function.

Example

The vertex of the graph of $y = \frac{2}{3}x^2 - \frac{4}{5}x - \frac{10}{3}$ is the point (1, −4), the absolute minimum of the parabola.

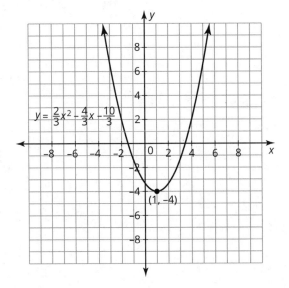

Vertical Line Test

The Vertical Line Test is a visual method used to determine whether a relation represented as a graph is a function.

Example

The equation $y = 3x^2$ is a function. The graph passes the Vertical Line Test because there are no vertical lines that can be drawn that would intersect the graph at more than one point.

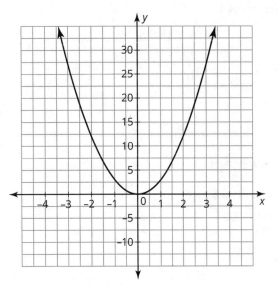

The equation $x^2 + y^2 = 9$ is not a function. The graph fails the Vertical Line Test because a vertical line can be drawn that intersects the graph at more than one point.

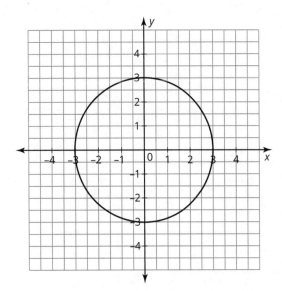

vertical motion model

A vertical motion model is a quadratic equation that models the height of an object at a given time. The equation is of the form $g(t) = -16t^2 + v_0t + h_0$, where $g(t)$ represents the height of the object in feet, t represents the time in seconds that the object has been moving, v_0 represents the initial velocity (speed) of the object in feet per second, and h_0 represents the initial height of the object in feet.

Example

A rock is thrown in the air at a velocity of 10 feet per second from a cliff that is 100 feet high. The height of the rock is modeled by the equation $y = -16t^2 + 10t + 100$.

X

---

x-intercept

The point where a graph crosses the x-axis is the x-intercept.

Y

---

y-intercept

The point where a graph crosses the y-axis is the y-intercept.

Z

---

zero of a function

A zero of a function is a real number that makes the value of the function equal to zero, or $f(x) = 0$.

Example

The zero of the linear function $f(x) = 2(x - 4)$ is (4, 0).

The zeros of the quadratic function $f(x) = -2x^2 + 4x$ are (0, 0) and (2, 0).

Zero Product Property

The Zero Product Property states that if the product of two or more factors is equal to zero, then at least one factor must be equal to zero.

Index